13⁵⁰

OSCAR
ZÚÑIGA
cuentos '79

AUTOMATIC TRANSMISSIONS
AUTOMOTIVE

Mathias F. Brejcha

Associate Professor
Automotive Department
Ferris State College
Big Rapids, Michigan

American Technical Society ⬛ Chicago 60637

Preface

Automatic Transmissions—Automotive covers fundamentals of operation, diagnostic procedures, and specific servicing instructions for current passenger car automatic transmissions. Transmission functions and the development of early models is reviewed, plus an operational description of typical 2-speed and 3-speed units. The development of the torque converter, planetary gear sets, and the use of hydraulic control systems are illustrated.

Pressure control systems, pumps and valves, and the fundamentals of automatic shifting are discussed in the text. Also treated in detail are planetary gear control devices such as *friction bands, one-way clutches,* and *multiple disc clutches.*

The various types of hydrodynamic units used in automatic transmissions are described, and a distinction is made between the early *fluid coupling* and the *fluid torque converter,* bringing in such fluid flow fundamentals as *vortex* and *rotary flow.*

The parts of a planetary gear assembly are reviewed and various gearing definitions are given. The five laws of planetary gear operation are carefully spelled out, as well as *overdrive, freewheeling, gear reduction* and *reaction members.*

The composition, properties and limitations of transmission fluids are shown. Methods of sealing fluids in an automatic transmission are explained.

A comprehensive procedure for removing, disassembling, repairing and reassembling a complete transmission is given in detail to enable the student to grasp every action and why it is taken. In the final chapter, summaries of the characteristics of current passenger car automatic transmissions are included from such major car manufacturers as Ford, American Motors, Chrysler, and General Motors.

The author, Mr. Mathias Brejcha, has been for almost a decade, an Instructor, then Assistant Professor in automotive power systems at Ferris State College. In addition to his college preparation, leading to a Master of Science degree, he has had service training at the General Motors Institute, and both Ford and Chrysler Training Centers. He has also had years of field experience.

The Publishers

Contents

Chapter		Page
I. DEVELOPMENT OF AUTOMATIC TRANSMISSIONS		1
The Power Train		2
Engine Characteristics		3
Transmission Functions		4
Transmission Development		5
Operational Description		15
Control Systems		16
II. HYDRODYNAMIC UNITS		29
The Fluid Coupling		35
The Fluid Torque Converter		42
III. PLANETARY GEARS IN OPERATION		62
The Planetary Gear Assembly		63
Gearing Definitions		64
The Laws of Planetary Gear Operations		65
Combining Gear Reduction and Direct Drive		81
Planetary Gear Ratios		84
IV. PLANETARY GEAR SYSTEMS IN AUTOMATIC TRANSMISSIONS		86
3-Speed Chrysler TorqueFlite		88
Ford C-6 and C-4		98
G.M. 2-Speed Units		104
V. HYDRAULIC SYSTEM FUNDAMENTALS		110
Fluid and the Hydraulic Lever		111
Pascal's Law		112
A Basic Hydraulic System		116
The Hydraulic Jack		120
The Hydraulic Hoist		122

VI. HYDRAULIC SYSTEM FUNDAMENTALS—PUMPS AND VALVES . 125

    Hydraulic Pumps 125
    Hydraulic Valves 130

VII. THE AUTOMATIC TRANSMISSION HYDRAULIC SYSTEM—
    FUNDAMENTALS OF OPERATION 142

    The Pressure Supply System 143
    Throttle Valve System 152
    Vacuum Modulator Valve System 156
    Governor Valve System 159
    Manual Valve 161
    Servo Assemblies 162
    Clutch Assemblies 163
    Automatic and Manual Shift Systems 166
    Semi-Automatic Shifting 187
    Accumulator Units 187

VIII. AUTOMATIC TRANSMISSION FLUIDS AND SEALS 192

    The Fluid 192
    Development of Transmission Fluids 193
    Sealing the Fluid 196

IX. PRINCIPLES OF DIAGNOSIS 207

    Step I   Listen to the Customer and Verify Complaint . . . 208
    Step II   Check the Fluid Level and Fluid Condition 209
    Step III Quick Check of Linkage and Engine Idle 214
    Step IV Stall Test (Optional) 216
    Step V   Road Test 220
    Step VI Pressure Testing 228

X. AUTOMATIC TRANSMISSION SERVICE 240

    Periodic Maintenance 240
    External Fluid Leaks 245
    Overhauling an Automatic Transmission 254
    Towing 280

XI. SUMMARY/CHARACTERISTICS OF
    CURRENT AUTOMATIC TRANSMISSIONS 286

    Chrysler Corporation (TorqueFlite 904 and 727) 286
    Ford Motor Company (C-4, C-6, and FMX Cruise-O-Matic) . . 290
    American Motors Corporation (Flash-O-Matic,
      Shift Command, Torque Command) 300
    General Motors Corporation (Powerglide, Torque Drive,
      Jetaway, Pontiac 2-Speed, Super Turbine 300, and
      Turbo-Hydramatic 400 and 350) 301

GLOSSARY 321

INDEX 336

Automatic Transmission

Automatic Transmission—Power Train

Development of Automatic Transmissions

Jetaway, Hydra-Matic, Torque-Flite, and Cruise-O-Matic are some of the familiar names used for automatic transmissions in the auto trade. To understand how each operates appears to be a monumental task. However, the objective of this book is to present a simple, comprehensive study of the fundamentals of automotive transmissions that covers operation, trouble diagnosis, and servicing. This background will add immeasurably to your automotive knowledge in preparation for earning a living in an expanding service industry.

The ultimate goal of this text is to create an awareness that automatic transmissions are more alike in design and operation than they are different. The differences that do exist are primarily in component sizes and structure and some minor variations in hydraulic control systems. This should not interfere in applying fundamental principles to individual transmissions.

The differences that exist in both operation and service among the various manufacturers' products are best learned through their current operation and service manuals. Although specific transmissions are not presented in detail the text deals with current production units when applicable to the discussion. While concentration is on passenger car automatic transmissions, such transmissions are also used in both diesel and gasoline engines in light and heavy duty trucks. Thus, general knowledge gained in one area is easily applied to allied kinds of work.

The study of this text is but one experience in a series of experiences needed for a complete understanding of automatic transmissions. This means that the individual should learn to apply his knowledge of fundamentals, then review service manuals for particular transmissions, drive passenger cars equipped with the various transmissions to get the feel of how they perform, and finally to get involved in the actual diagnosis and servicing of transmissions.

In keeping with the objective of presenting *fundamentals,* this book briefly reviews the theory of automotive power transmission and the evolution of transmission design and production. Then it treats of the fluid torque converter, planetary gearing, and hydraulic control systems in order to build toward an understanding of total transmission operation. Later chapters deal with trouble diagnosis and servicing based on the study of these operational fundamentals and the basic transmission models.

A review of transmission Fundamentals for students who have not had previous training is appended at the back of the text. Since stick shifts are becoming a decreasing part of transmission servicing it is assumed that they can be studied in a basic level text, therefore they are not included in Automatic Transmissions—Automotive.

The Power Train

The term *power train* includes all the drive components between the engine flywheel and the drive wheels. Typically, this includes a clutch, a transmission or gear box, a drive shaft, U-joints, a differential assembly, and the rear axle.

In this power train the gear ratio(s) of the transmission and rear axle ring gear and pinion are used to control engine rpm and provide the necessary torque. The transmission here alters torque. Since both the vehicle load changes and engine output changes, the transmission must provide suitable gear ratio changes, usually three or four, that permit the engine to efficiently propel any given load. In Fig. 1-1, the ideal transmission gear ratios should adjust the engine's load to produce the same torque curve at all speeds. Optimum engine performance is the objective, and the transmission is designed to make a significant contribution to engine performance as well as to transmit power.

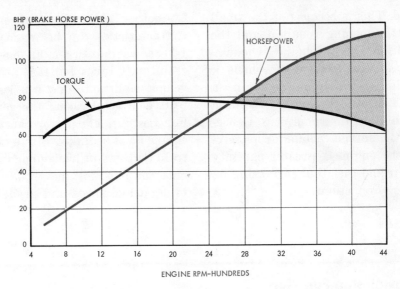

Fig. 1-1. Relationship of brake horsepower (bhp) to torque (Ram-Charger engine).

Engine Characteristics

The primary function of the internal combustion engine is to produce *torque* (turning or rotary force) for powering the automotive vehicle. Horsepower, which is often used loosely to describe the output of an engine, is simply the product of torque and speed (motion). That is, torque and speed produce *horsepower*. A specific horsepower can be the result of high torque and low speed; or low torque and high speed.

The first illustration shows a typical relationship of horsepower to torque. Fig. 1-1 shows that, as engine rpm increases, both torque and horsepower increase together until the mid range is reached in engine speed. It is at this mid range that engine efficiency reaches a maximum before gradually decreasing, with a resulting decrease in torque. Although absolute horsepower may continue to rise, effective utilization, or performance, drops off. Torque is thus seen to be the prime performance factor.

Another engine characteristic is that the engine will not produce any more output than is demanded by the vehicle load. For example, at 2,500 rpm, with the transmission in neutral, little torque is pro-

3

duced. This is because of the small throttle opening required and the resulting high engine vacuum. When a load (weight of vehicle × friction) is placed on the engine, a wider throttle opening is required to maintain the same rpm. Consequently, engine vacuum drops, giving the engine a greater capacity for air and fuel, thus increasing its power production.

Another observation of engine characteristics can be made. Fig. 1-1 shows that when an engine's crankshaft turns too fast and develops too little torque, it is less effective in accelerating the vehicle. For best vehicle performance the engine must be linked with a power train that will utilize and adapt engine output to the *road load* (weight and speed and grade).

Transmission Functions

A typical driveshaft *torque curve* (engine torque × transmission gear ratio(s) against road load on full throttle acceleration to 100 mph) is shown in Fig. 1-2 for a 3-speed automatic transmission. Road load in this case refers to driveshaft torque required to keep the vehicle moving at a particular speed. Observe the driveshaft torque curve; the greatest amount of torque is available at start because engine torque is multiplied by the torque converter (the converter ratio being greatest at start) and by the transmission first gear ratio. Because the converter ratio decreases rapidly once the vehicle begins moving, the driveshaft torque decreases rapidly up to 20 mph.

During 1st gear operation this converter effect gives a smooth

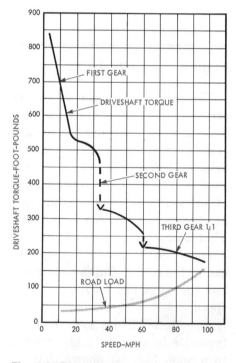

Fig. 1-2. Torque curve of a typical driveshaft showing its relationship to gear ratios.

transition in torque drop when compared to the sudden torque changes observed for second and third gears. If the vehicle is to accelerate, the driveshaft torque must exceed the road load requirement. When the condition is such that the driveshaft torque and road load are equal, the vehicle speed is then fixed. Fig. 1-2 illustrates this point.

At 5 mph the road load torque of 25 lb-ft and the driveshaft torque of 850 lb-ft gives a reserve of 825 lb-ft for acceleration. As the vehicle continues to accelerate to 100 mph the road load increases and the driveshaft torque decreases until finally the transmission (1) shifts into third gear, (2) the engine rpm is at maximum but at less than full torque, and (3) the road load and driveshaft torque reach an equilibrium. No further vehicle speed is possible. It should be rather evident in Fig. 1-2 that engine and transmission work together to provide this performance.

Transmission Development

The role of the automobile transmission has not changed throughout the years. Although its main function is that of a torque and speed changer, it also provides for a reverse and a neutral, and for engine braking. Great strides have taken place in its design and development to keep pace with the evolution of the automobile.

The American passenger car got along nicely for the first 30 to 40 years of its life with one basic transmission layout, a manually shifted 3- or 4-speed sliding gear box, Fig. 1-3, equipped with a foot operated friction clutch for engaging and disengaging engine power during shifts. The early versions were very simple and usually rugged in construction and operation.

During the same period, manually operated transmissions with planetary gears were also being developed—a 3-speed version was used in the 1904 Cadillac, and of more popular vintage the old Model T Ford used a 2-speed planetary gear box design that saw years of popularity until it was dropped in 1928.

Despite these early successes auto industry engineers were searching for the ideal transmission: one which would provide ease of driver operation, smooth shifts, and infinitely variable ratios to give the engine the ultimate in performance assist. The fully auto-

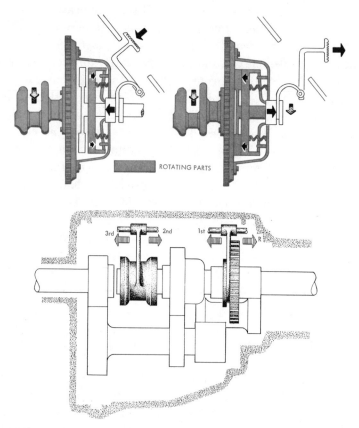

ROTATING PARTS

Fig. 1-3. Foot operated clutch used in older cars and on some heavy vehicles; and a manually operated 3-speed sliding gear box.

matic transmission was the answer, and the industry proceeded to pass through several important stages.

1928 Cadillac introduced the synchromesh transmission.

1933 Reo brought out a semi-automatic transmission. This unit had planetary gear sets which used centrifugal weights to control them. This permitted the gears to shift automatically from low speed into drive once the car was moving. A single plate, conventional friction clutch was still used.

1934 Chrysler introduced automatic overdrive.

1937 Oldsmobile introduced the next semi-automatic transmission design. Planetary gears were used and controlled by a combination of hydraulic and mechanical devices. The friction clutch was used and so were conventional gears for reverse operation.

1938 Chrysler introduced the fluid coupling, thus making it possible to idle the engine with the transmission in gear. This paved the way to the successful use of automatically shifted spur gear transmissions which Chrysler made famous. These semi-automatic designs were known by various trade names: Prestomatic, Tip-Toe Shift, and Gyromatic. In later designs the fluid coupling was replaced by a fluid torque converter and called the Chrysler Torque-Drive and the Plymouth Hydrive. Note in Figs. 1-4 and 1-5 that a pedal operated clutch was still used, but only for the purpose of changing operating ranges.

1940 General Motors Hydra-Matic first appeared in Oldsmobile. This design marked the first use of a fluid coupling in combination with a 4-speed planetary, fully automatic transmission, Fig. 1-6.

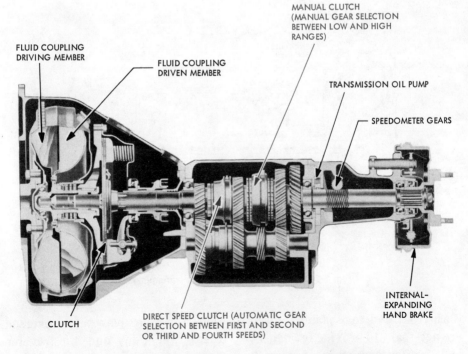

MANUAL CLUTCH
(MANUAL GEAR SELECTION BETWEEN LOW AND HIGH RANGES)

FLUID COUPLING DRIVING MEMBER

FLUID COUPLING DRIVEN MEMBER

TRANSMISSION OIL PUMP

SPEEDOMETER GEARS

CLUTCH

DIRECT SPEED CLUTCH (AUTOMATIC GEAR SELECTION BETWEEN FIRST AND SECOND OR THIRD AND FOURTH SPEEDS)

INTERNAL-EXPANDING HAND BRAKE

Fig. 1-4. Fluid coupling with manual gear box. (Chrysler Corp.)

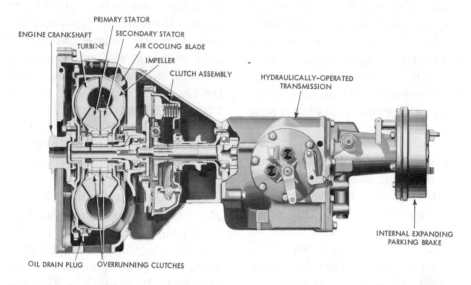

Fig. 1-5. Fluid Torque-Drive with manual and hydraulically operated gear box. (Chrysler Corp.)

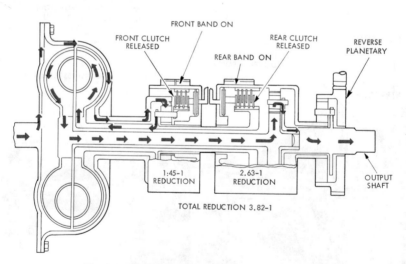

Fig. 1-6. The original Hydra-Matic transmission.

Both front and rear planetary sets are necessary to provide for neutral and the forward gears. In reverse, the front planetary gave a reduc-

tion, the rear planetary reversed the power flow, and the reverse planetary added a further reduction.

8

POWER FLOW SUMMARY

	DIRECT CLUTCH	LOW BAND	REVERSE BAND
NEUTRAL	OFF	OFF	OFF
DRIVE	ON	OFF	OFF
LOW	OFF	ON	OFF
REVERSE	OFF	OFF	ON

NOTE: NO AUTOMATIC SHIFTING

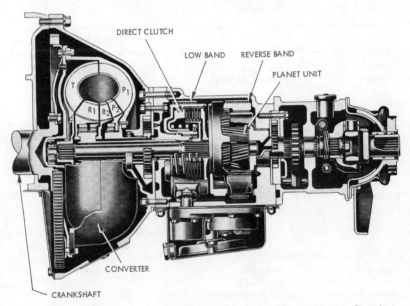

Fig. 1-7. First design Buick Dynaflow. (Buick Div., General Motors Corp.)

1948 Buick introduced the Dynaflow, Fig. 1-7, which was the first passenger car with automatic transmission to successfully use the fluid torque converter. The multiple pinion planetary gear box provided direct, low and reverse gear ratios. The drive selection of the transmission connects the fluid converter to the output shaft with no additional gearing. The maximum torque multiplication of the converter is 2.25-1. A low gear ratio of 1.82-1 is provided for extra pulling power or engine braking.

Following the Buick Dynaflow development, the industry proceeded to grow into the popular use

TABLE 1-1. INTRODUCTION OF SIGNIFICANT EARLY TRANSMISSIONS

Car Make	Transmission Trade Name	Model Year
		GENERAL MOTORS
Oldsmobile	Hydra-Matic	1940
Cadillac	Hydra-Matic	1941
Pontiac	Hydra-Matic	1948
Buick	Dynaflow	1948
Chevrolet	Powerglide[1]	1950
		FORD MOTOR COMPANY
Lincoln	GM Hydra-Matic	1950
Mercury	Merc-O-Matic[2] (Fig. 1-8)	1951
Ford	Ford-O-Matic	1951
		CHRYSLER CORPORATION
Chrysler and Imperial	Powerflite (Fig. 1-9)	1953
Dodge	Powerflite	1954
DeSoto	Powerflite	1954
Plymouth	Powerflite	1954
		OTHER MANUFACTURERS
Packard	Ultramatic (Fig. 1-10)	1949
Nash	GM Hydra-Matic	1950
Studebaker	Studebaker (Fig. 1-11)	1950
Kaiser-Frazer	GM Hydra-Matic	1951
Rambler	GM Hydra-Matic	1953
Willys	GM Hydra-Matic	1953

[1]The first design Powerglides, 1950-52, were almost exact copies of the early Buick Dynaflow. Automatic shifting was not introduced in the Powerglide until 1953 when the fluid torque converter and hydraulic control system were redesigned to produce a two speed automatic shift transmission. The planetary gear train remained the same.

[2]The Merc-O-Matic and Ford-O-Matic transmissions were identical in design and operation. Produced by Borg-Warner, they differed only in torque capacity.

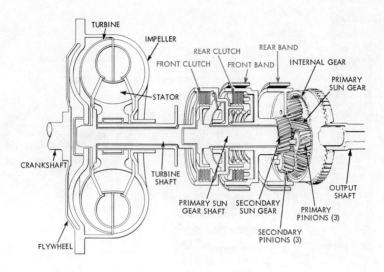

POWER FLOW SUMMARY CHART

OPERATING RANGE	FRONT BAND	FRONT CLUTCH	REAR BAND	REAR CLUTCH
NEUTRAL	OFF	OFF	OFF	OFF
DRIVE				
INTERMEDIATE	ON	ON	OFF	OFF
HIGH	OFF	ON	OFF	ON
LOW	OFF	ON	ON	OFF
REVERSE	OFF	OFF	ON	ON

Fig. 1-8. The original Ford-O-Matic 3-speed power train. (Ford Motor Co.)

of automatic transmissions, Table 1-1.

The Ford-O-Matic, Fig. 1-8, is composed of a 3-element torque converter and a multiple pinion gear system to produce three forward speeds and reverse. The converter provides a maximum torque multiplication of 2.1-1. Normal drive starts through the torque converter and intermediate gear ratio,

1.48-1 and automatically shifts to direct or converter drive only. A manual low range, 2.44-1 gear ratio, was used for extra pulling power or engine braking.

The Chrysler Corporation Powerflite, Fig. 1-9, was a 2-speed transmission, using a 3-element torque converter and two planetary gear sets, providing a low, direct, and reverse gear ratio. For forward

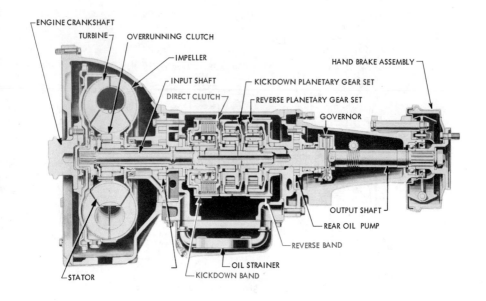

ENGINE CRANKSHAFT
TURBINE
OVERRUNNING CLUTCH
IMPELLER
INPUT SHAFT
DIRECT CLUTCH
KICKDOWN PLANETARY GEAR SET
REVERSE PLANETARY GEAR SET
HAND BRAKE ASSEMBLY
GOVERNOR
OUTPUT SHAFT
REAR OIL PUMP
REVERSE BAND
OIL STRAINER
KICKDOWN BAND
STATOR

POWER FLOW SUMMARY CHART

	DIRECT CLUTCH	KICKDOWN BAND	REVERSE BAND
NEUTRAL	OFF	OFF	OFF
DRIVE AUTOMATIC LOW DIRECT DRIVE	OFF ON	ON OFF	OFF OFF
LOW	OFF	ON	OFF
REVERSE	OFF	OFF	ON

Fig. 1-9. PowerFlite transmission and power flow. (Chrysler Corp.)

drive operation, the power flow starts through the converter, maximum torque multiplication 2.7-1, and low gear ratio of 1.72-1, and automatically shifts to direct or converter drive only. The transmission can be manually locked in low range for extra pulling power or engine braking.

Shown in Fig. 1-10 is the early designed Packard Ultramatic. This transmission used a 4-element converter, and a multiple pinion planetary gear box similar to the Buick Dynaflow, to provide direct, low and reverse. A direct clutch was used in the converter. Like the Dynaflow, the power flow in forward

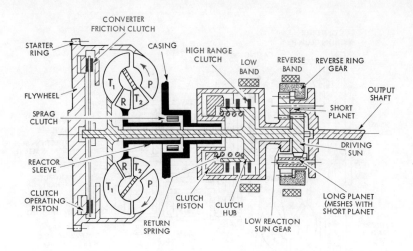

POWERFLOW SUMMARY CHART

	CONVERTER CLUTCH	HIGH CLUTCH	LOW BAND	REVERSE BAND
NEUTRAL	OFF	OFF	OFF	OFF
DRIVE CONVERTER & HIGH RANGE	OFF	ON	OFF	OFF
HIGH RANGE	ON	ON	OFF	OFF
LOW	ON	OFF	ON	OFF
REVERSE	OFF	OFF	OFF	ON

Later versions provided for low ratio in automatic drive range

Fig. 1-10. Packard Ultramatic transmission; power train is identical to current Power-Glide and other 2-speed transmissions.

drive passed through the converter to the output shaft without additional gearing assists. The direct drive clutch in the converter, however, was affected by an automatic shift. For part-throttle and cruising conditions the direct clutch was applied to provide a solid drive through the converter. For performance conditions the converter direct clutch was off and could provide a maximum torque multiplica-tion of 2.4-1. Low range, 1.82-1 gear ratio, could be manually engaged for extra power and engine braking.

The Studebaker automatic transmissions, Fig. 1-11, were produced by Borg-Warner. A 3-element torque converter with a direct drive clutch was augmented by two planetary gear sets, providing three forward speeds and reverse. Normal drive started through the

13

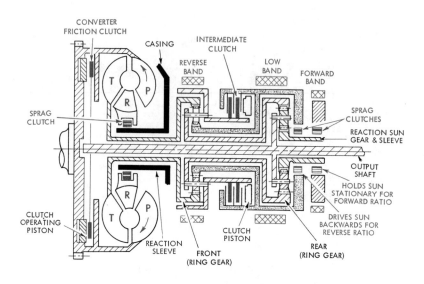

STUDEBAKER (BORG WARNER) EARLY DESIGN
3 SPEED TRANSMISSION

POWER FLOW CHART

	CONVERTER CLUTCH	INTERMEDIATE CLUTCH	FORWARD BAND	FORWARD SPRAG	LOW BAND	REVERSE BAND	REVERSE SPRAG
NEUTRAL	OFF	OFF	OFF	OFF	OFF	OFF	OFF
DRIVE INTERMEDIATE	OFF	ON	ON	ON	OFF	OFF	OFF
DIRECT DRIVE	ON	ON	ON	OFF	OFF	OFF	OFF
LOW	OFF	OFF	ON	ON	ON	OFF	OFF
REVERSE	OFF	OFF	OFF	OFF	OFF	ON	ON

Later versions provided for low range ratio in automatic drive range.

Fig. 1-11. Studebaker (Borg-Warner) transmission.

converter, maximum torque multiplication 2.15-1, and intermediate gear ratio, and then shifted to solid direct drive both in the converter and gear set. The gear ratios were as follows: 1st, 2.31-1; 2nd, 1.43-1; 3rd, 1-1. Low range was manually engaged for extra pulling power or engine braking.

By 1955 the automatic transmission had firmly established itself and was offered as standard or optional equipment by all automobile manufacturers. In today's car market, over 90% of the automobiles sold are equipped with automatic transmissions.

Operational Description

How an automatic transmission operates is an exciting story. The basic principles of operation can best be learned by a brief overview of how a typical automatic transmission works. This is easy because all self-shifting automatic transmissions operate in basically the same manner: a fluid torque converter is combined with a planetary gear set whose various gear ratios are automatically selected by a hydraulic control system, Fig. 1-12. This combination of fluid torque converter and planetary gears is currently used in a number of transmission families: the Chrysler TorqueFlite, the Ford Cruise-O-Matic, and G.M. Hydra-Matic families.

One of the great advantages of automatic shifting is that it takes the gear selection job away from the driver who is not always skilled in sensing the correct gear ratio needed by the engine at a particular throttle opening and road load (*road load* is a function of weight, speed and grade.) Whether the result is overspeeding or lugging the engine, the engine or the drive train is eventually damaged by an unskilled driver. There is also the direct hazard to a manual gear box by the uncoordinated operator or the unorthodox speed shifter. The driver of an automatic transmission equipped automobile needs only to select an operating range and step on the accelerator, as in Fig. 1-13.

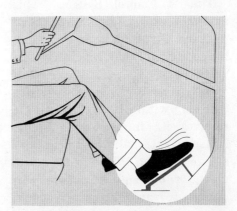

Fig. 1-13. Only the pressure on the accelerator is needed to operate the completely automatic transmission.

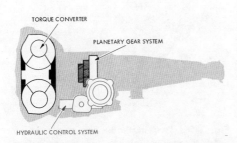

TORQUE CONVERTER

PLANETARY GEAR SYSTEM

HYDRAULIC CONTROL SYSTEM

Fig. 1-12. Automatic transmission systems.

Control Systems

Here's how it works. The transmission has a system of controls that (1) link it to the engine for influencing automatic shifts, and (2) to the driver for manual selection of an operating range. These controls are respectively referred to as the *throttle control system* and *manual control system* and will respectively have the following function:

Manual Control System. Through linkage movement the driver positions a manual valve in the valve body of the hydraulic control system and thus programs the transmission for the selected operating range, Fig. 1-14.

Throttle Control System. This system senses engine torque and hydraulically sends a pressure signal to the hydraulic control system valve body. The *throttle control system* consists of a regulator valve assembly within the valve body. It receives its input torque signal either by external mechanical linkage responding to gas pedal movement, or by engine vacuum connected to an external vacuum control unit at the transmission, Fig. 1-15.

One more link-up for the trans-

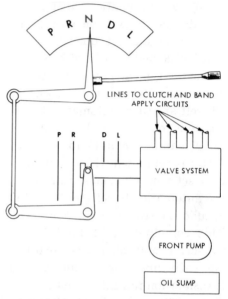

Fig. 1-14. Manual control linkage and manual valve establishes the selected operating range.

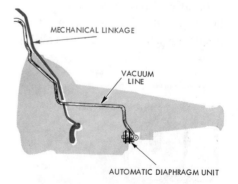

Fig. 1-15. Two methods are employed to send torque signals to the transmission: a mechanical linkage, or diaphragm control.

mission is necessary if automatic shifting is to take place. A governor system is provided to make the transmission sensitive to the road speed of the vehicle.

Governor Control System. This system senses the variations in road speed from the transmission output shaft rpm and, like the throttle system, sends a hydraulic pressure signal to the hydraulic control system valve body. The system is made up of a regulating valve assembly

equipped with centrifugal weights, Fig. 1-16.

The manual, throttle and governor links are part of the overall make-up of a much larger assemblage known as the hydraulic control system.

Hydraulic Control System. This system consists of an engine driven or front hydraulic pump and pressure regulator valve for supplying the necessary oil charge to the torque converter and furnishing an

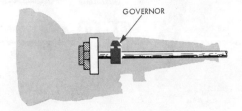

Fig. 1-16. Governor picks up road speed signal from the transmission output shaft.

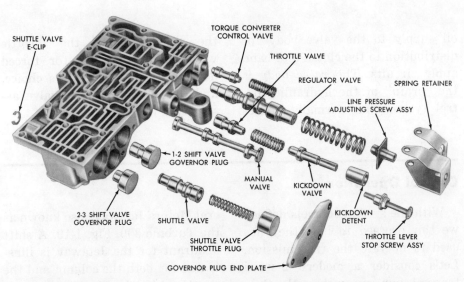

Fig. 1-17. Example of hydraulic control valve assembly, right side. (Chrysler Corp.)

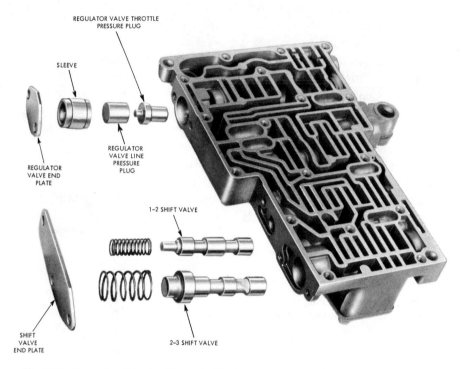

REGULATOR VALVE THROTTLE
PRESSURE PLUG

SLEEVE

REGULATOR
VALVE LINE
PRESSURE
PLUG

REGULATOR
VALVE END
PLATE

1-2 SHIFT VALVE

SHIFT
VALVE
END PLATE

2-3 SHIFT VALVE

Fig. 1-18. Example of hydraulic control valve assembly, left side. (Chrysler Corp.)

oil supply to the valve body for distribution to the clutch and band apply circuits. The *valve body* is the "brain" of the hydraulic control system and normally houses the manual valve, the throttle valve, a detent valve for forced downshifts by the driver's choice, and the automatic shift valve assembly, Figs. 1-17 and 1-18.

Control Operation

With the system controls defined we can proceed to how they are used to operate the transmission. Let's consider a modern 2-speed transmission, one such as the General Motors Jetaway, also known as the Turbine 300, Fig. 1-19. A shift quadrant for the Jetaway is illustrated for both the column and the console shifts in Fig. 1-20.

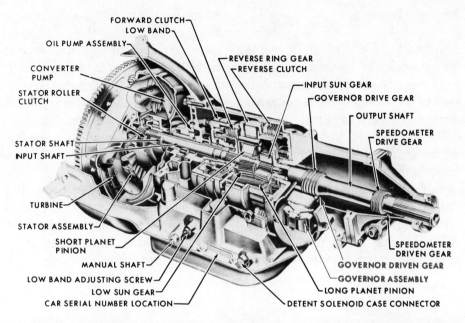

FORWARD CLUTCH
LOW BAND
OIL PUMP ASSEMBLY
REVERSE RING GEAR
REVERSE CLUTCH
CONVERTER PUMP
INPUT SUN GEAR
STATOR ROLLER CLUTCH
GOVERNOR DRIVE GEAR
OUTPUT SHAFT
SPEEDOMETER DRIVE GEAR
STATOR SHAFT
INPUT SHAFT
TURBINE
STATOR ASSEMBLY
SHORT PLANET PINION
SPEEDOMETER DRIVEN GEAR
MANUAL SHAFT
GOVERNOR DRIVEN GEAR
LOW BAND ADJUSTING SCREW
GOVERNOR ASSEMBLY
LOW SUN GEAR
LONG PLANET PINION
CAR SERIAL NUMBER LOCATION
DETENT SOLENOID CASE CONNECTOR

Fig. 1-19. Jetaway drive and automatic transmission. (Oldsmobile Div., General Motors Corp.)

PARK R N D L

Fig. 1-20. Shift quadrants of 2-speed transmission, steering column and floor types. (Oldsmobile Div., General Motors Corp.)

Park and Starting

To start the engine and provide for safety, the manual selector lever must be positioned in *park* or *neutral*. A safety switch prevents starting in reverse, drive, or low operating ranges. Whenever the engine starts a power flow enters the torque converter since it is attached to the engine crankshaft. The power flow passes through the torque converter and exits by way of its turbine shaft (input shaft of the transmission) into the plan-

etary gear set. With no band or clutches applied, the planetary gears are free to spin and do not transfer motion to the output shaft, Fig. 1-21. Apply-oil flow to the friction units and shift valve is cut off by the manual valve, Fig. 1-22.

With the selector lever in *park*, all friction units are released as in *neutral;* however, a spring force is applied to a parking pawl that engages the heavy teeth spaced around the front face of the planet carrier, locking the output shaft to the transmission case, Fig. 1-23.

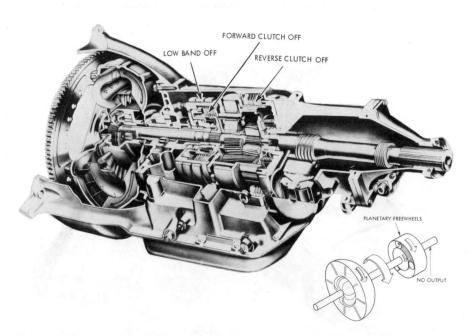

Fig. 1-21. Neutral—output shaft is stationary; clutches and bands are released. (Oldsmobile Div., General Motors Corp.)

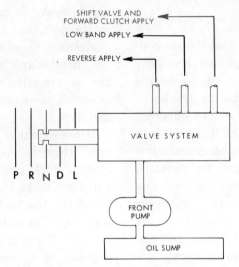

Fig. 1-22. Neutral—manual valve cuts off apply oil to friction units.

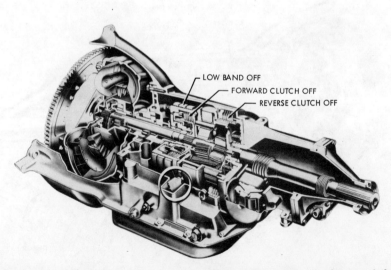

Fig. 1-23. Park—all members as in neutral; parking pawl engages teeth around the planetary carrier; direct manual action activates the linkage while spring action holds the pawl engaged, locking the output shaft. (Oldsmobile Div., General Motors Corp.)

Drive

In *drive* range, the torque converter and transmission low gear combine to multiply engine torque in response to engine throttle opening and the vehicle moves smoothly forward. When the upshift into *high* or *direct drive* occurs, the low band is released and the forward clutch applied. Applying the forward clutch locks the planetary gear set and the result is a 1:1 ratio, Fig. 1-24. The low band application in *automatic low* is actually accomplished by manual control and is not an automatic shift function. The forward clutch ap-

ply, however, is caused by an automatic shift.

Keeping in mind the purpose of the throttle and governor systems, the automatic shift timing is achieved as shown in Figs. 1-25 and 1-26.

If acceleration takes place at a light throttle opening, the regulated throttle pressure at the shift valve spring end is light. This combined throttle and spring pressure keeps the shift valve in a *closed* position. Since a gear ratio change depends on engine torque vs road speed, the regulated governor pressure opposes the throttle and spring resistance at the opposite

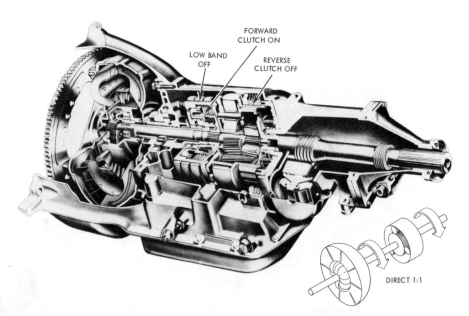

FORWARD
CLUTCH ON

LOW BAND
OFF

REVERSE
CLUTCH OFF

DIRECT 1:1

Fig. 1-24. Drive—transmission starts automatically in *low*; upshift to *drive* depends on car speed and throttle opening. (Oldsmobile Div., General Motors Corp.)

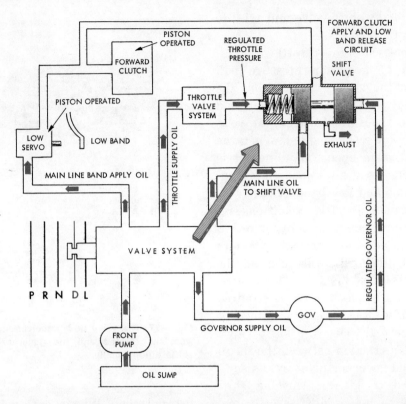

Fig. 1-25. Drive-Automatic Low—simplified; main line oil is routed via manual valve to low servo for low band application; in automatic low the shift components in the low valve shift system are charged with oil pressure to trigger the shift valve.

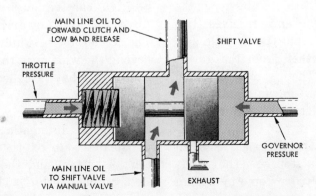

Fig. 1-26. Drive-Direct—governor pressure overcomes combined throttle and spring tension to open shift valve; main line oil applies forward clutch and also releases the low band.

end of the shift valve and tries to open the valve.

Thus, at light throttle a minimum of governor pressure will move the shifter valve from the *closed* to the *open* postion and cause the shift to occur at relatively low vehicle speed. When the shift valve opens mainline oil is directed to the forward clutch apply line and low band release.

Heavier throttle conditions required for rapid acceleration or hill grades add more throttle pressure to the normal resistance of the shifter valve spring. This means that more vehicle speed is required to raise the necessary governor pressure to open the shift valve. This interaction between the throttle and governor pressures is engineered to give a variable shift point to match any throttle and road load condition.

The valve body, or brain, works like a computer. It is programmed for the operating range by the manual valve and receives two signals, one from the throttle system and another from the governor system. These signals are then transmitted to an automatic shift valve and determine the shift point, Fig. 1-27.

On closed throttle, such as when braking for a stop, governor pressure is simply overcome by spring tension and the transmission shifts back to low gear just before the

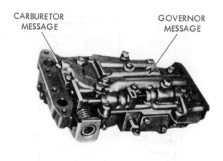

CARBURETOR MESSAGE   GOVERNOR MESSAGE

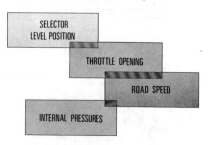

SELECTOR LEVEL POSITION

THROTTLE OPENING

ROAD SPEED

INTERNAL PRESSURES

Fig. 1-27. The valve body receives signals from the throttle and the governor and shifts automatically.

vehicle stops. Within safe vehicle speed ranges that will permit the engine to accelerate and not over-speed itself, the shift valve *open* position can be overruled for a *forced downshift* by driver's choice. The accelerator is simply depressed beyond the wide open throttle position into what is called *through-detent*.

When the selector is in the *low* position, the automatic shift valve is isolated out of the hydraulic control system and the transmission cannot *upshift*. The manual valve directs the mainline oil to the low servo piston for low band apply, Figs. 1-28 and 1-29. *Low* is designed for engine braking when descending steep grades and may also be used to hold the transmission in low gear for maximum pulling.

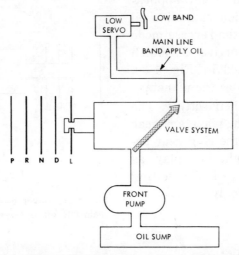

Fig. 1-28. Manual valve directs main line oil to the low band apply circuit; this is the same low gear used for automatic low.

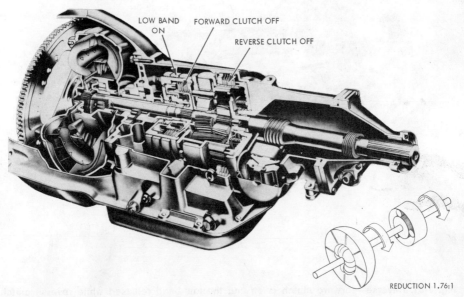

Fig. 1-29. Low range—forward clutch released; low band applied.

Reverse

Reverse is accomplished by the use of a multiple disc clutch that is caused to function by the application of transmission main line oil upon selection of the reverse mode of operation. This activates a clutch piston, as indicated by Fig. 1-30, which in turn causes the planetary gears to change their setting. The same portion of the planetary gear set, with the reverse ring gear being held, is brought into play, as illustrated in Fig. 1-31. This setting is used in *reverse* only.

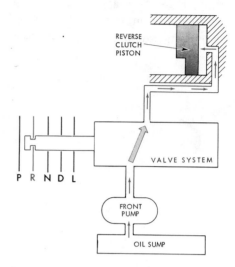

Fig. 1-30. Reverse—manual valve directs main line oil to reverse apply circuit.

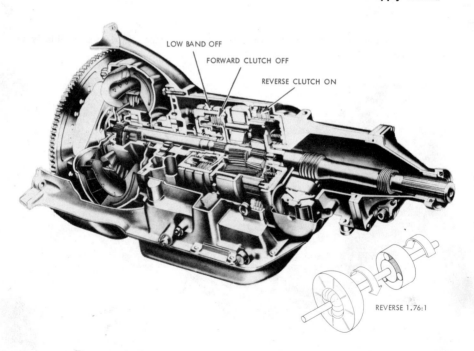

Fig. 1-31. Reverse—forward clutch is off and the low band released while reverse clutch is applied.

Checking On Your Knowledge

The following questions give you the opportunity to check up on yourself. If you have read the chapter carefully, you should be able to answer the questions.

If you have any difficulty, read the chapter over once more so that you have the information well in mind before you go on with your reading.

1. Name the components that make-up the conventional power drive train of a passenger car.
2. What are the three basic functions of a transmission?
3. Why is it necessary to provide for gear ratio changes in the transmission?
4. How is engine volumetric efficiency related to horsepower?
5. What is meant by *driveshaft torque?*
6. When does a vehicle reach the point of no further acceleration?
7. When is the vehicle road load the greatest? Explain your answer.
8. What happens to the torque converter ratio as the driveshaft torque or road load decreases?
9. What are some advantages of an automatic transmission over a manual gear shift transmission?
10. In what year was one of the first planetary gear boxes used in an American passenger car?
11. What significant transmission developments occurred in the following years: 1928, 1933, 1934, 1937, 1938, 1940, and 1948?
12. What major development made the fully automatic transmission possible?

13. Answer the following questions on a basic automatic transmission hydraulic system:
    a. Name the system that links the driver to the transmission for selection of the operating range.
    b. Name the system that links the engine to the transmission for the purpose of providing a torque signal.
    c. Name the system that links the vehicle speed to the transmission for the purpose of providing a speed signal.
    d. Name the system that provides the main working hydraulic pressure for the transmission.
    e. What is the job of the transmission front pump?
    f. What is the valve body?
14. From what source does the governor pick up the vehicle speed signal?
15. What are the two current methods used for sending a torque signal to the transmission?
16. Answer the following questions on automatic shift fundamentals:
    a. Name the hydraulic pressure signal that works to keep the shift valve closed.
    b. Name the hydraulic pressure sig-

POWER FLOW SUMMARY (SEE QUESTION 19)

2-SPEED AUTOMATIC TRANSMISSION

OPERATING RANGE	LOW BAND	~~FORWARD~~ *HI* CLUTCH	REVERSE CLUTCH
NEUTRAL	OFF	OFF	OFF
DRIVE			
LOW	ON	OFF	OFF
DIRECT	OFF	ON	OFF
LOW	ON	OFF	OFF
REVERSE	OFF	OFF	ON

nal that opposes the first pressure signal and works to open the shift valve.

17. Explain how the interaction between throttle and governor signal pressures on the shift valve produces a variable shift point.

18. Explain how the automatic transmission shift system is a hydraulic computer.

19. All current 2-speed transmissions use the same basic gear design and friction control elements. Study the power flow summary chart and get to know when these friction elements are applied for each operating range.

Hydrodynamic Units

Chapter

2

Hydrodynamic drive units, the fluid coupling and the fluid torque converter, have been used in semi- and fully-automatic transmissions on millions of American passenger cars since the introduction of the fluid coupling in 1938 and the fluid torque converter in 1948. At least one such hydrodynamic unit has been used since in all past and present automatic passenger car transmissions.

Hydrodynamic drive units are not an American development but European. Dr. Hermann Fottinger, a German engineer working with the Vulcan ship yards in Stettin, Germany, built the first experimental fluid drive unit, a torque converter, in 1908. This was developed and used as a speed reducer for high horsepower steam turbines for ship propulsion, Fig. 2-1 left. A modern version with stator is shown in Fig. 2-1 right.

Fottinger's torque converter gave a speed reduction of 5:1 and operated at an efficiency of 85 percent. His converter, however, was soon replaced by the geared turbine drive which was less expensive and even more efficient.

Further progress on fluid drives continued at the Vulcan yards along with marine application of the diesel engine. Diesel engines had then reached a stage where they were beginning to be used for very large marine installations. However, these engines had an objectionable torsional vibration that was imparted to the gear drives and into the ship structure.

In order to dampen these vibra-

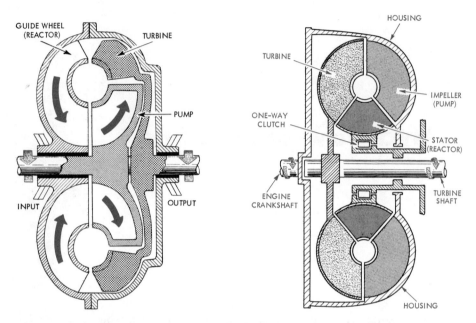

Fig. 2-1. The Fottinger torque converter; the guide wheel, now called the reactor or stator, is the name used by the inventor; and a modern three element converter coupling used in passenger cars. (Ford Motor Co.)

tions a fluid drive unit was designed which was a modification of the original Fottinger converter. It was found that by eliminating the reaction member a functional two member fluid coupling was created which developed no extra torque but which had a very high efficiency of 98 percent, Fig. 2-2. Marine hydraulic couplings continue to be used today.

The coupling and the converter in their early stages were two distinct and separate units and were not combined as a single unit, as is common in current practice. The greater efficiency of the fluid cou-

pling over the converter resulted in its wider use.

Some attempts were made, however, to take advantage of both the coupling and converter characteristics. The Fottinger drives were applied to some locomotive transmissions which used a converter and a fluid coupling in series. The transition from converter drive to coupling drive was made by emptying the fluid from the converter and then filling the coupling which had previously been empty.

In the years between World War I and World War II much of the work on fluid drives took place in

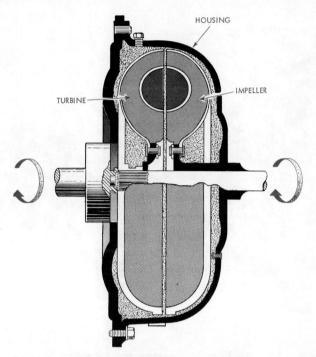

Fig. 2-2. Simplified fluid coupling.

England and Germany. Alan Coats, a young engineer, with Vickers in England, made a significant discovery when he saw the possibility of using roller clutches or free wheeling devices on the reaction member for transforming a fluid converter into a fluid coupling within a single drive unit. He obtained a U.S. patent in 1930 and is considered to be the inventor of the converter-coupling. Coats died while his work was still in the experimental stages but his invention is employed in modern converters. The converter-coupling concept continued to be developed in Europe following the Vickers-Coats development, with several other patents being filed.

In the meantime, Harold Sinclair, a British engineer, after extensive work on the two member fluid coupling, found a successful application in motor buses and automobiles as a fluid flywheel and eventual adoption in the United States in 1938 by the Chrysler Corporation under license.

It was not until after World War II that a converter-coupling was applied to an American passenger car. In 1948, the Buick Motor Division of General Motors

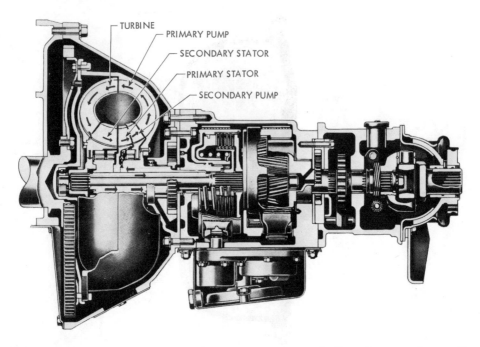

TURBINE
PRIMARY PUMP
SECONDARY STATOR
PRIMARY STATOR
SECONDARY PUMP

Fig. 2-3. Dynaflow 1948 model, the first passenger car application of a converter-coupling.

Corporation introduced a five element fluid unit on its newly designed Dynaflow transmission, Fig. 2-3.

In the past twenty years most of the success with converter work has occurred in the United States. Converter applications have been made extensively to passenger cars, trucks, and buses. A wide variety of heavy duty construction machinery also uses converters, such as wheeled and track laying tractors, loaders, cranes, lift trucks, graders, earth movers, and large farm tractors.

In modern passenger cars the torque converter has gradually taken over as the prime fluid drive unit. The fluid coupling has not been used in American automatic transmissions since 1965. When using the term *torque converter* in connection with automatic transmissions it is understood that it has the dual function. It must act as a torque multiplier with infinitely variable ratios from its maximum torque output to unity (1:1); then it becomes a simple fluid coupling, Fig. 2-4, which is its second function.

The converter offers several other desirable operating features.

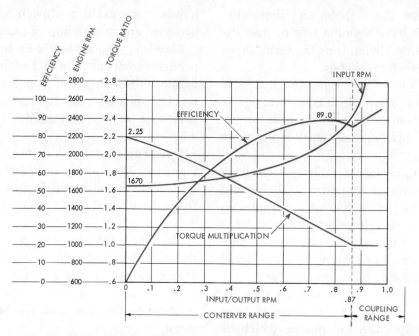

Fig. 2-4. A torque converter performance curve. (Chrysler Corp.)

It is a simple and rugged unit that operates as a clutch in a constant oil bath that gives unlimited life and requires no maintenance such as did the foot operated friction clutch which it eliminated. Since it is a fluid unit it provides a silky, smooth attachment of the engine power to the vehicle that avoids any sudden friction engagement shock to the power train components and results in their longer life and reduced repair costs. Another dividend is the excellent dampening of engine vibration that is taken up by the fluid before it extends into the transmission and drive line. The converter can be likened to a cushion that protects the power train from shocks and vibrations and prevents lugging or stalling of the engine.

Although a variety of fluid torque converter designs have been used in automatic transmissions, the simple *three element unit* (impellor, turbine and stator) is popularly used and the discussion of converter operation will concentrate on this unit.

Definitions—Torque Converter Operation

Element. An element is a single row of flow directing blades. In the simple torque converter the impeller, the turbine, and the stator each have a single row of flow directing blades, thus the term, *three element converter.*

Fluid Coupling. A hydrodynamic drive which transmits power without ability to change torque. Its maximum efficiency is unity, or 1:1.

Hydrodynamic Drive. A drive that transmits power solely by fluid action in a closed recirculation path. An impeller delivers large quantities of fluid moving at high speed into a turbine which is forced to rotate and deliver power.

Impeller. This is the power input member. An impeller is commonly called a pump, which is technically accurate. Use of the word *impeller* is recommended, however, to avoid confusion with pressure and other kinds of pumps.

Member. A member is an independent component of a hydrodynamic unit such as an impeller, a reactor, or a turbine. It may comprise one or more elements, Fig. 2-5.

One-Way Clutch. A device that transmits torque only in one direction. The roller design is favored for use with stator operation, Fig. 2-6.

Reactor (stator). The reaction member of a fluid torque converter. It is commonly called a stator. Reactor is preferred because it describes the function with the basic word.

Stator (See Reactor).

Torque Converter. A hydrody-

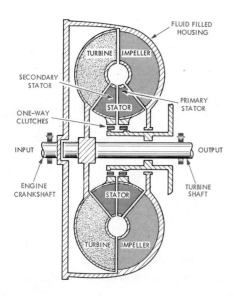

Fig. 2-5. Three member, four element converter; the stator member is made of two elements mounted on separate overrunning clutches that can freewheel independently; used in early converters.

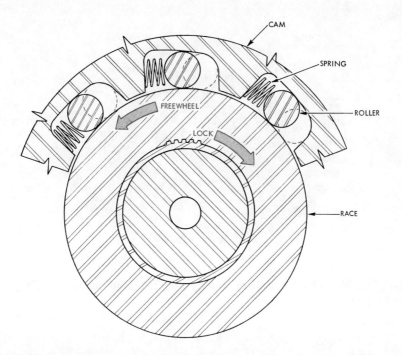

Fig. 2-6. Viewed from rear, typical cross section of one-way roller clutch. (Buick Div., General Motors Corp.)

namic drive which transmits power; it has the ability to change torque. An operational feature of the converter is that it can also perform as a *fluid coupling* when the reactor begins to freewheel in the same direction as the impeller (Fig. 2-2).

Turbine. The output member of a fluid coupling or a converter.

The Fluid Coupling

The operation of a fluid coupling is an introduction to the operation of a torque converter. The knowledge of how a typical fluid coupling is constructed and operates gives a better understanding of why the converter requires curved turbine blades and the addition of a *reactor* (stator).

The actual construction of a fluid coupling is very simple. It consists of impeller and turbine members of identical structure contained in a housing filled with oil, Fig. 2-7

35

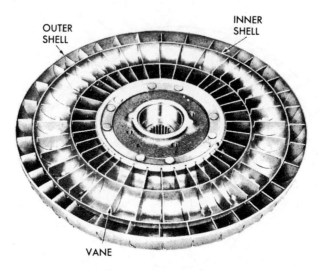

OUTER SHELL

INNER SHELL

VANE

Fig. 2-7. Coupling members (impeller and turbine) are identical. (Pontiac Div., General Motors Corp.)

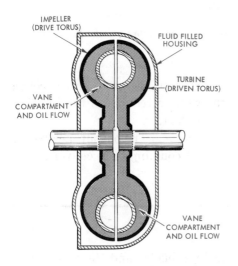

IMPELLER (DRIVE TORUS)

FLUID FILLED HOUSING

TURBINE (DRIVEN TORUS)

VANE COMPARTMENT AND OIL FLOW

VANE COMPARTMENT AND OIL FLOW

Fig. 2-8. Coupling turbine and impeller members in a housing. (Pontiac Div., General Motors Corp.)

and 2-8. The coupling members face one another closely with the impeller *driven* by the engine and the turbine *driving* the wheels through the transmission and axle.

Operation

When starting the car, or accelerating under heavy load, here is what happens inside a fluid cou-

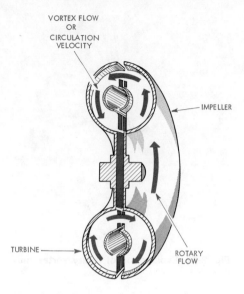

Fig. 2-9. Rotary and vortex flow shown. (Chrysler Corp.)

Fig. 2-10. Swinging bucket shows both rotary and vortex forces.

pling. As the engine drives the impeller, energy is imparted to the fluid between the impeller vanes with the impeller spin-up resulting in a fluid flow of two separate motions. One is a *rotary flow* in the direction of the impeller rotation. The other is a *vortex flow* that circulates the oil between the coupling members caused by the pumping action of the centrifugal force of the rotating impeller, Fig. 2-9.

This is sometimes difficult to understand. However, some examples and illustrations should clarify. Any time there is a spinning mass, the mass (in this case the oil) follows the rotational movement, but it also creates a centrifugal force. This dual effect is illustrated by a

bucket of water that is being swung in a circle, Fig. 2-10.

As the bucket is swinging the water is following the circular path of the bucket. At the same time it is developing a centrifugal force that keeps the water in the bucket as it passes through the overhead position. The water is confined by the solid side and bottom of the bucket and cannot discharge (fly) outward so it is forced to follow the bucket rotation only.

In a fluid coupling, however, the centrifugal force of the oil is not confined. The oil at the center of the spinning impeller follows the curved shell and is discharged along the outer diameter and into the turbine to establish a circular path

37

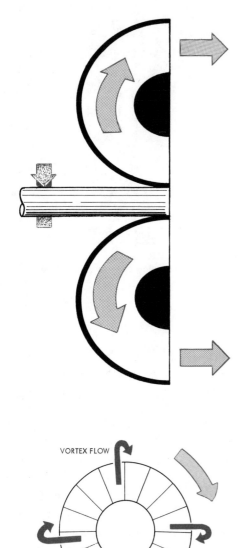

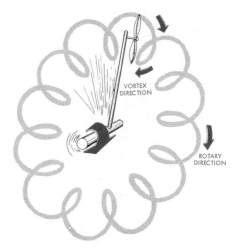

Fig. 2-12. Explanation of rotary vortex motion.

VORTEX FLOW

ROTARY FLOW

IMPELLER

Fig. 2-11. View of oil discharged from impeller—vortex flow; front view of impeller showing pumping action on fluid.

between the impeller and the turbine, Fig. 2-11 top and 2-11 bottom. The combination of rotary and vortex flow sets up an oil motion that follows the course of a rotating corkscrew. It is like watching the blade tips of a rotating pinwheel at the end of a stick with the stick itself turning about a center Fig. 2-12.

With the corkscrew oil action created by the rotation of the engine driven impeller, the turbine is pushed around ahead of the oil, striking on the turbine blades. A fluid clutch is thus established, with the turning torque on the turbine never exceeding impeller input torque.

Let's define these two flows:

Vortex flow. The crosswise or circulatory flow of oil between the blades of the members caused by the centrifugal pumping action of the impeller.

Rotary flow. The flow of the fluid trapped between the blades of the members assumes the direction of the impeller rotation.

Speed Ratio

The striking force of the fluid on the turbine can be explained from a slightly more technical viewpoint. In doing this it becomes necessary to define another term that is used when talking about a fluid coupling or a torque converter.

The number of revolutions which the turbine makes relative to one rotation of the impeller is its *speed ratio*. It is also a measure of *coupling* or *converter efficiency* and is expressed in percentage. For example, if the impeller rotation is 1,000 rpm and turbine rotation 900 rpm the speed ratio is 90 percent.

$$\text{speed ratio} = \frac{\text{turbine rpm}}{\text{impeller rpm}} \text{ or}$$

$$\frac{900}{1000} = 90\%$$

Just when the car starts to move there is an instant when the impeller is rotating and the turbine has not begun to move, a condition of *speed ratio zero*. During this situation the following rotary and vortex flow conditions are in effect:

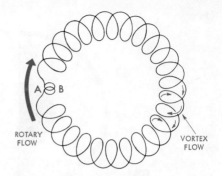

Fig. 2-13. Rotary and vortex flow during the condition of zero speed ratio.

1. Since the turbine is stationary the vortex flow cycles through the turbine unopposed giving a massive cross circulation between the coupling members, Fig. 2-13.
2. The stationary turbine also opposes the rotary flow and the moving oil does not favor rotary flow, also Fig. 2-13.

The effect of the oil striking on the turbine is determined by the strength of the respective oil flows. The impact and its result is illustrated by the vector diagram in Fig. 2-14. The diagram shows the movement of both the vortex flow and the rotary flow and the obvious fact that at the moment of impact it cannot move in two directions at the same time. The oil direction which results from the impact of the two flows will be at some intermediate angle resultant to the rotary and the vortex action, as de-

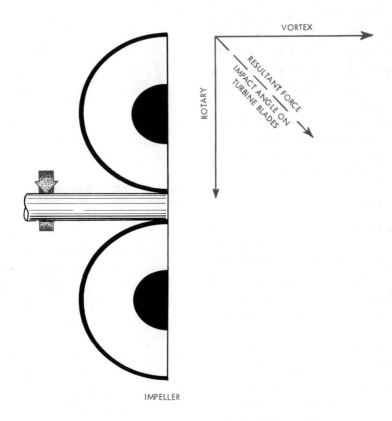

Fig. 2-14. Vector diagram of impact force of rotary and vortex flow.

termined by the speed ratio, or drive condition.

Going back to the *coupling start condition,* it is evident that the high rate of vortex flow does not have a favorable oil impact on the turbine blades; however, it is sufficient to get the turbine moving, as in Fig. 2-15. Considerable slipping takes place because the oil impact is only striking a glancing blow on the straight blades of the turbine.

As the turbine begins to rotate and catch up to impeller speed the vortex flow gradually slows down because of the counter pumping action of the turbine, Fig. 2-16. The speed ratio increases, going from zero to 90 percent, where car cruising speed is established. This makes it difficult for the oil to follow the vortex path and easy to follow the rotary path. Finally, at high efficiencies, the oil mass and momentum are almost entirely rotary at the coupling point, Fig. 2-17.

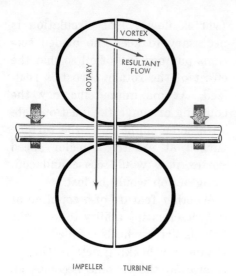

Fig. 2-15. Vortex and rotary impact angle with turbine stationary.

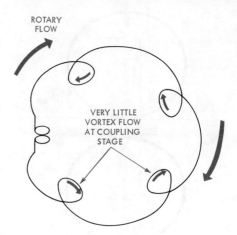

Fig. 2-17. At the coupling point.

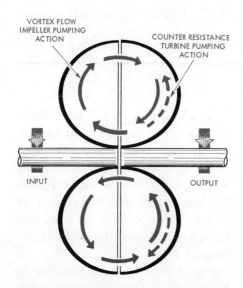

Fig. 2-16. As the turbine begins to turn a counter pumping action builds up.

It should be apparent that as the speed ratio increases to the coupling point the impact thrust of the oil on the turbine blades becomes more effective. At the coupling point the oil impact on the blades is almost direct, giving greatest efficiency, Fig. 2-18.

The change from a state of *coupling slip* to a state of *coupling full torque* occurs quite rapidly and is effective in controlling excessive engine *run-up* in the process. When full torque capacity is reached the turbine is carried along at nearly impeller speed solely by the fluid friction between the body of oil in each member. The resistance of oil to the shearing action between the impeller and turbine maintains a constant transfer of power during cruising.

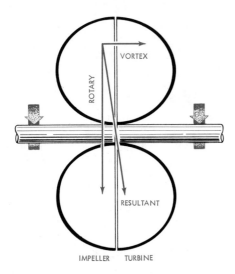

Fig. 2-18. Vortex and rotary impact with turbine at coupling point.

In all instances, whether within a coupling or a converter, no torque is transmitted unless there is a circulation of oil through the members (vortex flow). This circulation is necessary to keep the bladed sections pumped full of oil so that the effect of the rotary thrust is realized. At maximum efficiency the coupling or converter must operate with some slippage. If the turbine turned at exactly impeller speed vortex flow would cease and coupling action would be lost.

Another feature of a coupling or converter is the ability to keep the vehicle drive wheels coupled to the engine for braking action. On deceleration the turbine becomes an impeller and drives the oil against the normal impeller and engine compression. Both units are non-effective at idling speed and this results in a desirable automatic disengagement of engine power to the drive wheels.

The Fluid Torque Converter

An understanding of fluid coupling construction and operation makes it easier to study the torque converter and see how it is possible to multiply torque through fluid action. Although other and more complicated combinations have been used, the practice in current design of automatic transmissions is to use this three element combination: an impeller (pump), a turbine, and reactor (stator), Fig. 2-19.

A *split guide ring,* Fig. 2-20, is built into the impeller and turbine for greater operational efficiency. Since the center of the vortex flow sets up a *turbulence* which results in a loss of efficiency, the guide ring is used to provide a smooth, uniform flow between the impeller and turbine.

Fig. 2-21 shows the impeller as an integral part of the housing which in manufacturing production

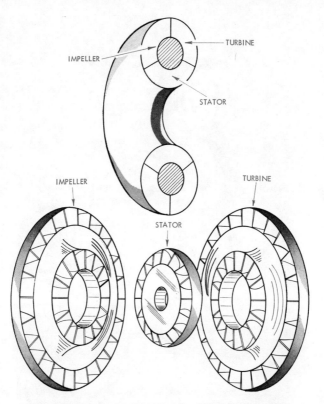

Fig. 2-19. Torque converter of the three element type.

is welded to the cover and encloses the turbine and the reactor. The reactor incorporates a one-way clutch and mounts on a support which is part of the transmission front pump assembly.

Another construction feature is the design of the impeller and turbine blades illustrated in Fig. 2-22. The curved shape of the impeller blades in a backward direction gives added acceleration and energy to the oil as it leaves the im-

peller, while the curved shape of the turbine vanes is designed to absorb as much energy as possible from the moving oil as it passes through the turbine.

Turbine vane curvature has two functions which give the turbine its excellent torque absorbing capacity. It reduces shock losses due to sudden change in oil direction between the impeller and turbine, Fig. 2-23. It also takes advantage of the hydraulic principle that the

43

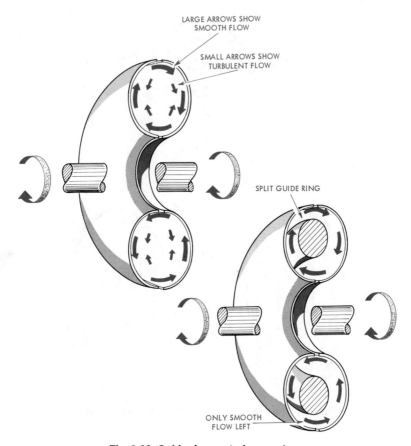

LARGE ARROWS SHOW
SMOOTH FLOW

SMALL ARROWS SHOW
TURBULENT FLOW

SPLIT GUIDE RING

ONLY SMOOTH
FLOW LEFT

Fig. 2-20. Guide ring part of converter.

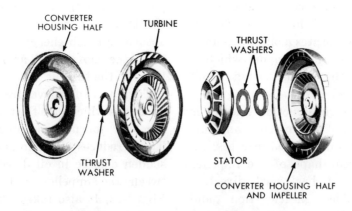

CONVERTER
HOUSING HALF

TURBINE

THRUST
WASHERS

THRUST
WASHER

STATOR

CONVERTER HOUSING HALF
AND IMPELLER

Fig. 2-21. Impeller as part of housing. (Ford Motor Co.)

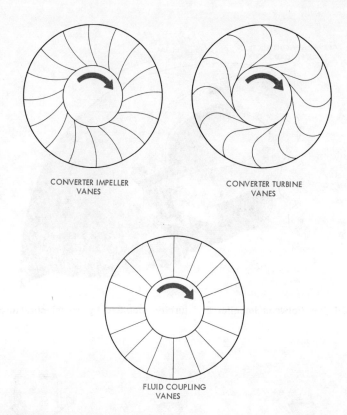

CONVERTER IMPELLER
VANES

CONVERTER TURBINE
VANES

FLUID COUPLING
VANES

Fig. 2-22. Comparison of converter impeller and turbine blades to coupling member blades. (Buick Div., General Motors Corp.)

more the direction of a moving fluid is diverted the greater the force the fluid exerts on the diverting surface. The two functions are illustrated in Fig. 2-24.

A fluid jet stream directed against a flat surface exerts a force on the plate but not without a shock loss caused by the breakdown of the smooth liquid flow, Fig. 2-24, left. By curving the inlet side, Fig. 2-24, center, the shock loss is reduced

considerably but the force on the flat surface remains the same. The plate surface, Fig. 2-24, right, is curved at both inlet and outlet, keeping the fluid smooth and greatly increasing the force of the fluid jet stream on the plate.

The third bladed member of the converter is the reactor (stator). Its function is to give directional control to the oil as it leaves the turbine and re-enters the impeller,

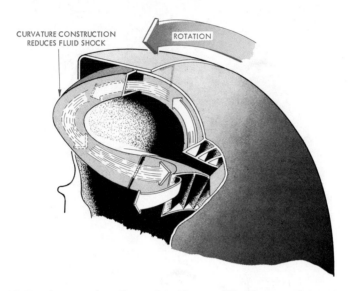

Fig. 2-23. Oil flow between impeller and turbine modified by vessel curvature. (Chrysler Corp.)

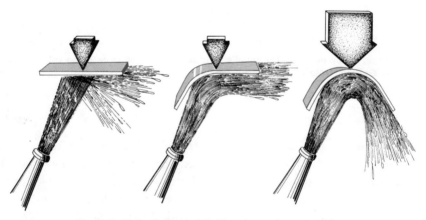

Fig. 2-24. Path of diverted fluid under various conditions.

Fig. 2-25. This action permits the reactor to perform the same function in the converter circuit as the fulcrum serves in a lever or gear system.

Converter Operation

Impeller and Turbine.   As in the fluid coupling, converter operation starts with the impeller putting the

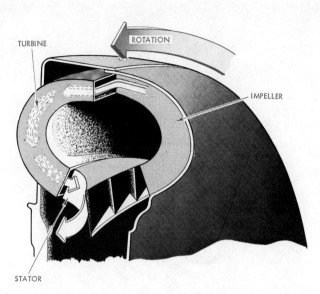

Fig. 2-25. Stator design redirects fluid flow to assist impeller rotation. (Chrysler Corp.)

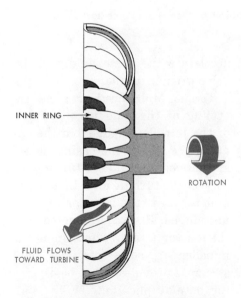

Fig. 2-26. Impeller operation—fluid flow.

fluid in motion, the engine furnishing the energy input. The rotating impeller creates the same centrifugal pumping action (described under fluid coupling operation) which results in acceleration of the fluid and a jet-like discharge into the turbine, Fig. 2-26.

The curved turbine blades absorb energy from the fluid until the force of fluid is great enough to overcome the turbine resistance to motion (turbine output is the input into the transmission).

Fig. 2-27 shows that at this point of operation the impeller and turbine are acting as a fluid coupling but have no torque multiplication effect. However, it should be noted that the turbine vanes have reversed the fluid flow.

The greatest amount of force occurs when the vane surface reverses the incoming jet flow rather

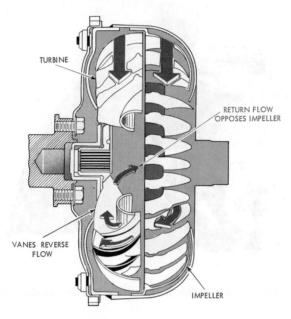

TURBINE

RETURN FLOW
OPPOSES IMPELLER

VANES REVERSE
FLOW

IMPELLER

Fig. 2-27. Fluid coupling action at point at which reversal of turbine flow occurs.

than just deflecting it. However, the reverse flow of fluid back to the impeller would work against impeller rotation and lug the engine.

Reactor (Stator). To correct this condition a reactor or stator is employed between the turbine out-flow and the impeller in-flow to reverse the direction of the oil and make it flow in the same direction as the impeller rotation, Fig. 2-28. Instead of the fluid bucking the impeller and interfering with it, the unexpended energy in the oil now assists the impeller. The reactor (stator) becomes a reaction member aiding the function of the impeller. Through this boost the impeller has another opportunity to

accelerate the same fluid and develop greater torque.

Torque Multiplication. The recycling of the fluid permits more of the impeller input from the engine to be used in increasing the jet stream velocity and the turning effort on the turbine even though engine torque to the impeller remains unchanged. It should be noted that the reactor (stator), by helping the impeller to accelerate the fluid stream, provides the basis for torque multiplication. This is similar to torque multiplication by reduction gear, Fig. 2-29. For passenger car applications, engineering design of the three element converter is to keep the torque output

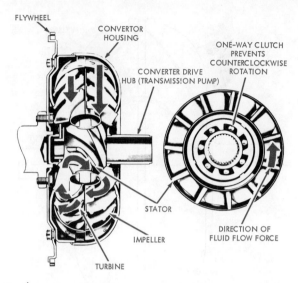

Fig. 2-28. Stator operation with converter in torque multiplication stage.

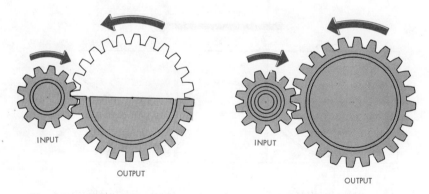

Fig. 2-29. Fluid torque multiplication gives the same effect as gear reduction.

within the general range of 2:1 to 2.5:1, otherwise overheating will result from heavy driving loads.

During torque multiplication, vortex flow actually moves the fluid through the impeller, to the turbine, to the reactor, and back through the impeller, Fig. 2-30. It is the acceleration of the vortex movement that results in torque multiplication. Since vortex flow is greatest at stall conditions the greatest torque boost takes place at this time. As the speed ratio in-

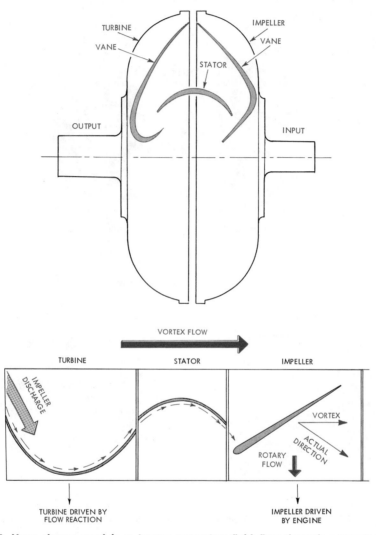

Fig. 2-30. Vane shapes used in a torque converter; fluid flow through converter during torque multiplication. (Allison Div., General Motors Corp.)

creases it is known that the vortex flow decreases; and therefore torque multiplication is gradually reduced. At about 90 percent speed ratio, or when the turbine speed is about 9/10 of impeller speed, there is no longer any torque multiplication. The rotary flow of the fluid is the predominant influence and the converter enters a coupling phase, Fig. 2-31.

A comparison can be made to the

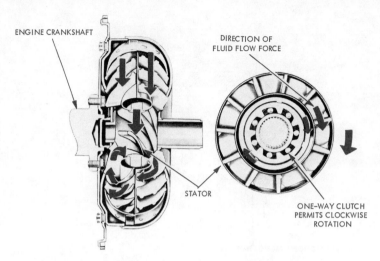

ENGINE CRANKSHAFT

DIRECTION OF
FLUID FLOW FORCE

STATOR

ONE-WAY CLUTCH
PERMITS CLOCKWISE
ROTATION

Fig. 2-31. Coupling phase of converter operation. (Ford Motor Co.)

fluid coupling operation. As the turbine catches up with the impeller, the angle at which the fluid exists from the turbine is constantly changing. Finally, in the converter coupling phase the fluid exiting from the turbine strikes the *back* of the reactor (stator) blades. The reactor no longer is needed and the one-way clutch *releases* to permit the stator to freewheel and rotate with the impeller and turbine.

(Stall is a condition where the impeller is rotating and the turbine is stationary. The maximum stall and torque is when the turbine is stationary and the engine drives the impeller at wide open throttle.)

Newton's Law. The ability of the torque converter to multiply torque can also be understood by applying Newton's Law of Physics,

"For every action there is an equal and opposite reaction." In the converter, the impeller, the turbine, and the reactor are points of action and reaction with respect to oil flow. During the period of torque multiplication the *reaction* of the stationary reactor (stator) blades to the oil is in the same direction as the impeller rotation, Fig. 2-32. In accordance with Newton's Law the reaction of the turbine blades on the oil must be equal to the combined reactor and impeller torque (A + B = C). Turbine torque, therefore, is greater than impeller torque by the amount of the reactor (stator) *reaction torque.* Therefore C − B = A.

Using Newton's Law again, it is obvious why a coupling cannot increase torque. Without a stator or

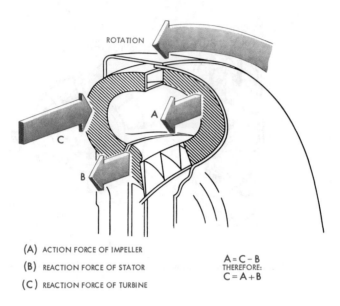

ROTATION

(A) ACTION FORCE OF IMPELLER

(B) REACTION FORCE OF STATOR

(C) REACTION FORCE OF TURBINE

A = C – B
THEREFORE:
C = A + B

Fig. 2-32. Newton's law as applied to converter torque multiplication. (Chrysler Corp.)

reactor the fluid coupling has only two points of action and reaction—the impeller and the turbine. The impeller action on the fluid is opposed only by the reaction of the turbine so the action-reaction between the two must always equal one another.

Cooling the Hydraulic Fluid. When the converter is multiplying torque, the *recirculating vortex flow* causes considerable heat to be generated and it becomes necessary to provide some type of cooling to keep the fluid from overheating. Two type of cooling systems are used, *oil-to-air* and *oil-to-water*.

In both types, *feed oil* under low pressure from the transmission front pump and regulator valve is constantly cycling oil into and out of the converter with the outflow returning to the transmission sump. In the oil-to-water system used with larger engines, the oil is simply routed through a water cooler lower tank or side tank, Figs. 2-33 and 2-34.

The oil-to-air system requires a *cooling shroud cover*, tacked over the rear half of the converter, which is provided with fins to pick up the air in the space between converter and the shroud, Fig. 2-35. As the converter revolves, a centrifugal air pump action develops. A low pressure area is formed between the shroud and fin pockets

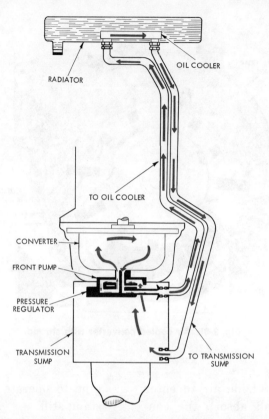

Fig. 2-33. Oil cooling circuit for the converter, bottom tank of radiator. (Ford Motor Co.)

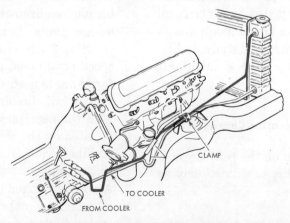

Fig. 2-34. Another converter oil cooler circuit, side tank design. (Oldsmobile Div., General Motors Corp.)

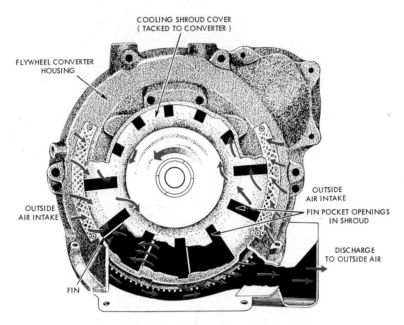

COOLING SHROUD COVER
(TACKED TO CONVERTER)

FLYWHEEL CONVERTER
HOUSING

OUTSIDE
AIR INTAKE

OUTSIDE
AIR INTAKE

FIN POCKET OPENINGS
IN SHROUD

DISCHARGE
TO OUTSIDE AIR

FIN

Fig. 2-35. Air cooled converter with shroud.

which allows outside air to enter the pockets and absorb the converter heat.

After the air passes over the converter it is expelled by centrifugal force through a housing outlet back to the atmosphere. A study of Fig. 2-35 will reveal the detailed air action.

Converter Operating Characteristics

In operation on the road the converter provides effortless driving characteristics:

1. At *engine idle* it acts as an automatic clutch and permits the en-

gine to operate and the car to stand still.

2. It automatically adjusts its torque output to drive shaft torque requirements within its design limits. It acts as a *fluid coupling* for level road, constant speed conditions, but when performance is needed for acceleration or hill climbing it responds with the necessary extra torque dictated by the slowdown of the turbine from increased drive shaft torque.

3. As the converter is a fluid unit, it acts as a natural *shock absorber* during gear ratio changes and adds to shift smoothness.

Converter Capacity or Size

When discussing converters it is important to note another characteristic or behavior pattern. A mechanical gear transmission will take on any amount of torque up to the *clutch slip point;* a torque converter will however absorb only a given amount of engine torque and no more. For example, as the throttle control opens and engine torque starts to rise, the engine will be permitted to speed up only to the point where engine torque reaches converter torque capacity. When converter torque capacity is reached, engine rpm stabilizes and

the converter slips. This is referred to as the *converter stall speed.* (Converter stall speed will be explained later where stall speed testing is covered.)

It should be apparent that the converter has the added job of controlling engine rpm, and in essence, must be carefully designed to take advantage of the engine torque output for most efficient operation (the converter and engine must be matched). As another approach, the engine rpm, by virtue of converter design, is controlled by the load which the impeller imposes on the engine as it attempts to drive the turbine. Naturally, as the ve-

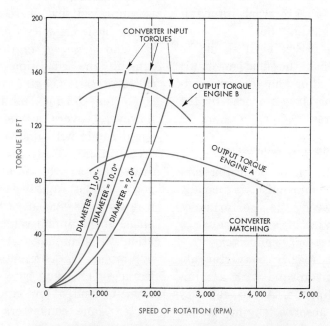

Fig. 2-36. Matching of converter design to the engine.

hicle picks up momentum and turbine speed increases, the engine torque required to drive the impeller falls off and engine speed steadily rises.

If too small a converter is used for a particular application the engine will operate at higher rpm than desired before the converter can transmit *maximum torque.*

In the situation where too large a converter is used, the engine would not have the ability to drive the impeller at a speed which would permit it to operate at maximum power. Both size extremes result in an undesirable *overspeed* or *underspeed* condition. The normal practice is to match the converter and engine at a stall speed that enables the engine to reach its maximum torque, Fig. 2-36.

From the preceding it should be apparent that the field mechanic should not alter the converter-engine size match engineered by the manufacturer.

Variable Capacity Converters

In the design of a torque converter a compromise is usually made between the performance characteristics of a *high capacity* and a *low capacity converter.*

A high capacity converter absorbs engine torque with a minimum of slippage. A low capacity converter absorbs engine torque with greater slippage, but produces more fluid torque for acceleration. A high capacity converter gives pleasing light throttle starts and a low coupling point for excellent highway cruising efficiency. A low coupling point means that the torque multiplication under heavy throttle cannot stretch itself over a wide vehicle speed range. The converter, for example, may be designed to reach coupling phase under full throttle at 45 mph. The automatic gear ratios continue to function to give engine performance. With the low coupling point and the low engine speed inherited from a high capacity converter, full throttle engine performance is not at optimum.

When acceleration performance is improved by decreasing converter basic capacity *light throttle feel* and *coupling tightness* suffer, causing the condition commonly called *excessive engine run-up.* The converter torque multiplication, however, covers a wider vehicle speed range with improved engine acceleration. This presents one drawback as the *high coupling point* does not rapidly achieve highway cruising efficiency. The torque phase at maximum vehicle acceleration is sometimes stretched to 90 mph. To eliminate the dilemma of choosing between a high capacity and a low capacity converter some converters were designed with *variable pitch stator*

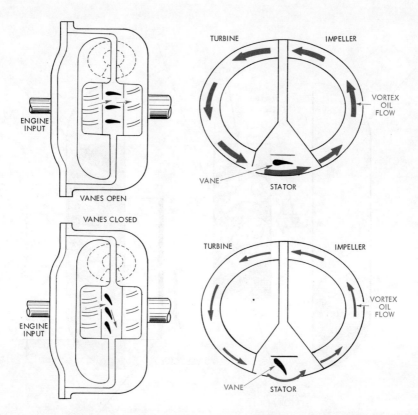

Fig. 2-37. Variable stator vane open, and closed. (Allison Div., General Motors Corp.)

blades. A simple illustration of variable pitch stator blades is shown in Fig. 2-37.

Fig. 2-38 shows how the *exit angle* of the stator blades affects the converter capacity. This is directly related to the amount of fluid acceleration that must take place in the impeller to bring the velocity of the fluid at the stator exit to match the velocity of the fluid exiting from the pump. The greater the change, the greater is the capacity.

As shown in Fig. 2-39, the high angle position causes the re-entry oil from the stator to have greater momentum and a more favorable thrust angle for impeller propulsion. In the various technical writings on passenger car automatic transmissions there appears to be disagreement as to what the stator blade angle is in reference to *open* and *closed positions* on variable pitch converters. To avoid confusion we refer to the *open blade*

57

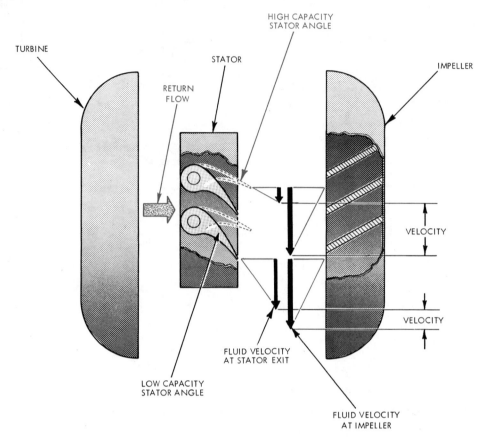

Fig. 2-38. Exit angle from stator as it affects pump capacity. (Allison Div., General Motors Corp.)

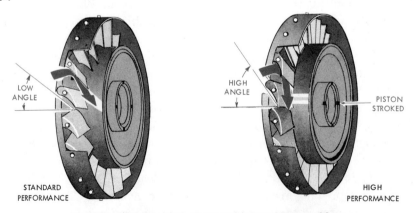

Fig. 2-39. Variable pitch stator at high and low positions.

position as low angle and *the closed blade position* as high angle, Fig. 2-39.

Another factor works to lower converter capacity as the stator blades are moved to high angle. The blades cause a restriction in flow which decreases the amount of fluid passing through the impeller. As a result the impeller can add more energy to the fluid. Since the quantity of fluid is less it can be accelerated at a faster rate and thus improve engine performance.

Advantages. A torque converter with a variable stator offers these advantages:

1. In the high capacity range the tighter converter allows starts with a minimum of engine speed.
2. The high capacity also gives a very efficient coupling.

3. In the low capacity range engine speed is allowed to increase for high performance starts, giving more input to the converter.

4. Extension of the *torque multiplication range* is increased to higher speeds in the low capacity range. High performance engines with *low axle ratios* have had coupling points as high as 90 mph.

5. A transition from the high capacity converter to low capacity converter and vice versa can be easily and smoothly accomplished, as seen in Fig. 2-40.

6. When the control pressure triggers the stator valve, the high pressure feed is cut off and the circuit to the stator piston exhausted. Converter low pressure

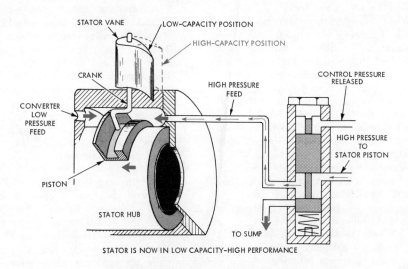

Fig. 2-40. Operation of a variable stator.

feed then moves the piston and stator blades to the high capacity position.

With the exception of one older design which set the stator blades at any position between high and low angles, the standard practice is to position the blades in either high or low angle.

The variable capacity converter was first introduced in the Buick Dynaflow and was subsequently adopted for use in the other multi-turbine converter drives that were soon to follow. After more than a decade the multi-turbine converter drives faded from the scene; however the variable capacity concept was kept alive and was used in some of the three element converter type applications until the production year of 1968. Today's automatic transmissions are of the 2 and 3-speed design, using the simple three element converter of the conventional fixed blade design.

ANSWER THE CIRCLED QUESTIONS

Checking On Your Knowledge

The following questions give you the opportunity to check up on yourself. If you have read the chapter carefully, you should be able to answer the questions.

If you have any difficulty, read the chapter over once more so that you have the information well in mind before you go on with your reading.

1. What is a hydrodynamic drive?
2. What is the difference between the function of a fluid coupling and a fluid torque converter?
3. What significant contributions did the following European engineers make in the field of hydrodynamic drives? Dr. Hermann Fottinger, Alan Coats, and Harold Sinclair.
4. When was the first fluid coupling for passenger car application introduced in the United States?
5. When was the first fluid torque converter for passenger car application introduced in the United States?
6. What are some desirable operating advantages of a hydrodynamic drive as it applies to passenger cars?
7. Answer the following questions on fluid coupling operation:
   a. What are the two members that make-up a fluid coupling? Briefly state their job function.
   b. What two forces are set up in the fluid mass as a result of impeller spin-up?
   c. Define the following terms: *rotary flow, vortex flow,* and *speed ratio.*
   d. Explain speed ratio as a reflection of coupling or converter efficiency.
   e. Briefly explain how the resultant force or impact angle of the fluid discharge from the impeller to turbine changes as the coupling efficiency changes from a speed ratio of zero to 90 percent plus.
   f. Why does the effect of vortex flow in the fluid mass get less as the speed ratio increases?
   g. What is the coupling speed ratio when the impeller speed is 1,800 rpm and the turbine speed 1,000 rpm?
8. Answer the following questions on fluid torque converter operation?
   a. Name the major parts that make up a simple three element torque converter.

b. What is the guide ring function?

c. Name the input member of the torque converter; the one connected to the engine.

d. Name the output member of the torque converter; the one connected to the input shaft of the transmission.

e. Name the reactor member of the torque converter; the one mounted on an overrunning clutch and serves as the torque multiplier.

f. Why are the impeller and turbine blades designed with a curved shape?

g. What is the function of the stator during the torque multiplication phase of operation?

h. What is the function of the stator during the coupling phase of operation?

i. Why is the stator mounted on a one way clutch?

j. In relation to impeller rotation, what direction does the stator freewheel during the coupling phase of operation?

k. What would be the characteristic of the vehicle performance should the overrunning clutch fail to hold the stator stationary during the torque multiplication phase of operation?

l. What is a stall condition? Describe maximum stall.

m. When does the torque converter produce its maximum torque output?

n. What happens to converter torque output as the turbine speed approaches impeller speed?

o. What is the converter torque ratio when the speed ratio is 90 percent plus?

9. Name the two types of cooling systems used to prevent overheating of the torque converter.

10. What are the comparisons between the performance characteristics of a high capacity and low capacity converter?

11. What are the advantages of a variable capacity converter?

12. What is the blade position of a variable pitch stator for high performance?

13. Applying Newton's Law of Physics, "For every action there is an equal and opposite reaction", explain why a fluid torque converter can multiply torque and a fluid coupling cannot multiply torque.

Chapter 3

Planetary Gears In Transmissions

Planetary gears have been associated with the American automobile since its very beginning at the turn of the century. They were among the first type of gearing used in passenger car and light truck transmissions and offered the advantage of minimum driver skill when changing gears (gear ratios). The sliding gear boxes in the early years did not feature synchronized shifts and it was a skillful art to change gears on the move.

Design restrictions confined the planetary gear boxes to two speeds and a reverse, although it is on record that the 1906 Cadillac used a 3-speed planetary transmission. These early versions were not without their problems. They were noisy, had short bearing life (the practice at that time was to use

bushing mounted pinions), and at times *chattered* or *grabbed* during shift changes because of uneven brake band application.

Advances in the sliding gear transmission design eventually lead to its popularity over the planetary designs and the almost universal use of sliding gear transmissions in passenger cars and trucks. The Ford Model T, however, used a planetary transmission until the year 1928.

Planetary gears staged a comeback in the 30's with the introduction of the Borg-Warner *automatic overdrive* and the General Motors' Hydra-Matic transmission. Research and development in helical gears, alloy steels, heat treatment of metal, and needle bearings eliminated many of the deficiencies of the early types of planetary gears.

Planetary gears today have a wide range of applications, varying from passenger car and truck automatic transmissions to steering and final drive mechanisms of track and wheel driven construction machinery, and as *reduction gears* for aircraft propeller drives. These are just a few modern examples of the planetary gear applications in power transmission.

The Planetary Gear Assembly

The heart of the automatic transmission is the planetary gear system. It is therefore essential to review the basic construction of a simple planetary gear set as an introduction to how planetary gears operate.

A simple planetary gear set, Figs. 3-1 and 3-2, consists of a *sun* gear or center gear which is surrounded and in constant mesh with the *planet gears or pinions* which are mounted and free to rotate on individual support pins of the *planet carrier,* and within the *internal gear* (so-called because the gear teeth are cut on the inner circumference) which surrounds and

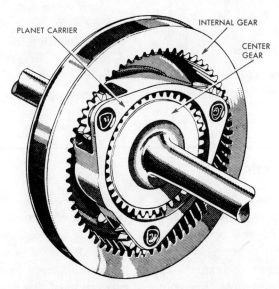

PLANET CARRIER

INTERNAL GEAR

CENTER GEAR

Fig. 3-1. Simple planetary gear assembly. (The sun gear is sometimes called the center gear.)

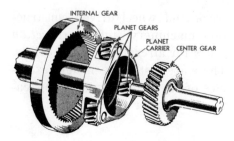

Fig. 3-2. Planetary gear assembly—exploded view.

is in *constant mesh* with the planet pinions.

The planetary gear set gets its name from the action of the planet pinion gears. As will be observed in later discussion, they have the ability to turn on their own centers and at the same time revolve around the sun gear. This is similar to the earth turning on its axis and rotating around the sun.

By studying Figs. 3-1 and 3-2, several major advantages of planetary gears are realized:

1. All members of the planetary gear set share a common axis, which results in a structure of compact size.

2. Planetary gears are always in full and constant mesh, eliminating the possibility of gear tooth damage from gear clash or partial engagement. The full and constant mesh feature also permits automatic and quick gear ratio changes without power flow interruption.

3. Planetary gears are strong and sturdy and can handle larger torque loads for their compact size than any other gear combinations in a standard transmission. This is because the torque load as it passes through the planetary set is distributed over the several planet pinion gears which in effect allows more tooth contact area to handle the power transmission.

4. The location of the planetary members makes it relatively easy to hold the members or lock them together for ratio changes.

Gearing Definitions

Whether a *gear train* is set up as *a simple, compound,* or *planetary system,* much of the terminology used in describing how they work and affect the power train is the same. It is necessary at this point to review some gearing definitions that are essential for undertaking the task of planetary gear operation.

Gear Ratio. The number of revolutions the input gear makes to one revolution of the output gear. In a simple gear combination three revolutions of the input gear to one of the output gear gives a ratio of 3:1.

Gear Reduction. Torque is multiplied and speed decreased by the factor of the gear ratio. For example, a 3:1 gear ratio will change an input torque of 180 lb-ft and an input speed of 2,700 rpm to 540 lb-ft and 900 rpm respectively. (No account is taken for *frictional losses* which are always present.)

Overdrive. It produces the opposite effect of a gear reduction. Torque is reduced and speed is increased by the factor of the gear ratio. A 1:3 gear ratio would change the previously mentioned input torque and speed used for

gear reduction to 60 lb-ft and 8,100 rpm.

Direct Drive. The gear ratio is 1:1 with no change occurring in the torque and speed input.

Freewheeling. There is a power input with no transmission of power output.

Reaction Member. In a planetary gear set, reference is made to the *stationary planetary member* grounded to the transmission case. This is accomplished through the use of friction and *wedging devices* known as *bands, disc clutches,* and one way *clutches*. These will be discussed and illustrated later in the chapter.

The Laws of Planetary Gear Operation

The operation of a planetary gear train is governed by five basic laws which provide the key to understanding the various power flows in all automatic transmissions. They are the laws of *neutral, reduction, overdrive, direct drive,* and *reverse*. Carefully study them one at a time.

Law of Neutral

When there is an input, but no reaction member, the condition is neutral.

In Fig. 3-3 the sun gear serves as the driving input member and the internal gear is free to rotate

since it is not grounded to any part of the transmission. The planet carrier is held stationary by the weight of the car on the rear wheels. This causes the planet pinion gears to rotate on their pins and drive the internal gear opposite the sun gear or input direction.

In automatic transmissions neutral is accomplished as in the above manner, or achieved by de-clutching the converter turbine input to the transmission. Lately, and in recent production of automatic transmissions the 2-speed Jetaway (T-300), Powerglide, and Torque-Drive are the only units that pick

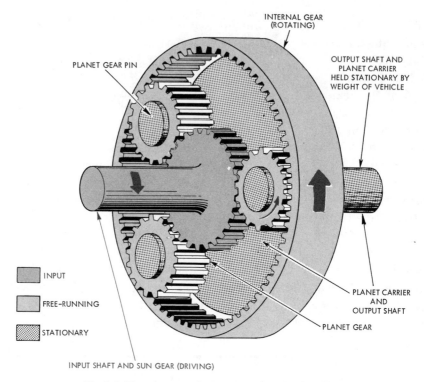

INTERNAL GEAR
(ROTATING)

PLANET GEAR PIN

OUTPUT SHAFT AND
PLANET CARRIER
HELD STATIONARY BY
WEIGHT OF VEHICLE

INPUT

FREE–RUNNING

STATIONARY

PLANET CARRIER
AND
OUTPUT SHAFT

PLANET GEAR

INPUT SHAFT AND SUN GEAR (DRIVING)

Fig. 3-3. Planetary gear set during neutral operation.

up neutral through the gear set. All others *de-clutch* the converter turbine input and avoid using a gear set for *neutral*.

Law of Reduction

When there is a reaction member and the planet carrier is the output, the condition is gear reduction.

There are two reduction possibilities that meet the requirements for the law of reduction. In Fig. 3-4 a brake band used typically in automatic transmissions is *applied*

to the internal gear and holds it against rotation. The band itself is rigidly anchored to the transmission case when applied and serves as the *grounding medium* for the *reactionary internal gear*.

This first illustration of reduction shows the input sun gear driving the pinion gears on their pins opposite the input direction. Since the pinion gears cannot move the stationary internal gear, a reaction force is set up which causes the pinions to walk around the internal gear as they rotate and to move

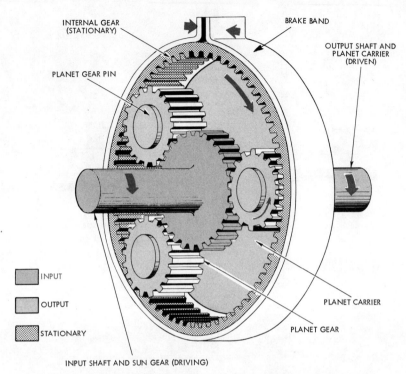

INTERNAL GEAR
(STATIONARY)

BRAKE BAND

OUTPUT SHAFT AND
PLANET CARRIER
(DRIVEN)

PLANET GEAR PIN

INPUT

OUTPUT

STATIONARY

PLANET CARRIER

PLANET GEAR

INPUT SHAFT AND SUN GEAR (DRIVING)

Fig. 3-4. Planetary gear set during reduction, with internal gear held.

the carrier in a forward direction at a reduced speed. If the input torque is 100 lb-ft and the gear reduction is 1.5:1, then the output torque is increased to 150 lb-ft.

The other reduction combination is set up with the sun gear stationary and power input applied to the internal gear, Fig. 3-5. The planet pinions now rotate on their pins and walk around the sun gear to produce another forward reduction effect on the carrier. This kind of planetary gear *reduction power flow* is used for second gear oper-

ation in the current series of Chrysler's TorqueFlite, Ford's C-4 and C-6, and G.M.'s Turbine 350 and 400.

In place of a band for connecting a selected planetary reaction member solidly to the transmission case, the *sprag clutch*, the *roller clutch*, and the *multiple disc clutch* are also used as *grounding components* for reduction. The sprag and roller clutches are both classified as *one-way clutches* and are rather interesting devices. They are self initiating in the exact timing of their

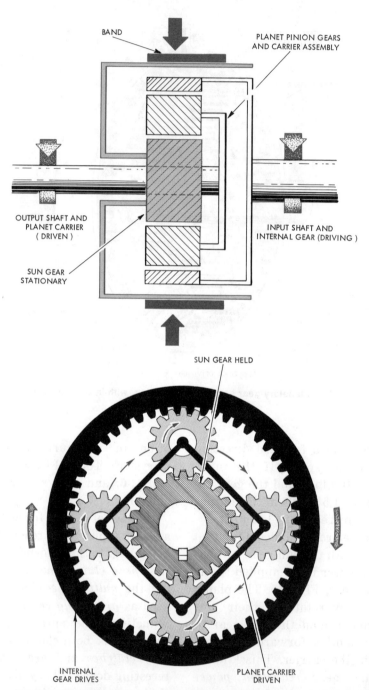

BAND

PLANET PINION GEARS
AND CARRIER ASSEMBLY

OUTPUT SHAFT AND
PLANET CARRIER
(DRIVEN)

INPUT SHAFT AND
INTERNAL GEAR (DRIVING)

SUN GEAR
STATIONARY

SUN GEAR HELD

INTERNAL
GEAR DRIVES

PLANET CARRIER
DRIVEN

Fig. 3-5. Planetary gear set during reduction, with sun gear held.

hold and *freewheeling actions,* and require no hydraulic controls. They operate solely by mechanical means, and both use a wedging action when they *self-apply.* This self operating feature permits simplified transmission design and easy maintenance, with space saving, and no adjustment requirements.

A study of Figs. 3-6 and 3-7 will show the wedging (ON position) and freewheeling (OFF position) action of these clutches. Both illustrations could be reversed to show the inner race as the stationary member and the outer race as the rotating or drive member. In actual practice the stationary race

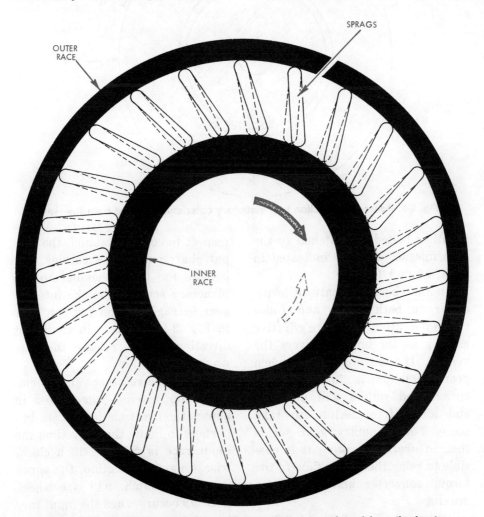

Fig. 3-6. Sprag clutch action with stationary outer race—viewed from the front.

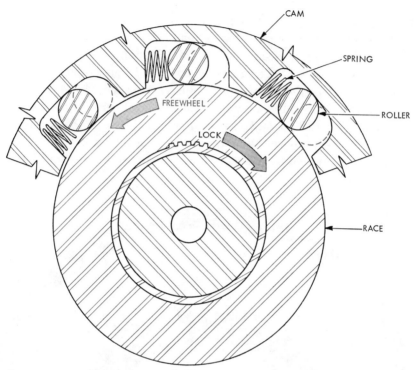

Fig. 3-7. Roller clutch action with stationary outer cam—viewed from the rear.

is either bolted or clutched to the transmission case, as indicated in Figs. 3-8 and 3-9.

Another behavior pattern is peculiar to both sprag and roller clutch operation. They are effective as long as the engine powers the vehicle. If *coasting* occurs when gear reduction is in effect, the sprags and rollers will unwedge and allow freewheeling to take place. The planetary gear set is then in *neutral*, making it impossible to relay the power flow to the torque converter and engine for braking.

Reviewing Figs. 3-8 and 3-9 in respect to coasting action, the output shaft and planet carrier now become the input member to the planetary set, causing the internal gear in Fig. 3-8 and the sun gear in Fig. 3-9 to rotate in the input direction and to release the one-way clutch.

For future reference in determining the *gearing power flow* in automatic transmissions it is important to know that any time the input race is rotating in a clockwise (engine) direction, the sprag or roller clutch will freewheel. *Lock-up* occurs when the input race is rotated counter-clockwise.

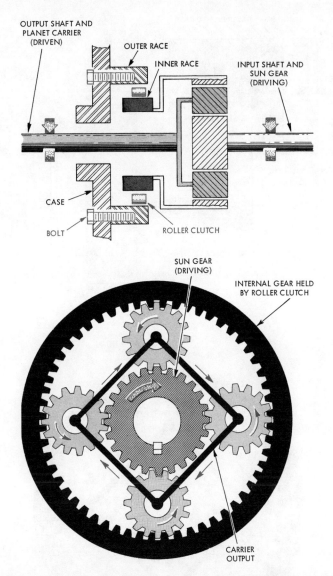

OUTPUT SHAFT AND
PLANET CARRIER
(DRIVEN)

OUTER RACE

INNER RACE

INPUT SHAFT AND
SUN GEAR
(DRIVING)

CASE

BOLT

ROLLER CLUTCH

SUN GEAR
(DRIVING)

INTERNAL GEAR HELD
BY ROLLER CLUTCH

CARRIER
OUTPUT

Fig. 3-8. Planetary Gear Set in reduction, internal gear held by roller clutch action.

Although the freewheeling action of a sprag or roller clutch on coast or deceleration is not a hazard for normal driving, it is definitely un-safe when transmission gear reductions need to be used for controlling vehicle speed on descending steep hills or mountain grades. To

71

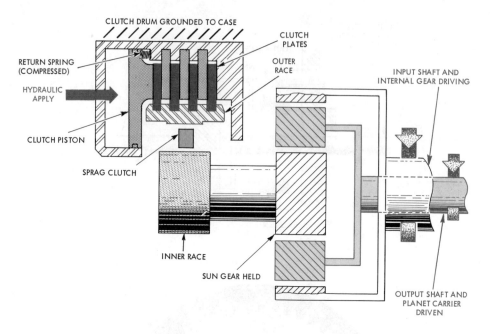

CLUTCH DRUM GROUNDED TO CASE

CLUTCH PLATES

RETURN SPRING (COMPRESSED)

OUTER RACE

HYDRAULIC APPLY

INPUT SHAFT AND INTERNAL GEAR DRIVING

CLUTCH PISTON

SPRAG CLUTCH

INNER RACE

SUN GEAR HELD

OUTPUT SHAFT AND PLANET CARRIER DRIVEN

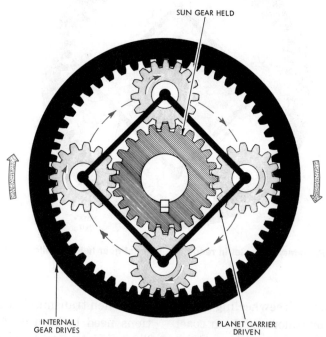

SUN GEAR HELD

INTERNAL GEAR DRIVES

PLANET CARRIER DRIVEN

Fig. 3-9. Planetary gear set in reduction, sun gear clutched to transmission case by multiple disc clutch apply and one-way clutch action.

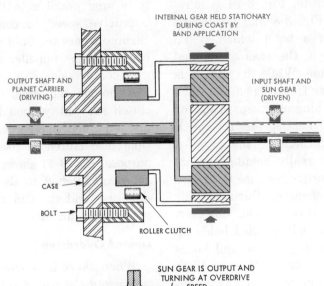

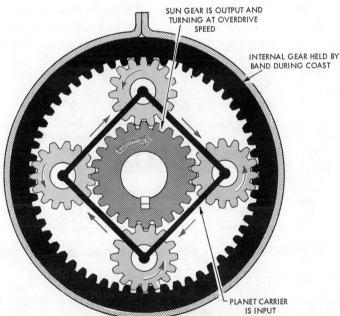

Fig. 3-10. Planetary gear set in reduction showing band apply for braking during coast. Band is applied at all times during drive or coast conditions.

overcome this deficiency the driver can select an operating range, such as *manual low,* which will elimin- ate the freewheeling and return positive gearing action to the engine for braking and a safe descent.

To illustrate, Fig. 3-10 is a re-design of Fig. 3-8 and shows the addition of a band which would be applied in the case of manual low operation. While the vehicle is under power from the engine, such as in climbing a steep grade or while using *manual low* for maximum performance, the *applied band* is not really holding against the drive torque because the *roller clutch* is effective. During grade descent or deceleration, however, the band already applied holds up against coasting torque and keeps the internal gear reactionary. With the planet carrier serving as the input to the gear set during coasting

it is now possible to transfer an overdrive speed to the converter turbine where the fluid attempts to overspeed the impeller against engine compression.

Although the band and roller clutch are widely used for the reduction function, on occasion a multiple disc clutch is used for this purpose. Fig. 3-11 shows the internal gear clutched to the transmission case and the sun gear acting as the input drive.

Law of Overdrive

When there is a reaction member and the planet carrier is the input, the condition is overdrive.

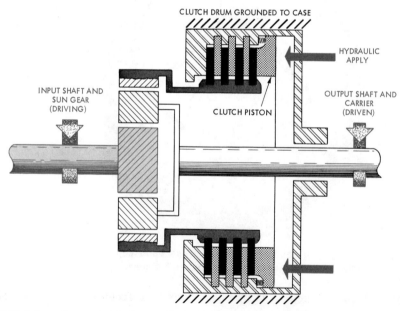

Fig. 3-11. Internal gear clutched to the transmission case, with sun gear driving. No roller clutch or band is needed for drive or coast.

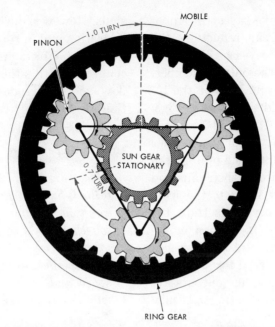

Fig. 3-12. Planetary gear set in overdrive, with sun gear stationary—showing pinion carrier vs ring gear travel.

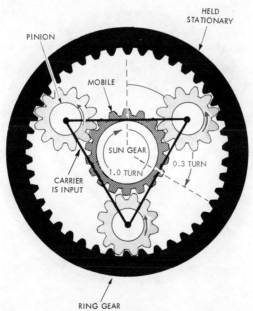

Fig. 3-13. Planetary gear set in overdrive, with ring gear stationary—showing pinion carrier vs sun gear travel.

Since overdrive gives the opposite effect of gear reduction, the planet carrier serves as the input rather than as the output member, with either the sun gear or the internal gear held stationary, Figs. 3-12 and 3-13. It should be noted that even with the planet carrier as the power input, the pinions are still free to rotate on their pins and to *walk* as they react to the fixed planetary member. This time, the turning and walking action moves the output member at an increased speed and at reduced torque.

Overdrive planetary outputs are not used in automatic transmissions. However, during *coast* or deceleration and in *reverse* operation, overdrive effects are usually encountered within the gearing power flow and the reader should know the law of overdrive.

Law of Direct Drive

Direct drive or high gear is obtained by clutching or locking any two members of the gear set together. This can also be interpreted to mean that driving any two members at the same relative speed and in the same direction will give the same effect.

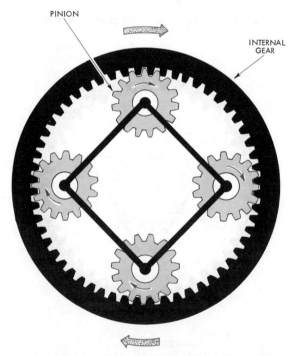

Fig. 3-14. Planetary gear set in direct drive sequence, with internal gear driving. As clockwise power is applied to the internal gear the planet pinions are rotated clockwise.

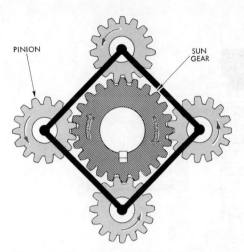

Fig. 3-15. Planetary gear set in direct drive sequence, with sun gear driving. Clockwise power applied to planet pinions.

The principle of direct drive is shown and explained in the following sequence of illustrations, Figs. 3-14, 3-15, and 3-16. In automatic transmissions a multiple-disc clutch or fluid clutch is used to lock any two members of a planetary gear set for direct drive.

Although the fluid clutch was used for years in the G.M. Hydra-Matic *controlled coupling* it has no current application. Its uniqueness, however, is worthy of attention.

Fig. 3-17 shows a typical multiple-disc clutch which in this case locks the internal gear and planet carrier together. *Apply* and *release*

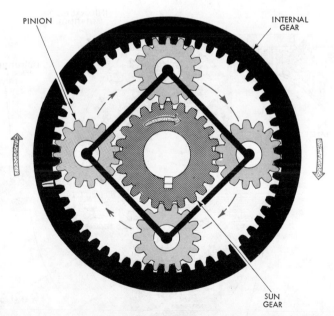

Fig. 3-16. Planetary gear set in direct drive. Clockwise power applied to the sun gear and to the internal gear meets at the planet pinions preventing the pinions from rotating on their centers. If the pinions cannot rotate on their centers, it is obvious that the planet pinions are trapped solidly beween the sun gear and the ring gear and must turn with them at the same relative speed.

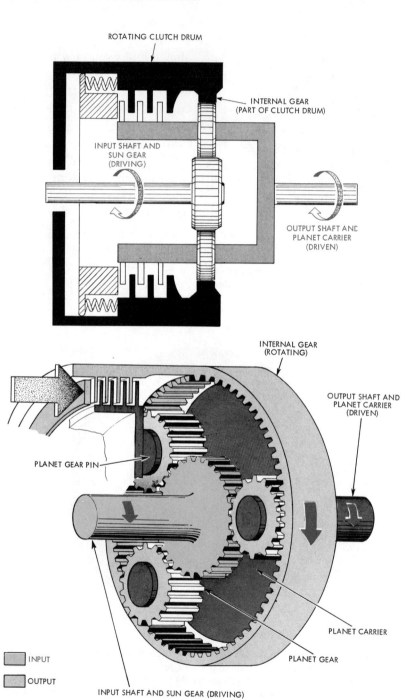

ROTATING CLUTCH DRUM

INTERNAL GEAR
(PART OF CLUTCH DRUM)

INPUT SHAFT AND
SUN GEAR
(DRIVING)

OUTPUT SHAFT AND
PLANET CARRIER
(DRIVEN)

INTERNAL GEAR
(ROTATING)

OUTPUT SHAFT AND
PLANET CARRIER
(DRIVEN)

PLANET GEAR PIN

PLANET CARRIER

PLANET GEAR

INPUT

OUTPUT

INPUT SHAFT AND SUN GEAR (DRIVING)

Fig. 3-17. Multiple disc clutch for locking internal gear and planet carrier in direct drive.

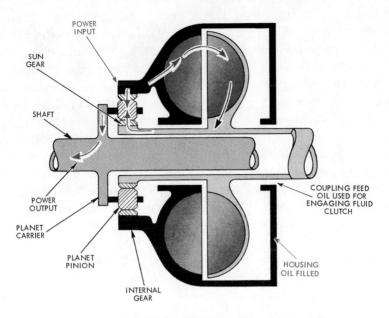

Fig. 3-18. Fluid clutch filled and engaged for direct drive.

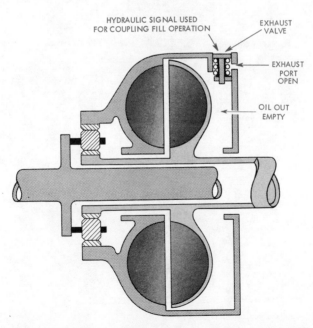

Fig. 3-19. Fluid clutch emptied and disengaged for gear reduction.

of the clutch is controlled by the transmission valve body.

Fig. 3-18 illustrates how a fluid clutch is used for direct drive. The fluid clutch is nothing more than a fluid coupling with a *drive* and a *driven member* enclosed in a housing.

When the housing is filled with oil the drive member transmits power through the oil to the driven member for direct drive. In this case the internal gear (input) through the fluid clutch drives the sun gear at the same relative speed.

The *exhaust valve* is used to empty the coupling when direct drive is not needed, Fig. 3-19. When the hydraulic close signal is released from the exhaust valve, spring pressure and the rotating force of the coupling opens the valve. At the same time the oil supply for the coupling fill is cut off by the valve body control and the centrifugal effect of the rotating coupling dumps the coupling oil out through the exhaust valve.

For *coupling fill* the exhaust valve is closed by a hydraulic signal followed by coupling feed oil. Essentially, the exhaust and fill

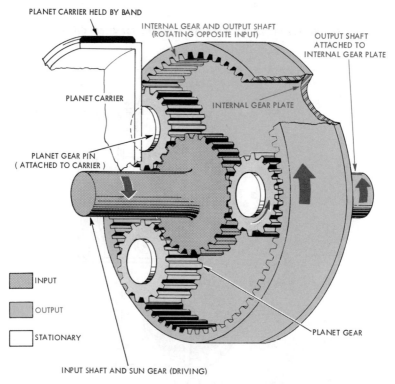

Fig. 3-20. Typical reverse gear operation.

operations are controlled by the *transmission valve body.*

Law of Reverse

When the planet carrier, but not the planet gears, is held against rotation, reverse is the result (for simple planetary set only). Reverse rotation and one that is popularly used in most present 3-speed automatic transmissions is shown in Fig. 3-20 With the planet carrier held by a band application the sun gear input rotation is reversed by the planet gears with the reverse motion then picked up by internal gear and output shaft at a reduction. If the internal gear served as input, the sun gear would be in reverse overdrive.

Combining Gear Reduction and Direct Drive

It is possible to use a single planetary gear assembly as a 2-speed transmission if the basic requirements for reduction and direct drive are satisfied. A band and multiple disc clutch are combined

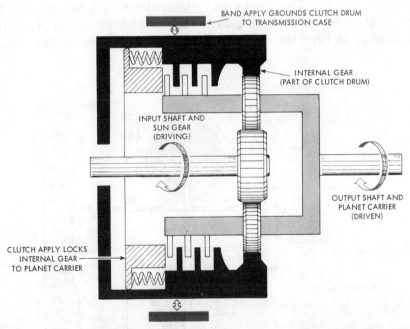

BAND APPLY GROUNDS CLUTCH DRUM TO TRANSMISSION CASE

INTERNAL GEAR (PART OF CLUTCH DRUM)

INPUT SHAFT AND SUN GEAR (DRIVING)

OUTPUT SHAFT AND PLANET CARRIER (DRIVEN)

CLUTCH APPLY LOCKS INTERNAL GEAR TO PLANET CARRIER

Fig. 3-21. A multiple disc clutch is used for the rear unit to lock the internal gear to the planet carrier for direct drive. The clutch is oil applied and spring released. For direct drive the clutch is applied and the band OFF. For gear reduction the band is applied and the clutch is OFF.

in Fig. 3-21 to illustrate the possibility. The band is used for holding the internal gear for reduction and the multiple disc clutch ties the internal gear and planet carrier together for direct drive.

It is the valve body controls that coordinate the apply and release of these friction units so that they do not fight one another, or permit a powerflow interruption during a gear change.

Fig. 3-22 shows how a sprag clutch and fluid clutch are combined for 2-speed operation. For gear reduction *the fluid clutch is empty* and therefore cannot transmit a power flow. The clockwise input rotation of the internal gear will attempt to turn the sun gear

counter-clockwise, Fig. 3-23, applying the sprags which will lock the inner race to the outer race, Fig. 3-24. But since the outer race is grounded to the transmission case the sprag clutch assembly now holds the sun gear and the end result is gear reduction.

When *the fluid clutch is filled* direct drive occurs as previously explained under the Law of Direct Drive. The important point is to note that the sprag releases independently of any valve body control. The oil filled clutch forces the sun gear and also the inner sprag race to rotate in a clockwise direction, along with the internal gear. This clockwise motion of the inner sprag race releases the wedging

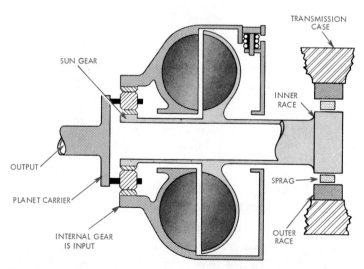

Fig. 3-22. When the coupling is empty and the sprag is ON the condition is reduction. When the coupling is full and the sprag is OFF the effect is direct.

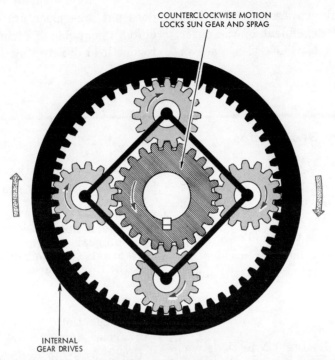

Fig. 3-23. Sun gear reversal locks inner sprag race to outer race and holds sun gear stationary.

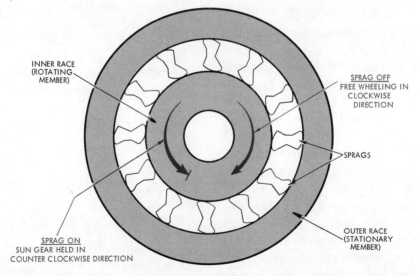

Fig. 3-24. The sun gear is held by the sprag clutch in reduction; sun gear rotation releases the sprag for direct drive. Front view.

action of the sprags and it is free to rotate independent of the outer race, Fig. 3-24. This release action does not take place until the fluid clutch is capable of picking up the torque load during its *oil fill.*

Planetary Gear Ratios

The *gear ratio* equals the number of revolutions the driving member makes while the driven member makes one revolution. It may also be expressed as the number of teeth on the driven member divided by the number of teeth on the drive member.

gear ratio =

$$\frac{\text{rpm driving}}{\text{rpm driven}} = \frac{\text{N teeth driven}}{\text{N teeth drive}}$$

The definition and calculation of *gear ratio* can be applied to any gear set—simple, compound, or planetary. In a simple or compound gear set the calculation of the gear ratio is easily determined by using a direct comparison of the number of gear teeth. However, for *planetary gear set ratios* a modified ratio formula must be used because the planet pinions rotate about two center points at the same time—during reduction or overdrive the pinion gears rotate on their own centers, plus they walk around the common rotational center of the sun and internal gears. The following formulas and examples should

clarify how gear ratios are calculated for a planetary gear set:

where,
N_s equals number of teeth on the sun gear (20)
N_i equals the number of teeth on the internal gear (50)

Example:

$$\frac{\text{Reduction}}{\text{(carrier driven)}} = \frac{N_s + N_i}{\text{N driving}}$$

With Sun Gear Driving and Internal Gear Fixed

$$\text{reduction} = \frac{20 + 50}{20} = 3.5:1 \text{ ratio}$$

Example:

$$\frac{\text{Overdrive}}{\text{(carrier driving)}} = \frac{\text{N driven}}{N_s + N_i}$$

With Internal Gear Driven and Sun Gear Fixed

$$\text{overdrive} = \frac{50}{20 + 50} = .71:1 \text{ ratio}$$

Example:

$$\frac{\text{Reverse}}{\text{(carrier fixed)}} = \frac{\text{N driven}}{\text{N driving}}$$

With Sun Gear Driving and Internal Gear Driven

$$\text{reverse} = \frac{50}{20} = 2.5:1 \text{ gear ratio}$$

Checking On Your Knowledge

The following questions give you the opportunity to check up on yourself. If you have read the chapter carefully, you should be able to answer the questions.

If you have any difficulty, read the chapter over once more so that you have the information well in mind before you go on with your reading.

1. Name the components that make up simple planetary gear set.
2. What are the several major advantages of planetary gears?
3. Define the following terms: gear ratio, gear reduction, overdrive, direct drive, freewheeling, and reaction member.
4. What is the gear train output speed when (a) the gear ratio is 1.5:1 and (b) the input speed is 1,000 rpm.
5. What is the gear train output torque when (a) the gear ratio is 1.5:1 and (b) the input torque is 250 lb-ft.
6. List and define the five laws that govern planetary gear operation.
7. What are the two reduction possibilities that meet the requirements for the law of reduction? Which of the two gives the greatest reduction?
8. For forward reduction, what member of the planetary is always the output?
9. For forward overdrive, what member of the planetary is always the input?
10. Name four devices that are used in automatic transmissions to ground or hold a planetary reaction member to the transmission case.
11. What are the two independent actions or motions of the planet pinions during reduction or overdrive operation?
12. What are the advantages of using a sprag or roller clutch in planetary gear operation?
13. What happens to a sprag or roller clutch application during vehicle coast? How does this affect the planetary gear set?
14. Relative to transmission input shaft rotation, in what direction does a sprag or roller clutch freewheel?
15. If the transmission must be used in manual low for vehicle braking, why must a band application supplement the sprag or roller clutch operation?
16. What is the most popular method used to lock two planet members together for direct drive?
17. In reference to Question 16, what is another technique that has been used to accomplish direct drive?
18. What is the purpose of the planet pinions during reverse operation?
19. For reverse reduction, indicate the planetary member used in the following roles: (a) input member (b) reactionary member (c) output member.

Planetary Gear Systems In Automatic Transmissions

The preceding chapter served as the basis for understanding the fundamentals of planetary gears, their function, construction, and operation. The objective in this chapter is to discuss the applica-

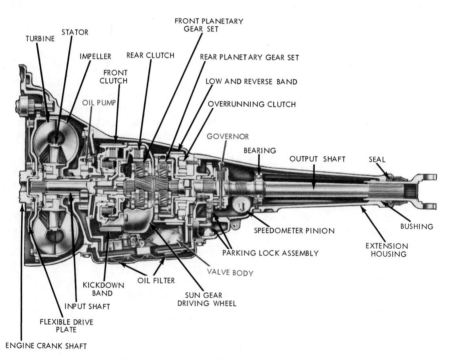

Fig. 4-1. TorqueFlite A-727 automatic transmission.

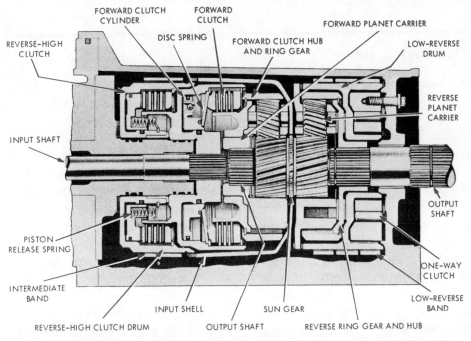

Fig. 4-2. C-4 gear train, clutches and bands. (Transmission converter is not shown.)

tion of these fundamentals to modern planetary gear systems used in 3-speed and 2-speed passenger car automatic transmissions.

Only one basic 2-speed design is currently used in automatic transmissions; however, several different 3-speed designs are in production among the automobile manufacturers. The Chrysler Torque Flite is selected for detailed study to show how the power flow in a typical 3-speed planetary system operates, Fig. 4-1. This same planetary system is also common to both the Ford C-4 and C-6 transmissions, Fig. 4-2, and the G.M.

Hydra-Matic 350. Other 3-speed automatic transmissions presently used by American Motors, Ford, and General Motors are summarized later.

When trouble shooting an automatic transmission it is an advantage to know what gear sets are operational for each gear ratio, also what band and clutch combinations control these individual gears. With this knowledge, noise and friction element problems can be isolated to one area of the transmission. With careful study, these trouble shooting procedures can be applied to any transmission.

Planetary System

(3-Speed Chrysler TorqueFlite)

The TorqueFlite Transmission combines a *three element torque converter* with a fully automatic 3-speed planetary system. The transmission consists of two multiple disc clutches, an overrunning roller clutch, two *servos* (a hydraulic piston that converts hydraulic force to mechanical force), two bands, and a compound planetary gear system consisting of two planetary gear sets sharing a *common sun gear*. The above design provides three forward gear ratios, reverse, and neutral. The hydraulic system is made up of a front pump, a valve body, and a governor, as shown in Fig. 4-1.

The torque converter is attached to the crankshaft through a *flexible drive plate.* Converter cooling is provided by circulating the transmission fluid through an oil-to-water cooler located in the radiator lower tank. The torque converter assembly is of welded construction and cannot be disassembled. The converter housing and transmission case are designed as a one piece casting.

Two versions of the TorqueFlite are manufactured, the A-904 for six cylinder and low torque V-8 engines, and the A-727 for high torque V-8 engines.

Operating Characteristics

The transmission operation is programmed by the traditional manual control of either the steering column or the console gearshift. The control has six selector lever positions: P (park), R (reverse), N (neutral), D (drive), 2 (second), and 1 (low). For safety, the engine cannot start in other than the *park* or *neutral* positions.

In *drive,* the transmission shifts through all three ratios automatically. Shift points are determined by throttle opening and car speed. If additional acceleration is desired while in drive, the transmission will downshift (depending on vehicle speed) to second or *breakaway* (first gear) when the accelerator pedal is completely depressed. On *closed throttle downshifts,* the transmission shifts 3-1 taking advantage of the smooth free wheeling action from the overrunning roller clutch.

Second position is used to operate the transmission in the first two gears only—third gear is blocked out of operation. The 1-2 automatic shift occurs the same as in *drive.* This range is suitable for heavy city traffic where the driver may desire to use part throttle second range operation for more precise control. It may also be used on long down-grades where additional engine braking is needed, or for extra pulling power.

Low or *first position* keeps the transmission in first gear only. This position provides added braking and handling ease in mountain driving and exceptional pulling qualities in sand and snow. If low range is selected at an excessive car speed, the tranmission shifts to second gear and remains until the vehicle is slowed to a safe speed range. Once low gear is engaged, the transmission cannot upshift again.

Planetary Power Flow

Before proceeding with the details of operation, some basic facts need to be mentioned as a background for understanding the planetary system power flow. The power input to the transmission comes from the engine *torque flow* through the converter to the transmission input shaft and the multiple disc clutches in the transmission. The power flow through the planetary gear train will depend on the application of the clutches, bands, and the overrunning roller clutch. A power flow summary chart, Table 4-1, is provided as a quick reference to clutch engagement and band application.

Table 4-1 Powerflow Summary for Torqueflite A-904 & A-727 *

Range	Gear	Front Clutch	Rear Clutch	Kickdown Band	Low-Reverse Band	Over-Running Clutch	Park Pawl
Park		off	off	off	off	no movement	in
Reverse		on	off	off	on	no movement	out
Neutral		off	off	off	off	no movement	out
D-drive	first	off	on	off	off	holds	out
	second	off	on	on	off	overruns	out
	third	on	on	off	off	overruns	out
2-drive	second	off	on	on	off	overruns	out
	first	off	on	off	off	holds	out
1-low	first	off	on	off	on	holds	out

* Torqueflite discontinued rear pump in 1966

Note: of special concern to the reader is that all reference to direction of rotation in describing the gearing power flows is based on viewing the transmission front.

Neutral

In N (neutral) none of the clutches are engaged or bands applied. There is a power feed to the input shaft. However, when the front and rear clutches are not engaged no power is transmitted forward to the planetary gear sets and to the output shaft.

Breakaway (First)

In *breakaway* with either the D or 2 selection, the rear clutch is engaged and the overrunning clutch holds, Figs. 4-3 and 4-4.

The torque flows from the converter turbine through the input shaft to the rear clutch. With the rear clutch engaged the torque flow is able to turn the *annulus gear* (terminology preferred by Chrysler to describe the internal gear) of the *front planetary* in a forward direction. Since the front planet carrier is *splined* (locked) to the output shaft and the weight of the car, the annulus gear drives the front planetary pinions, rotating them in the same direction. The pinions, in mesh with the sun gear, rotate the sun gear in the reverse direction, Figs. 4-4 and 4-5.

The front and rear planetary sets share the same sun gear; therefore the sun gear rotates the rear planet pinions in the forward direction. The planet pinions, in mesh with the rear annulus gear, rotate the annulus gear and output shaft in the forward direction. The rear

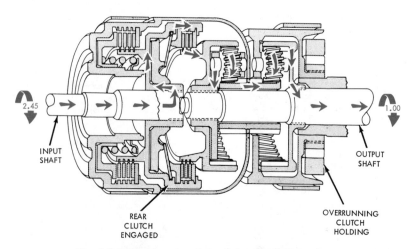

INPUT
SHAFT

REAR
CLUTCH
ENGAGED

OUTPUT
SHAFT

OVERRUNNING
CLUTCH
HOLDING

Fig. 4-3. Power flow in breakaway. (Chrysler Corp.)

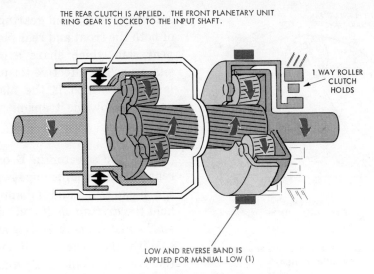

THE REAR CLUTCH IS APPLIED. THE FRONT PLANETARY UNIT
RING GEAR IS LOCKED TO THE INPUT SHAFT.

1 WAY ROLLER
CLUTCH
HOLDS

LOW AND REVERSE BAND IS
APPLIED FOR MANUAL LOW (1)

Fig. 4-4. Simplified power flow—breakaway.

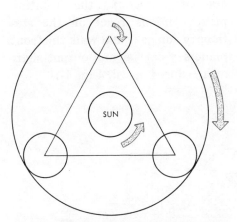

SUN

Fig. 4-5. Front planetary breakaway. The carrier will rotate once the output shaft goes in motion. The same gearing action in the front planetary will be maintained since the carrier turns at less than annulus (internal) gear speed.

planet carrier is held by the over-running clutch because of the action of the pinions as they rotate the rear annulus gear. The pinions must rotate the annulus gear against the weight of the car which makes the annulus gear *reactionary*. This results in the pinions attempting to walk the carrier in reverse direction of the output shaft. Applying a general rule of overrun clutch operation, note that the rear carrier transfers the reverse motion to the inner overrun clutch race and *lock-up* occurs, Figs. 4-4 and 4-6.

Lock-up of the overrun clutch is effective as long as the car is under *drive power*. On *coast*, with the rear wheels and the weight of the car attempting to work against the engine, the planetary gear action puts the overrun clutch in free wheeling. This results in a neutral gear condition, and therefore, en-

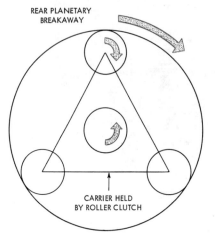

Fig. 4-6. Rear planetary breakaway, with carrier held by roller clutch.

gine braking is not possible during *coast breakaway.*

In summary, breakaway is a re-

sult of the compound gearing action of both the front and rear planetary gear sets which share a common sun gear. The effective torque ratio is 2.45:1, which is the maximum developed by the transmission.

Second

With the selector in D or 2 the rear clutch remains engaged while the kickdown band is applied to hold the *driving shell* and sun gear stationary, Figs. 4-7, 4-8, and 4-9.

With the rear clutch engaged, the front annulus gear and front planetary pinions all rotate in a forward direction. Applying the *law of reduction*, the rotating planet pinions react on the stationary sun gear and walk the front planetary carrier and output shaft at a reduced speed, Fig. 4-10.

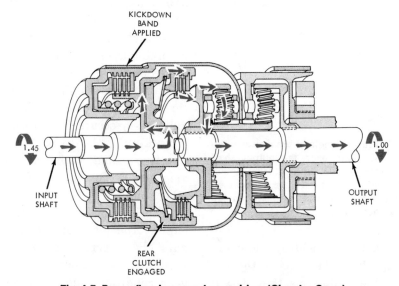

Fig. 4-7. Power flow in second gear-drive. (Chrysler Corp.)

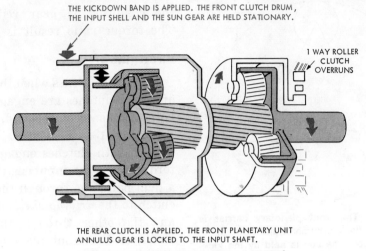

THE KICKDOWN BAND IS APPLIED. THE FRONT CLUTCH DRUM, THE INPUT SHELL AND THE SUN GEAR ARE HELD STATIONARY.

1 WAY ROLLER CLUTCH OVERRUNS

THE REAR CLUTCH IS APPLIED. THE FRONT PLANETARY UNIT ANNULUS GEAR IS LOCKED TO THE INPUT SHAFT.

Fig. 4-8. Simplified power flow—second.

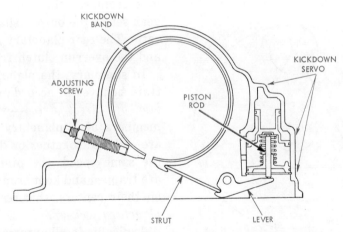

KICKDOWN BAND

KICKDOWN SERVO

ADJUSTING SCREW

PISTON ROD

STRUT

LEVER

Fig. 4-9. The TorqueFlite servo and linkage mechanism is used for applying the kickdown band around the front clutch drum.

The rear planetary in second gear goes along for the ride. The rear annulus gear attached to the output shaft drives the rear planet pinions in a forward direction. These pinions react on the stationary sun gear and walk the carrier in a forward direction resulting in a freewheeling overrun clutch, Fig. 4-11.

In summary, *second gear* is a result of a simple reduction action

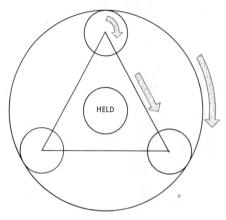

Fig. 4-10. The front planetary carrier is splined to the output shaft and turns at reduced speed. The sun is held by the kickdown band.

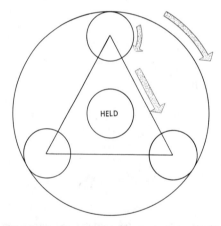

Fig. 4-11. The rear planetary-carrier and overrun clutch freewheel, and the planetary is ineffective. The sun gear, also common to the front planetary, is held by the kickdown band.

from the front planetary—when there is a reactionary member and the planetary carrier is the *output*,

the condition is gear reduction. The torque ratio result is 1.45:1.

Direct (third)

D (*direct*) occurs when the front and rear clutches are engaged and both bands are released, Figs. 4-12 and 4-13.

With both clutches engaged, the torque from the input shaft takes a dual path, one through the front clutch to the *driving shell sun gear* and the other through the rear clutch to the front planetary annulus gear. This dual input to the front planetary prevents the pinions from rotating and locks the gear set to the output shaft at 1:1 ratio. The rear planetary also locks and the overrun clutch freewheels.

In summary, the planetary gear train behaves in accordance to the *law of direct drive*—when two members of a planetary gear set are clutched together or driving at the same speed, the pinion gears are trapped and kept from rotating on their centers, this results in a *planetary lock-up*.

Typically, in all automatic transmissions *direct drive* locks up the drive clutches and planetary gears so that all motion within the power train is essentially at the same speed. When troubleshooting noise problems that are audible in direct drive or high gear it is not likely that the planetary gears or clutch assemblies are at fault.

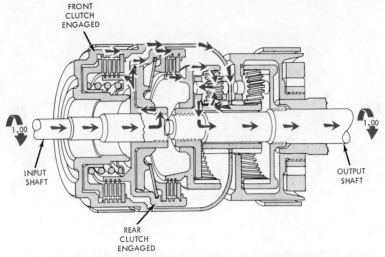

Fig. 4-12. Power flow in D (drive) position—direct. (Chrysler Corp.)

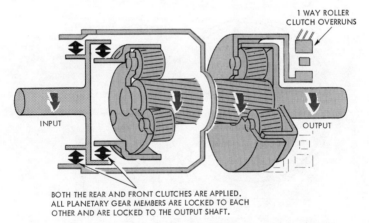

BOTH THE REAR AND FRONT CLUTCHES ARE APPLIED.
ALL PLANETARY GEAR MEMBERS ARE LOCKED TO EACH
OTHER AND ARE LOCKED TO THE OUTPUT SHAFT.

Fig. 4-13. Simplified power flow in D (drive) position—direct.

Low

In 1 (low), the rear clutch is engaged and the low and reverse band applied, Figs. 4-14 and 4-15.

A comparison of Fig. 4-3 and Fig. 4-14 will show that the power flow in *breakaway* and *low* is the same. The application of the low and reverse band assures that upon *coast* a holding force remains on the rear planetary carrier as the overrun clutch attempts to freewheel. This keeps the front and rear planetary gear sets effective for braking action through the driver's accelerator control until changed.

95

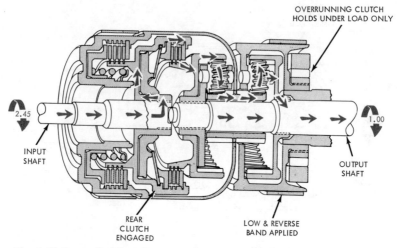

Fig. 4-14. Power flow in 1 (low) position—low or retarding. (Chrysler Corp.)

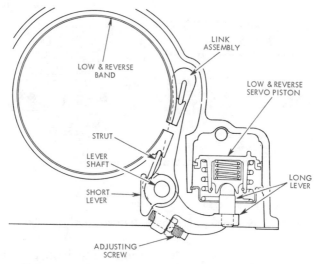

Fig. 4-15. TorqueFlite servo and linkage for holding the low and reverse drum, which is part of the rear planet carrier.

Reverse

In R (*reverse*), the front clutch is engaged to the driving shell and the sun gear. The low and reverse drum and rear planetary carrier are held stationary by the rear band, Fig. 4-16 and 4-17.

Engagement of the front clutch drives the shell and sun gear in a

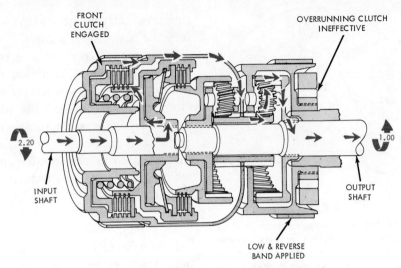

FRONT
CLUTCH
ENGAGED

OVERRUNNING CLUTCH
INEFFECTIVE

2.20

1.00

INPUT
SHAFT

OUTPUT
SHAFT

LOW & REVERSE
BAND APPLIED

Fig. 4-16. Power flow in reverse. (Chrysler Corp.)

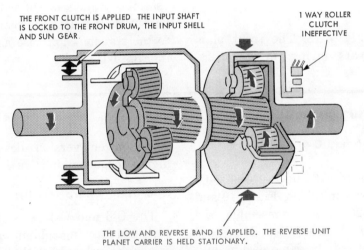

THE FRONT CLUTCH IS APPLIED THE INPUT SHAFT
IS LOCKED TO THE FRONT DRUM, THE INPUT SHELL
AND SUN GEAR

1 WAY ROLLER
CLUTCH
INEFFECTIVE

THE LOW AND REVERSE BAND IS APPLIED. THE REVERSE UNIT
PLANET CARRIER IS HELD STATIONARY.

Fig. 4-17. Simplified power flow—reverse position.

forward direction. With the rear carrier held stationary, the sun gear drives the rear planet pinions counter-clockwise. This reversing motion of the planet pinions also drives the rear annulus gear (splined to the output shaft) in the reverse direction at a reduced

97

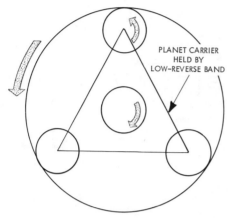

PLANET CARRIER
HELD BY
LOW–REVERSE BAND

Fig. 4-18. Reverse—planet carrier held by low-reverse band. Planet pinions reverse the motion of the sun gear and drive the rear annulus gear and output shaft in reverse.

speed, Fig. 4-18. The front planetary gears during reverse opera-tion are active, but do not enter into the power flow picture.

In summary, *reverse* is a result of a simple reduction action from the rear planetary—when the planetary carrier (but not the planet gears) is held against rotation, *reverse* is the outcome. In this case the sun gear is the input member which gives a reverse reduction of 2.20 :1.

Park

In *Park* (*P*) the transmission gear train remains in neutral. A manually activated linkage en-gages a pawl in the parking lock assembly which is splined to the output shaft to lock the rear wheels to the transmission case as shown in Fig. 4-1.

Planetary System

(Ford C-6 and C-4)

The Ford C-6 and C-4 Cruise-O-Matic transmissions, Fig. 4-19 and Fig. 4-20, closely resemble the Chrysler TorqueFlite. The gear trains are of the same design, and so are the clutch and band combina-tions with one exception. The C-6 has a low-and-reverse multiple disc clutch in place of the low-and-re-verse band used in both the C-4 and the TorqueFlite. The C-4 was in-troduced in 1964 and the C-6, which is a larger version design for higher torque engines, in 1966.

Operating Characteristics

The C-6 and C-4 use either the standard steering column or a con-sole shift selector with six posi-tions. Figs. 4-21 and 4-22, show the early and late design selector patterns. The change in selector design patterns was to accommo-date the Select-Shift feature of the transmissions in 1967. The Select-Shift had previously been available only in the Sports-Shift C-6 Cruise-O-Matic on the high performance Comet GTA and Fairlane GTA models.

The selector illustrated in Fig. 4-21 offers two drive ranges, D2 and D1.

In the *normal drive range* (D1) the car starts in low and upshifts automatically to *second* and *high* depending on throttle opening and road speed. On closed throttle the transmission downshifts from high to low at 10 mph.

D2 range starts out in *second gear* and upshifts to *high*. The closed throttle downshift back to

second gear occurs at 10 mph. This operating range is particularly used for car starts on slippery road surfaces, or for rocking the car with reverse when the car is stuck in a soft surface such as snow, mud, or sand.

Forced downshifts (kickdown) from *high* to *second* are possible at speeds below 65 mph in D1 or D2. A high to low forced downshift in D1 is available below 30 mph.

In *manual low* the transmission remains in low gear and will not upshift. When shifting from D1 or D2 into *low* the transmission downshifts to second and will not

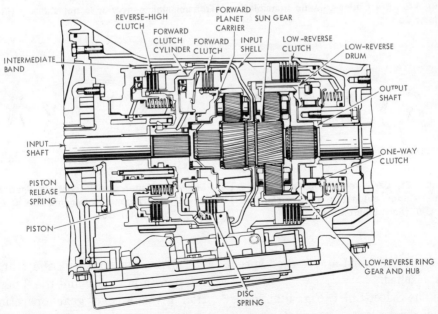

Fig. 4-19. C-6 gear train, clutches and band. (Transmission converter is not shown.) (Ford Motor Co.)

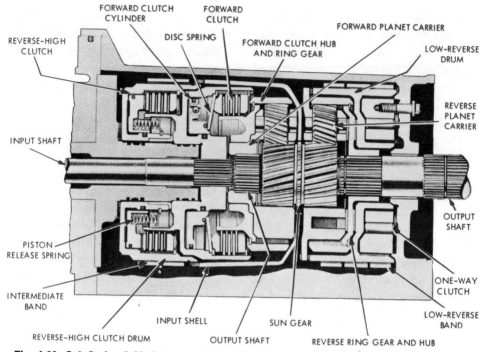

Fig. 4-20. C-4 Cruise-O-Matic transmission. (Transmission converter is not shown.) (Ford Motor Co.)

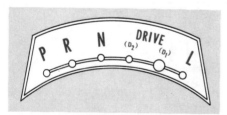

Fig. 4-21. Early selector pattern used for Dual Range automatic transmissions, C-4 & C-6. (Ford Motor Co.)

Fig. 4-22. Later selector pattern used for Select Shift automatic transmission, C-4 & C-6. (Ford Motor Co.)

engage low until a safe road speed is reached.

The Select-Shift, Fig. 4-22, gives the driver more manual control over the transmission.

The 1 position keeps the transmission in low gear and the 2 position gives second gear operation only. In D position, the transmission is fully automatic, starting in low gear, shifting into second, and then into high gear. With this shifting arrangement, the driver can elect to start in D and have fully automatic shifting, or start in 1, then shift to 2, and then into D at any speed or peak rpm.

On manual downshifting by the driver for braking or added performance full engine-transmission protection is built in. Shifting from D to 2 immediately downshifts the transmission to second gear, while the shift from D or 2 positions into 1 downshifts the transmission to low. If the road speed is too high when shifting to 1, the transmission selects second gear until road speed is at a safe level for the downshift into low.

Normal 3-2 and 3-1 kickdown features are available in D, which functions only at the appropriate road speeds.

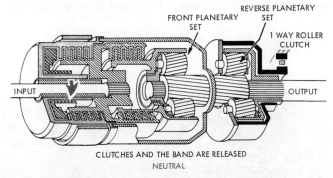

Fig. 4-23. Neutral—with bands and clutches in the OFF position, there is no input to the gear sets. (Ford Motor Co.)

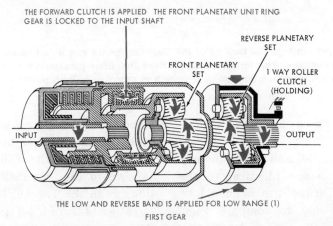

Fig. 4-24. Drive—first gear is a function of the front and the reverse planetary sets. (Ford Motor Co.)

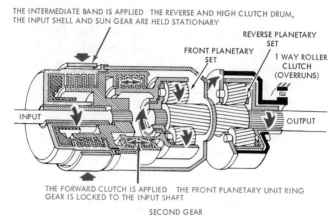

THE INTERMEDIATE BAND IS APPLIED THE REVERSE AND HIGH CLUTCH DRUM,
THE INPUT SHELL AND SUN GEAR ARE HELD STATIONARY

REVERSE PLANETARY
SET

FRONT PLANETARY
SET

1 WAY ROLLER
CLUTCH
(OVERRUNS)

INPUT

OUTPUT

THE FORWARD CLUTCH IS APPLIED THE FRONT PLANETARY UNIT RING
GEAR IS LOCKED TO THE INPUT SHAFT

SECOND GEAR

Fig. 4-25. Drive—second gear is a function of the front planetary gear set. (Ford Motor Co.)

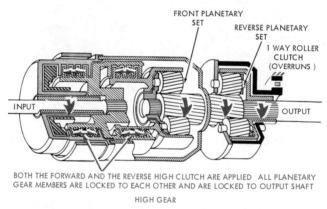

FRONT PLANETARY
SET

REVERSE PLANETARY
SET

1 WAY ROLLER
CLUTCH
(OVERRUNS)

INPUT

OUTPUT

BOTH THE FORWARD AND THE REVERSE HIGH CLUTCH ARE APPLIED ALL PLANETARY
GEAR MEMBERS ARE LOCKED TO EACH OTHER AND ARE LOCKED TO OUTPUT SHAFT

HIGH GEAR

Fig. 4-26. Drive—in high the locking of the planetary gears is a direct result of the input through the clutches. The forward clutch drives the front planetary ring gear and the reverse high clutch drives the sun gear (which is common to both planetary sets). (Ford Motor Co.)

Planetary Power Flow

Since the C-6 and C-4 planetary power flows are identical to the Chrysler TorqueFlite it should be necessary only to compare Figs. 4-23, 4-24, 4-25, 4-26, and 4-27 with the previous TorqueFlite sequence of power flow illustrations and detailed discussion. The overrunning clutch used in the C-6 and C-4 (shown in the illustrations) functions as in the TorqueFlite.

Tables 4-2 and 4-3 give power flow summaries of the current Select-Shift C-6 and C-4. It should be

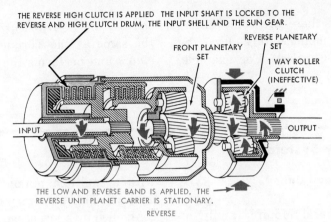

THE REVERSE HIGH CLUTCH IS APPLIED THE INPUT SHAFT IS LOCKED TO THE
REVERSE AND HIGH CLUTCH DRUM, THE INPUT SHELL AND THE SUN GEAR.

REVERSE PLANETARY SET

FRONT PLANETARY SET

1 WAY ROLLER CLUTCH (INEFFECTIVE)

INPUT

OUTPUT

THE LOW AND REVERSE BAND IS APPLIED. THE
REVERSE UNIT PLANET CARRIER IS STATIONARY.

REVERSE

Fig. 4-27. Reverse is the sole function of the reverse planetary unit. (Ford Motor Co.)

Table 4-2 Powerflow Summary for Ford C6 Select Shift, Ford Motor Co *

Range	Gear	Intermediate Band	Reverse High Clutch	Forward Clutch	Low Reverse Clutch	One-Way Clutch	Park Pawl
Park		off	off	off	off	off	in
Reverse		off	on	off	on	not affected	out
Neutral		off	off	off	off	off	out
D-drive	first	off	off	on	off	holds	out
	second	on	off	on	off	overruns	out
	third	off	on	on	off	overruns	out
2-drive	second	on	off	on	off	overruns	out
1-low	first	off	off	on	on	holds	out

* No rear pump since its introduction in 1966

Table 4-3 Powerflow summary for Ford C4 Select-Shift, Ford Motor Co *

Range	Gear	Forward Clutch	Reverse High Clutch	Intermediate Band	Low Reverse Band	One-Way Clutch	Park Pawl
Park		off	off	off	off	off	in
Reverse		off	on	off	on	not affected	out
Neutral		off	off	off	off	off	out
D-drive	first	on	off	off	off	holds	out
	second	on	off	on	off	overruns	out
	third	on	on	off	off	overruns	out
2-drive	second	on	off	on	off	overruns	out
1-low	first	on	off	off	on	holds	out

* No rear pump since its introduction in 1964

noted that there are some differences in nomenclature used by Ford and Chrysler. For example, the C-6 and C-4 *forward clutch* is the same as the TorqueFlite *rear clutch* and performs the same.

Planetary System

(G.M. 2 Speed Units)

The General Motors family of 2-speed transmissions—Buick Turbine 300, Olds Jetaway, Pontiac Tempest, Chevrolet Powerglides and Torque-Drive—combines a three element torque converter with a multiple pinion planetary gear set. This planetary gear set is controlled by a low servo and band, a forward clutch, and a reverse clutch which provides for *low, direct,* and *reverse* ratios, plus a *neutral.* The hydraulic system make-up is typical of other auto-

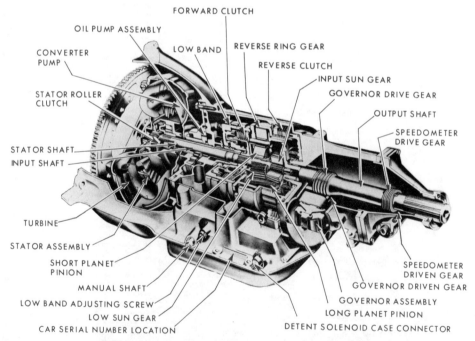

Fig. 4-28. Typical of GM 2-speed family of automatic transmissions.

matic transmissions and consists of a front pump, a valve body, and a governor, Fig. 4-28.

The Torque-Drive is not designed for automatic shifting and is defined as a semi-automatic transmission, therefore it does not have a governor or an automatic shift valve body.

Transmission converter cooling is either oil-to-water or oil-to-air, depending on the engine torque output. The converter is of welded construction and cannot be disassembled.

In the Turbine 300 and Jetaway transmissions a variable pitch stator was used in the converter through production year 1967.

The converter housing and transmission case are designed as a one piece aluminum casting.

Operating Characteristics

The operating characteristics of a General Motors 2-speed Transmission has already been discussed in Chapter I under the Jetaway heading, therefore only a brief review is presented here.

Normal drive starts through the torque converter and low gear ratio and automatically shifts to converter plus direct drive depending on throttle opening and road speed. For the Torque-Drive sometimes used in the Chevy II, Camaro, and Vega, normal drive starts through the converter and low gear, with the selector in *manual low*. It is then shifted to *direct drive* through the gear set when the selector-shift is manually shifted to *drive*.

With the automatic shift systems, forced downshifts (kickdown) are available for added acceleration at speeds below 60 mph.

The transmissions can be manually locked in low range for extra pulling power and engine braking. Because manual low is immediately engaged at any road speed, the driver should avoid selection above 40 mph.

Planetary Power Flow

The General Motors 2-speed transmissions are another example of a compound planetary gear arrangement still governed by the laws of planetary gear operation.

In this design set-up there are two sun gears, a low sun gear mounted to the forward clutch drum and an input sun gear splined to the input shift. There are three sets of multiple pinions mounted on the planetary carrier and in constant mesh with both sun gears and the reverse ring gear.

By closely following the power flow descriptions with the illustrations, the planetary operation can easily be determined.

Neutral

With the selector control in *neutral* (N) position, the output shaft

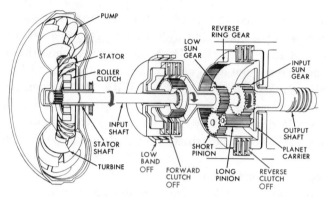

Fig. 4-29. Power flow—neutral.

remains stationary. The clutches and low band are released, so there is no reaction member to provide a positive drive. All gears are free to spin around their axes and no motion is imparted to the planet carrier, Fig. 4-29.

Manual Low

In *Low* (L) range the forward clutch is released and the low band is applied to the outside diameter of the forward clutch drum. With the low band applied, the low sun gear and flange assembly are held stationary. Drive is from the converter through the input shaft to the input sun gear in the planetary gear set. The input sun gear drives the long planet pinions, which are meshed with the short planet pinions. The short planet pinions are, in turn, meshed with the low sun gear. Since the low sun gear is held stationary with the low band applied, the short pinions walk around the low sun gear and carry

with them the planet carrier and the output shaft at a reduction of 1.82 to 1 in the low torque engines and 1.76 to 1 in the high torque engines, Fig. 4-30.

Direct Drive

With the selector control in *drive* (D) position, the transmission is started automatically in low gear. When the upshift into direct drive occurs, the low band is released and the forward clutch is applied. With the forward clutch applied, the clutch hub, which is splined to the input shaft, is locked to the low sun gear and flange assembly through the clutch plates. The low sun gear is meshed with the short pinions, the short pinions are meshed with the long pinions, and the long pinions are meshed with the input sun gear which is also splined to the input shaft. Since both sun gears now rotate with the input shaft because of the clutch apply, the short and long pinions

106

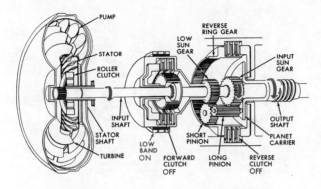

Fig. 4-30. Power flow—low, (manual low)

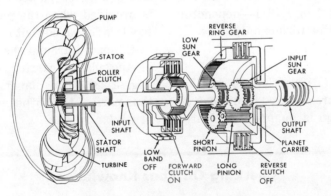

Fig. 4-31. Power flow—direct drive.

are trapped between the sun gears and cannot turn on their centers. This locks the planetary unit in a direct ratio 1:1. The planet carrier is part of the output shaft, and therefore, the output shaft rotates at the input shaft speed and in the same direction, Fig. 4-31.

Reverse

When the selector control is in *reverse* (R) position, the forward clutch and low band are released and the reverse clutch is applied, holding the reverse ring gear stationary. Drive is through the input shaft and input sun gear to the long pinions and then to the short pinions. The short pinions in mesh with the stationary ring gear walk around the inside of the ring gear in a reverse direction, carrying with them the planet carrier and output shaft, Fig. 4-32. The re-

107

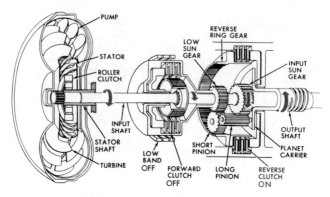

Fig. 4-32. Power flow—reverse.

verse ratios are the same as the low ratios 1.82:1 or 1.76:1—depending on the engine torque output.

Park

In *park* (P) position, all reaction members are released as in *neutral*. The linkage is manually activated and a *positive planet carrier lock* is provided when the parking lock pawl is engaged with the heavy teeth spaced around the front face of the planet carrier (shown in Fig. 4-28). The planet carrier is thus part of the output shaft when in *park*.

Checking On Your Knowledge

The following questions give you the opportunity to check up on yourself. If you have read the chapter carefully, you should be able to answer the questions.

If you have any difficulty, read the chapter over once more so that you have the information well in mind before you go on with your reading.

Chrysler TorqueFlite

1. What is the advantage of using a 3-1 closed throttle downshift in this transmission?
2. How does the transmission respond to a manual selection from *drive* to *low* at 80 mph?
3. How many gear ratios are available in *drive*? How many automatic shifts?
4. What two gears are available in the manual (2) position?
5. How is neutral attained in the trans-

mission?
6. What common planetary member is shared by the front and rear planetary sets?
7. State whether one or both planetary sets are effective in *breakaway*.
8. Name the planetary set that is effective in second gear operation.
9. Name the planetary set that is effective in reverse operation.
10. Briefly explain how the front and rear planetary sets are locked together for direct drive operation.
11. Name the reactionary planet mem-

ber and its holding mechanism in breakaway, second gear, and reverse.

12. In what gear or gears is the front clutch applied?
13. In what gear or gears is the rear clutch applied?
14. Why is the low and reverse band applied in *manual low?*

Ford C4 and C6

1. Describe the basic difference between the C-4 and C-6 transmissions.
2. What do the symbols C-4 and C-6 identify?
3. Compare the gear train power flows of the Ford C-4 and C-6 family to the Chrysler TorqueFlite family.
4. Name the C-4 equivalent of the following TorqueFlite nomenclature:

Front Clutch	Kickdown Band
Rear Clutch	Low and Reverse
Overrun Clutch	Band

5. Make a brief comparison of operating characteristics between the D2 and D1 operating ranges of the early design selector pattern.
6. In what year was the Select-Shift made standard for all C-4 and C-6 transmissions?
7. Briefly describe the Select-Shift operating characteristics in the 1, 2, and D positions.
8. What is the closed throttle downshift pattern in automatic drive? How does this compare to the TorqueFlite?

GM 2-Speed Transmissions

1. Give the trade names of the various G.M. 2-speed Transmissions.
2. What is the difference in operating characteristics between the Chevrolet Powerglide and Chevrolet Torque-Drive?
3. What action takes place in the planetary gears in *neutral?* Explain.
4. Name the reactionary member of the planetary gear set for low gear operation in manual low or automatic drive.

5. How many individual sets of long and short pinions are used in the planetary set?
6. What is the purpose of the long pinions?
7. What is the purpose of the short pinions? Relate this purpose to the gear set operation in low and reverse.
8. What planetary member is held stationary by the low band apply? By the reverse clutch apply?
9. Application of the forward clutch attaches the low sun gear to the input shaft. Explain how this causes the planetary set to lock-up for direct drive.
10. How does the transmission respond on a selector shift from D to L at 80 mph?

Troubleshooting a friction element or one-way clutch— *What is wrong?*

1. TorqueFlite: Vehicle does not move in D, 2, and 1 ranges; R works O.K.
2. TorqueFlite: Vehicle does not move in D and 2 ranges; 1 and R ranges O.K.
3. C-4 Select-Shift: No braking action in 1 and slipping reverse operation; D and 2 ranges work O.K.
4. C-4 Select-Shift: Slipping reverse operation and slipping third gear; 1 and 2 ranges plus 1st and 2nd gears D range work O.K.
5. C-4 Select-Shift: Vehicle creeps forward in neutral and engine lugs in reverse.
6. TorqueFlite: Transmission up-shifts 1-3 in D and stays in 1st gear in 2; Manual 1 and R are O.K.
7. G.M. Automatic 2 Speed: Vehicle has no reverse. Manual L and D ranges work O.K.
8. G.M. Automatic 2 Speed: Vehicle fails to move forward in D or L; reverse operation is O.K.
9. G.M. Automatic 2 Speed: Transmission slips on shift from L to D; L and reverse operation is O.K.

Hydraulic System Fundamentals*

The principal objective in the development of automatic transmission units was to relieve the driver of the physical effort and coordination required to operate a clutch pedal and a shift lever for gear changes. The more complex planetary gear trains used in fully automatic transmissions replacing the synchronized, constant mesh manual designs still require gear changes. These gear changes are brought about by means of *friction bands* and *multiple disc clutches* that are engaged by hydraulic pressure.

This pressure is produced by an engine driven hydraulic pump which is the heart of a total hydraulic system that functions to make the planetary transmission fully automatic. The transmission must start the car in motion smoothly, swiftly, and silently. It must select the proper gear ratio for any given engine torque output and vehicle speed combination and it must also respond immediately to the will of the driver.

The hydraulic system for the control and operation of an automatic transmission consists of the following, Fig. 5-1:

Fluid

Fluid source or reservoir (sump)

Source of pressure from a hydraulic pump

Hydraulic operating units to apply the bands and clutches

Control or valve systems for regulating pressures and directing fluid flows for auto-

---

*Based on training publications of the Chrysler Corporation.

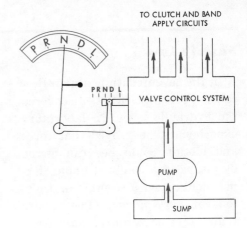

Fig. 5-1. Basic hydraulic control system.

matic and manual gear en-
gagements

Mechanical controls allow driver
selection of operating ranges

Before the operational details of
this system can be discussed, however, the reader must first know
the science of pressure hydraulics.

Fluid and the Hydraulic Lever

The word *hydraulic* comes from
the Greek word for water. For
many years the science of hydraulics was nothing more than storing
water, moving it from place to
place, and operating water wheels.

The machine age changed all of
this simplicity. Today's modern hydraulics involves a lot more science
and machine applications than ever
dreamed by the ancient Greeks.

Hydraulics involves the use of a
fluid, so let's proceed to "de-Greek"
hydraulics and begin with what a
fluid is:

Fluid. *A fluid can either be a
liquid or a gas. Since our subject
matter is hydraulics, the media
for transmitting force and motion takes place through the use
of a liquid. In automatic transmissions a mineral oil fortified
with additives is used.*

An essential part of pressure
hydraulics is to understand the
basic nature of a fluid, and how
it acts as a *lever arm* in transmitting force and motion. This is
defined in *Pascal's Law.*

111

Pascal's Law

In the seventeenth century, Pascal, a French scientist, discovered the hydraulic lever. In laboratory experiments, he proved that force and motion could be transferred by means of a confined liquid. Experimenting with weights and pistons of varying size, Pascal also found that *mechanical advantage* or *force multiplication* could be obtained in a pressure system, and that the relationships between *force* and *distance* were exactly the same as with a mechanical lever, Fig. 5-2. From the data Pascal collected, he formulated a law, which states:

Pressure on a confined fluid is transmitted equally in all directions and acts with equal force on equal areas.

To the novice learning hydraulics

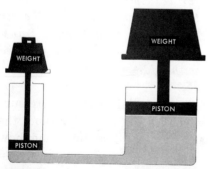

Fig. 5-2. Pressure is transmitted by fluids. (Chrysler Corp.)

this may sound like a mass of complicated words. Therefore, let's break it down into easy-to-understand parts, demonstrating it with the kind of equipment Pascal used in his experiments. To simplify the discussion of Pascal's Law, it is important to review two terms which are commonly used when talking about hydraulics, *force* and *pressure*. Actually, force and pressure are units of measurement used in hydraulics:

Force. *For our purposes, force can be defined as a push or pull on an object.*

A classic example of a kind of force is *gravity*. The force of gravity is nothing more than the weight of an object. If you weigh 175 pounds, you exert a downward force of 175 pounds on the floor on which you are standing.

In hydraulics, another type of force often encountered is *spring force*, Fig. 5-3. Spring force is the tension in the spring when it is compressed or stretched.

The reader by now has probably deduced that the engineering and household unit for force is the *pound*. Force can be measured, then, on any scale designed to measure weight:

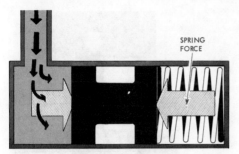

Fig. 5-3. Hydraulic force versus spring force. (Chrysler Corp.)

Pressure. *Pressure is force divided by area, or force per unit area.*

To illustrate pressure, Fig. 5-4, a uniform weight of 1000 pounds rests on a surface 100 square inches in area. The total force is 1000 pounds, the weight of the object; however, the force on each square inch of area is 1000 pounds divided by 100 square inches, or ten

pounds of pressure on the surface per square inch:

Pounds per square inch. *This is the unit for measuring pressure. It is abbreviated psi.*

Pressure on a Confined Fluid

Pressure is exerted on a *confined fluid* by applying a force to some area in contact with the fluid. For example, if a cylinder is filled with fluid, and a piston closely fitted to the cylinder has a force applied to it, pressure will be created in the fluid, Figs. 5-5 and 5-6.

If the fluid is not confined, no pressure will be created but a fluid flow will result. There must be a *resistance to flow* to create pres-

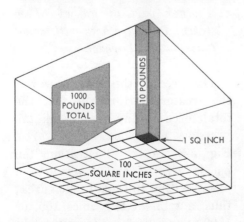

PRESSURE = 10 POUNDS PER SQUARE INCH

Fig. 5-4. Force is pressure divided by area. (Chrysler Corp.)

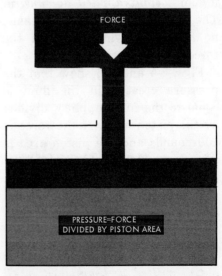

Fig. 5-5. Pressure is force on a confined liquid. (Chrysler Corp.)

113

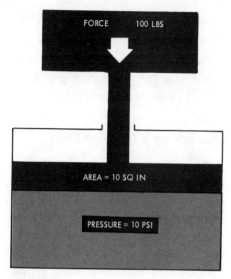

Fig. 5-6. Pressure is equal to the force applied. (Chrysler Corp.)

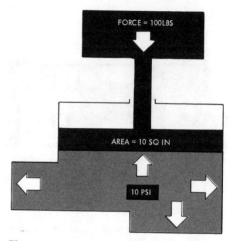

Fig. 5-7. Pressure is equal in all directions. (Chrysler Corp.)

sure. (In the illustrations, the applied forces used are that of gravity, of *weight applied downward*. The principle, however, is the same, no matter in what direction the force is applied.)

Figs. 5-5 and 5-6 show that the pressure created in the fluid is equal to the force applied, divided by the piston area. If the force is 100 pounds and the piston area is ten square inches, pressure equals ten psi. According to Pascal's Law, this pressure of 10 psi is equal everywhere in the trapped fluid Fig. 5-7:

Pressure on a confined fluid is transmitted undiminished in all directions.

No matter what shape the container is, no matter how large, this pressure will be maintained throughout, as long as the fluid is confined.

Force On An Area

Another part of Pascal's Law states: Pressure acts with equal force on equal areas.

The greater the area, however, the greater the force; in fact, the total force on any area equals *the pressure multiplied by the area,* Fig. 5-8. In the illustration, ten psi is created and applied to a piston with a 100 square inch area; thus, a total of ten times 100, or 1000 pounds of force is exerted. In fact, input force may be multiplied 100 to one, or even 1000 to one by

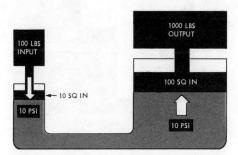

FORCE ON LARGE PISTON = 1000 LBS

1000 LBS OUTPUT

100 LBS INPUT

10 SQ IN

100 SQ IN

10 PSI

10 PSI

Fig. 5-8. Force is pressure multiplied by area. (Chrysler Corp.)

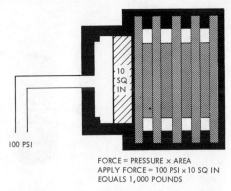

10 SQ IN

100 PSI

FORCE = PRESSURE × AREA
APPLY FORCE = 100 PSI × 10 SQ IN
EQUALS 1,000 POUNDS

Fig. 5-10. A hydraulic piston used for clutch application.

increasing the size of the output piston.

The servo and clutch pistons in an automatic transmission are working examples of how hydraulic pressure is transformed into a mechanical force to apply the bands and clutches, Figs. 5-9 and 5-10. If the transmission apply pressure is 100 psi, then a 5 sq in servo

BAND

DRUM

PRESSURE APPLY PASSAGE

STATIONARY ANCHOR

PISTON

STEM

SERVO BODY

RELEASE SPRING

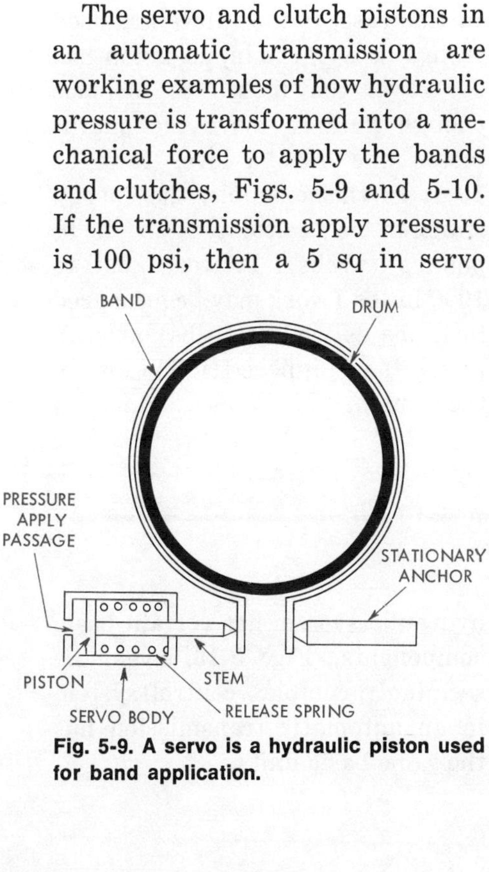

Fig. 5-9. A servo is a hydraulic piston used for band application.

piston and 10 sq in clutch piston would develop 500 pounds and 1000 pounds of apply force respectively.

Conservation of Energy and the Hydraulic Lever

The old *law of conservation of energy* says that *"energy can neither be created or destroyed."* The only way to get a large output force with a small input force is to make the input force travel farther.

In a mechanical set-up using the fulcrum and lever principle, Fig. 5-11, a 100 pound weight is used to move a 1000 pound weight with a lever. It should be obvious that to get an output ten times the input lever, the input lever arm has to be ten times as long. Thus, for every foot the 1000 pound weight moves, the 100 pound weight has to move ten feet. The energy transfer in this system can easily be measured

115

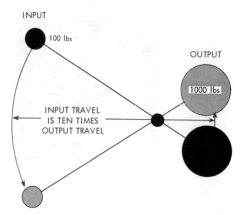

Fig. 5-11. The theory of the lever. (Chrysler Corp.)

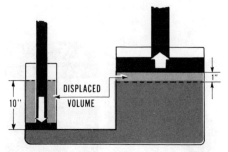

Fig. 5-12. The hydraulic lever. (Chrysler Corp.)

in foot-pounds. The 100 pound weight moves ten feet so the energy is 1000 foot-pounds. The 1000 pound weight moves one foot, and therefore, it also has 1000 foot pounds (ft-lbs) of energy. (*Work* is measured in *ft-lbs;* but *torque* is measured in *lbs-ft.*) In summation, if friction losses are ignored, 1000 pounds of energy is transferred in the system with no loss or gain, thus proving the *law of conservation of energy.*

The law of conservation of en-ergy can be related to hydraulics. Returning to a small and large piston illustration, Fig. 5-12, the same weight-to-distance relationship is established as with the lever. In this case, if the values are used from Fig. 5-8, the input piston has to travel ten inches to displace enough fluid to move the output piston one inch, a lever ratio of 10:1. In this example, the energy transfer is calculated in inch-pounds (in-lbs). It works out to 1000 in-lbs (work may be measured in in-lbs as well as ft-lbs) at each piston if you ignore friction loss in the system.

A Basic Hydraulic System

Now that you have been introduced to *Pascal's Law* and the principles of the hydraulic lever, let's look at how a simple hydraulic system works. Every pressure hydraulic system has certain basic components, Fig. 5-13, even the seemingly complex control system in an automatic transmission has the same basic units.

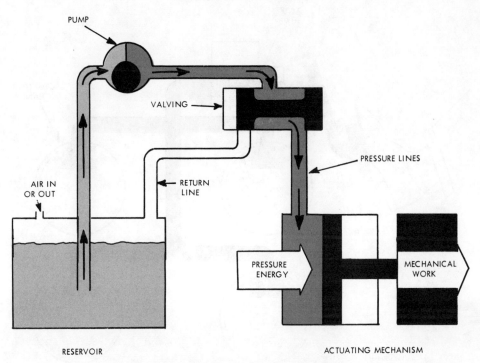

LINES CONNECT COMPONENTS

PUMP

VALVING

PRESSURE LINES

AIR IN
OR OUT

RETURN
LINE

PRESSURE
ENERGY

MECHANICAL
WORK

RESERVOIR

ACTUATING MECHANISM

Fig. 5-13. A basic hydraulic system. (Chrysler Corp.)

First a Reservoir

The reservoir (or sump) is a storehouse for fluid until it is needed in the system. In some systems where there is constant circulation of the fluid, the reservoir aids cooling by transferring heat from the fluid to the container and ultimately to the atmosphere.

In a brake system, the reservoir is part of the master cylinder, Fig. 5-14. In power steering, the power steering reservoir surrounds the pump housing. In automatic transmissions, the control system reservoir is the oil pan.

Then a Pump

The pump creates *flow* and applies force to the fluid. It pushes the fluid into the system and pressure is built up when the fluid encounters resistance.

Here's an important point to remember. The pump cannot create pressure by itself; it can only create flow. If the flow doesn't meet any resistance, it is referred to as a *free flow*, and there is no pressure build-up. There must be a blind alley, or a dead end, or a resistance to flow in the system to create pressure.

117

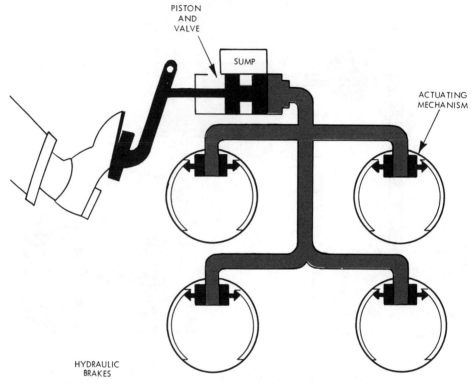

PISTON AND VALVE

SUMP

ACTUATING MECHANISM

HYDRAULIC BRAKES

Fig. 5-14. The brake system as an application of hydraulics. (Chrysler Corp.)

Pumps can be the *reciprocating piston type* (as in a brake master cylinder), or they can be *rotary* (like the front pump in an automatic transmission). In hydraulics, piston pumps are usually operated manually and rotary pumps are driven by an engine or an electric motor. In automatic transmissions, the *front pump* is driven by the engine through the converter hub, or if the transmission is also designed with a *rear pump*, it is driven by the output shaft.

Then Valving

Valving regulates and directs the fluid. Some valves just inter-connect passages, telling the fluid where to go and when. Other valves control or regulate *pressure* and *flow*. In a brake system, for instance, valving is done by the piston and *ports* in the master cylinder. In automatic transmissions the valving for controlling the shifts and shift quality is housed in a *control valve body*.

An Actuating Mechanism

The working or actuating mechanism changes *pressure energy* to *mechanical force*. This is where the flow from the pump runs into a dead end and causes pressure to build up. The pressure works against a *surface* and causes a force to be applied. In a brake system, there are eight actuating mechanisms, the wheel cylinder pistons, Fig. 5-14. In automatic transmissions there are the *servo pistons* and *clutch pistons* to apply the bands and clutches.

Finally the Lines

The individual components of a hydraulic system need to be tied together for the system to operate. These components are inter-connected by tubing, hoses, or passages that are machined or cast in the system housing and attachments. *Pressure lines* carry fluid from the pump to the actuating mechanisms and *return lines* release fluid to the sump when pressure is released. In many systems, such as brakes and automatic transmissions, the same lines perform both functions.

The Complete System

The preceding basic components make up any hydraulic system whether it is simple or complex. An understanding of how these components work, and of some basic facts about hydraulic systems, will let you approach any system with confidence. No matter how many lines and how many valves in the system, each has a basic function that can be studied apart from the rest.

Flow in A Circuit

Flow has been mentioned several times without giving it too much attention. Flow is what is coming out of the pump when it is pumping and is commonly measured in gallons per minute, abbreviated *gpm*.

If the system output is force and motion, there is continuous flow to the actuating mechanism. If the output is force only, there is very little flow in the system, only enough to maintain pressure and make up for normal leakage. The pump is still delivering fluid, but it is bypassed to the sump by a *regulator valve*.

In any pressure hydraulic system the components are kept full of fluid at all times. Thus, response to flow, or pressure build-up, is instantaneous. This is one reason that air, which is compressible, cannot be tolerated in a pressure system and must be bled out for proper operation of the system. Not only would air compress and thus hinder the hydraulic, also it would affect the transmission fluid.

The Hydraulic Jack

Let's look at a hydraulic jack circuit, examine it for basic component make-up and study how it works, Fig. 5-15.

The small piston is the *pump* and the large piston is the *actuating mechanism*. The large piston is used to raise a *load;* therefore its output will be *force* and *motion*. The system makes use of pressure and flow, *pressure* to supply force and *flow* to supply motion.

A reservoir and valving is needed to permit repeated *stroking* of the pump which results in raising the output piston another notch with each stroke. Two *check valves* are needed, one to keep the load from lowering on the intake stroke, the other to prevent pressure loss on the power stroke.

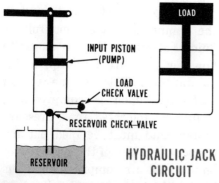

INPUT PISTON (PUMP)

LOAD

LOAD CHECK VALVE

RESERVOIR CHECK-VALVE

RESERVOIR

HYDRAULIC JACK CIRCUIT

Fig. 5-15. Diagram of hydraulic jack circuit. (Chrysler Corp.)

The component make-up of the hydraulic jack circuit meets the basic hydraulic system requirements. We are now ready to see how it operates, but first, let's look at two terms that need to be defined.

Atmospheric Pressure. It is the pressure exerted on everything around us because of the weight of the air. If a one square inch column of air as high as the atmosphere goes could be isolated, it would weigh 15 pounds at sea level. Since air is a fluid and it is confined to the earth's atmosphere, 15 pounds per square inch (psi) is exerted equally over everything on the earth's surface.

Atmospheric pressure does vary with altitude and weather conditions. A pressure of 15 psi is often referred to as *one atmosphere*. Denver, the mile high city, has an atmospheric pressure of less than one atmosphere.

Vacuum. Technically, a *vacuum* is the absence of pressure. Actually, any condition where pressure is less than one atmosphere is referred to as a vacuum. For example, when you sip on a straw a void is created in the straw which is below one atmosphere. The liquid in your glass, though, is still at atmospheric pressure; and it is the pressure difference that forces the liquid up through the straw.

Atmospheric pressure and *vacuum* will play an important part in a later discussion of hydraulic pump operation.

Intake Stroke

As we study the pump system in Fig. 5-16, we see that as the pump piston is stroked upward, a *partial vacuum* is created below it. Atmospheric pressure in the reservoir forces fluid past the reservoir check valve, which is unseated by the flow. The load is prevented from coming down by high pressure seating the load check valve and preventing any *back flow*.

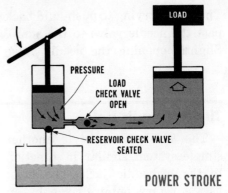

POWER STROKE

Fig. 5-17. Pressure stroke in a jack. (Chrysler Corp.)

builds up below it, seating the reservoir check valve and preventing return of the fluid to the sump. The load check valve opens and fluid is forced under the large piston, raising the load another notch.

Lowering

To lower the load, a third valve is connected, a manually controlled *needle valve* between the large piston and the reservoir, Fig. 5-18.

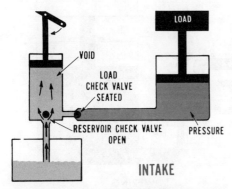

INTAKE

Fig. 5-16. Intake stroke in a jack. (Chrysler Corp.)

Power Stroke

When the pump piston is stroked downward, Fig. 5-17, the pressure

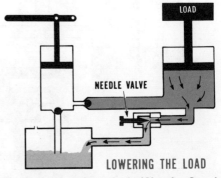

LOWERING THE LOAD

Fig. 5-18. Lowering a jack. (Chrysler Corp.)

The load is trying to push fluid back past the needle valve to the sump. Slightly opening the needle valve meters the fluid back to the reservoir, permitting gravity to bring the load down.

The Hydraulic Hoist

The *hydraulic hoist* is another simple system similar in function to the hydraulic jack. The hoist uses a rotary pump driven by an electric motor instead of the hand-powered piston pump. This gives a smooth, constant flow of fluid. One three position *spool valve* controlled by the operator, raises, holds, and lowers the load, depending on the valve position, Fig. 5-19.

Raise Position

The valve has three ports; these are connected to the pump output, the hoist cylinder, and the sump. In one position of the valve handle, flow from the pump is directed under the cylinder. The weight of the load causes pressure to develop and the hoist is raised. The reservoir port is blocked by a *valve land*.

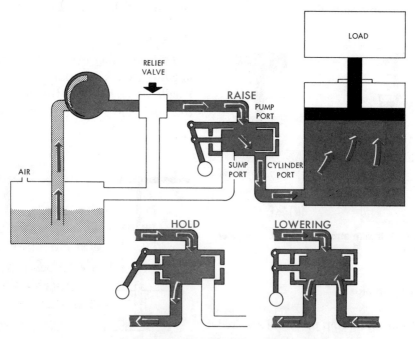

Fig. 5-19. A hydraulic hoist system.

Hold Position

In the *hold position* of the valve, the line to the hoist cylinder is blocked by one of the valve lands. This prevents the hoist from lowering or raising. The reservoir port is uncovered and pump delivery is bypassed to tank.

Lowering Position

For lowering, all three ports are open to each other. Pump *delivery* is bypassed to the reservoir along with the fluid under the hoist cylinder and gravity lowers the load.

Relief Valve

A *relief valve* is needed in the hydraulic hoist system to protect the system from overloading. For instance, if the control valve is left in the raise position when the cylinder is all the way up, there is no place for any more fluid to go. The pump, however, is still pumping and, if no relief is provided, pressure increases until something breaks or the motor stalls. The relief valve by-passes pump delivery to the reservoir and still maintains system pressure under the cylinder to prevent it from lowering.

The hydraulic jack and hydraulic hoist are simple but basic examples of the hydraulic lever. We can now build upon this basic background in the next two chapters, getting a more detailed look at hydraulic pumps and valving. Finally we will look into the workings of an automatic transmission hydraulic control system.

Checking on Your Knowledge

The following questions give you the opportunity to check up on yourself. If you have read the chapter carefully, you should be able to answer the questions. If you have any difficulty, read the chapter over once more so that you have the information well in mind before you go on with your reading.

1. What is a fluid?
2. State Pascal's Law.
3. Briefly discuss Pascal's findings of the relationship between a mechanical lever system and pressure system.
4. What is the difference between force and pressure?
5. How much apply force is developed by a 90 psi pressure head working on a 10 sq in clutch piston?
6. Briefly discuss, "The law of conservation of energy can be related to hydraulics."
7. Briefly describe the following basic components that make up a pressure hydraulic system. Relate these components to an automatic transmission pressure hydraulic system:

    reservoir   valving
    pump   actuating mechanism

8. Why can't air be tolerated in a hydraulic pressure system?
9. There are two check valves used in a hydraulic jack circuit. Explain why.
10. Briefly explain the terms: *atmospheric pressure* and *vacuum*.
11. Hydraulic jack operation: What causes the fluid from the sump to move into the pump cylinder on the intake stroke.

12. Hydraulic hoist operation: What is the purpose of the three-position spool valve? How is this spool valve controlled?
13. Hydraulic hoist operation: Why is a relief valve needed in the system.
14. Hydraulic hoist operation: What causes the fluid from the sump to move into electric driven pump?

Hydraulic System Fundamentals— Pumps and Valves*

Chapter

6

Hydraulic Pumps

A *hydraulic pump* is a mechanism through which an external source of power is used to apply force to a liquid. In automatic transmissions, the front pump drive, Fig. 6-1, is keyed to the converter hub, therefore the external source of power is the engine.

In most cases a hydraulic pump must provide a flow of fluid under pressure from which force and motion are transmitted. The pump is the heart of any pressure hydraulic system. When it fails to operate to specifications, the system encounters partial or total failure.

Rotary hydraulic pumps are widely used in pressure hydraulic systems. Although there are many types of rotary pumps, we will con-

fine our discussion to those used in current automatic transmission applications.

Rotary Pumps

All *rotary pumps* used in pressure hydraulic systems work on the same operating principle. Fluid is trapped in chambers that are constantly expanding and contracting —expanding at the pump inlet to draw fluid into the pump and contracting at the outlet to force fluid into the system under pressure, Fig. 6-2.

Most of these pumps have two round members, with the *inner drive member* turning inside the outer. The members are on different centers, therefore, at one point

*Based on training publications of the Chrysler Corporation.

125

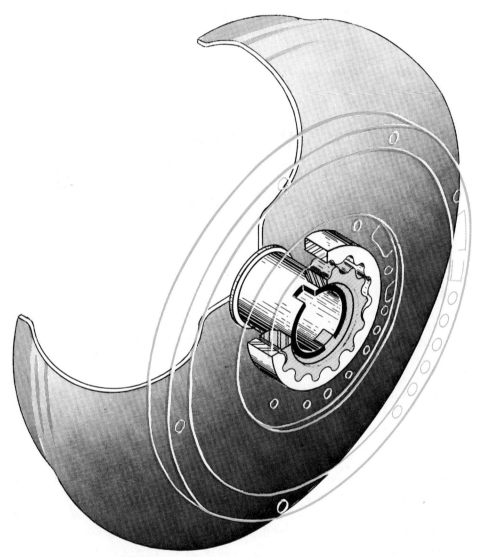

Fig. 6-1. Oil pump in automatic transmission driven by converter hub or drive sleeve.

there is no clearance between them, and the clearance varies through a half revolution to the point of maximum clearance, Fig. 6-3.

The pumping mechanism lobes, or gears, form sealed chambers between the members. These pumping chambers are carried around

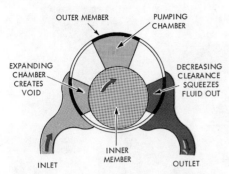

Fig. 6-2. Diagram of a rotary pump. (Chrysler Corp.)

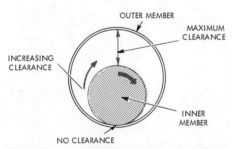

Fig. 6-3. Rotary pumps have two round members on different shaft centers. (Chrysler Corp.)

by rotation of one or both members.

Using Fig. 6-2, here is how the pumping action takes place. At the point where clearance begins to increase, the pumping chamber expands in size, creating a *void*. The *inlet* is located at this void and atmospheric pressure in the sump forces fluid into the void.

The size of the chamber continues to increase until rotation carries it past the inlet to the point

of maximum clearance. For a few degrees of travel at maximum clearance, the chamber neither increases nor decreases.

The outlet is located where the clearance is decreasing. Here, the pumping chamber decreases in size and fluid is squeezed out of the chamber and into the system under pressure. Succeeding chambers follow each other closely so a smooth, continuous output is obtained.

Internal-External Gear And Rotor Pumps

The two pumps under discussion are commonly referred to as the *IX gear pump* and the *IX rotor pump;* the term IX is used as an abbreviation for *internal-external*. They are called internal-external pumps because the gear or lobe members of the moveable outer ring are pointed toward the center. Figs. 6-4 and 6-5 show the component makeup of a typical IX gear and IX rotor pump assembly.

In the *IX rotor pump of the lobe design* both rotor members turn together. The inner rotor is the drive member and carries the outer rotor by meshing of the lobes, Fig. 6-6. A pumping chamber is formed between the lobes. As the lobes separate from mesh, the chamber increases at the inlet. At the outlet, the lobes are meshing again, decreasing the chamber size and squeezing the fluid out into the sys-

127

Fig. 6-4. Internal-external gear pump, Turbo Hydra-Matic 350. (Oldsmobile Div., General Motors Corp.)

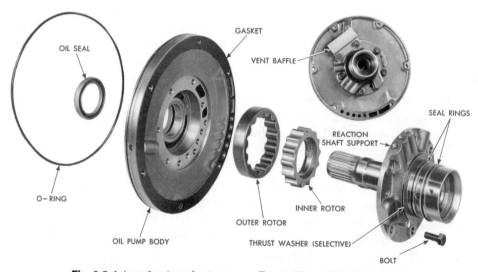

Fig. 6-5. Internal-external rotor pump, TorqueFlite. (Chrysler Corp.)

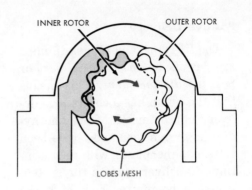

Fig. 6-6. Internal-external rotor design. (Chrysler Corp.)

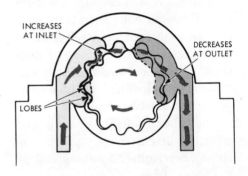

Fig. 6-7. Internal-external rotor design flow pattern. (Chrysler Corp.)

Fig. 6-8. IX gear pump.

tem, Fig. 6-7. The inlet is sealed from the outlet by the close clearance between the lobe tips at the point of maximum displacement.

The pumping action of the IX gear pump is similar to the IX rotor pump, Fig. 6-8. As the inner gear drives the outer gear, the space between the teeth increases as they pass the inlet port and then decreases as they pass the outlet port. There is a crescent-shaped divider between the two gears. In this case, oil is trapped between the divider and the gear teeth of both gears and carried to the outlet.

129

Positive Delivery

The IX rotor, and IX gear pumps are classified as *positive delivery* or *positive displacement*. This means that the pump has a continuous delivery characteristic. Once the hydraulic system demands have been satisfied, the pump will then continue to deliver against the system pressure no matter how high the pressure. This pressure build-up could have no end; therefore, it is necessary to provide a relief valve to protect against overloads which could cause some weak point in the system, a valve seal or line component, to give way or burst.

The volume delivery or output of positive displacement pumps is simply determined by the speed of the pump drive.

Pump Efficiency

As pump parts become worn or damaged, fluid can leak back from the contracting (output) chambers to the expanding (intake) chambers, causing loss of efficiency.

Efficiency is the actual pump output with respect to displacement. Thus, if a pump has a displacement of 100 cu in per revolution, but twenty cu in are leaked internally, its efficiency is eighty percent.

Loss of efficiency does not mean pressure is lost, because pressure will build up as long as some fluid is being pumped and is not leaking off somewhere else in the system. Loss of efficiency, however, often slows down the application of pressure and the movement of working mechanisms.

Hydraulic Valves

Valves are used in hydraulic systems to control the operation of the *actuators*. In automatic transmissions this means control over the servo and clutch pistons, their apply and release. It is common to refer to a group of valves built into a single assembly as the *control valve body assembly*, Fig. 6-9.

The valves assert their authority in the circuit by regulating pressure; by creating special pressure conditions; by deciding how much oil will flow in portions of the circuit; and by directing the oil where to go.

In construction they vary from a simple ball and seat to a many element spool type valve train.

Hydraulic valves can be divided generally into two classes, those that *direct* flow and pressure and those that *regulate* or control flow and pressure.

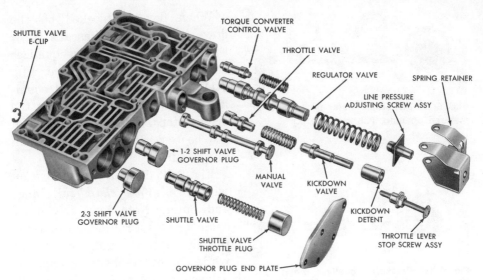

Fig. 6-9. Control valve body assembly. (Chrysler Corp.)

Valves that direct flow and pressure are like an ON/OFF switch. They simply connect or disconnect passages without restricting the fluid flow or changing the pressure while the passages are connected. These valves are usually called *directional* or *relay valves*, and have but the simple function of turning ON and OFF.

Regulator valves are valves which change pressure of the oil as it passes through the valve. It does this by bleeding off (or exhausting) some of the volume of oil supplied to it.

Let's look at some of the directional control and regulating valves typically used in automatic transmissions (or in any hydraulic control system).

Orifice

The simplest means of controlling flow and pressure is by an orifice. An *orifice* is a restriction. It slows down fluid flow either to create back pressure or to delay pressure build-up downstream.

When fluid is pumped to an orifice, there is not enough room for it to go through all at once, and a *back pressure* is created on the pump side. If there is a flow path on the downstream side, a *pressure difference* is maintained across the orifice; pressure is lower on the downstream of the orifice, Fig. 6-10, as long as fluid continues to flow throughout. In hydraulic circuits, the orifice is a simple means of lowering pressure.

131

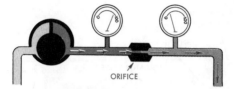

Fig. 6-10. An orifice acts as a fixed or metered opening. (Chrysler Corp.)

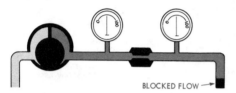

Fig. 6-11. Pressure equalizes when flow through orifice stops on the blocked side. (Chrysler Corp.)

When flow is blocked on the downstream side, Pascal's Law then applies and pressure equalizes on both sides of the orifice, Fig. 6-11. The pressure does not equalize, however, until flow across the orifice stops. The orifice then can also be used to delay the application of pressure.

Fig. 6-12 shows a *clutch position* with two *apply chambers*, inner and outer. Note how the inner chamber gets a rapid feed to apply the clutch for initial engagement while the outer chamber apply is delayed by an orifice. By not engaging the clutch with full force, a

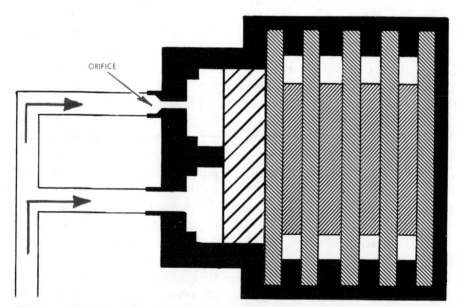

Fig. 6-12. An orifice gives delaying action. (Oldsmobile Div., General Motors Corp.)

harsh *clutch apply* is not experienced by the driver. Eventually, the flow across the orifice ceases and full pressure in both chambers apply against the clutch piston for *maximum holding power*.

In automatic transmissions the change from one gear ratio to another requires a delicate control of the rate of release of one friction clutch or band in favor of an alternative friction device also requiring a precise rate of application. Small restriction orifices are engineered and used throughout the hydraulic paths to obtain a timed sequence for a quality shift so that the engine does not flare up, nor the two gear ratios fight one another.

The density of automatic transmission fluid does not vary appreciably, thus a rate of flow through an orifice can be considered to depend solely on the apply pressure in spite of small variations in viscosity and temperature.

Check Valves

A check valve in its simplest form is a one-way directional valve. It permits flow in a hydraulic line in one direction only. The two most common kinds of check valves are the *ball check* and *poppet check*.

The *ball check valve*, Fig. 6-13, consists of a steel ball and a seat, although there may be a light spring to hold the ball against the

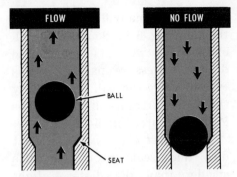

Fig. 6-13. One-way ball type check valve. (Chrysler Corp.)

seat in some applications when no pressure is applied. When pressure is applied on the seat side the ball is forced off the seat and permits flow. Pressure on the opposite side holds the ball against its seat and blocks flow in the reverse direction.

In automatic transmission valve control body assemblies, the ball check plays an important part in

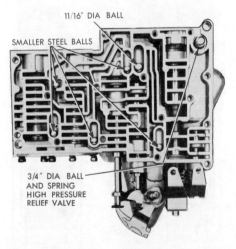

Fig. 6-14. Ball type check valves are used to direct flow patterns in transmissions.

directing the many flow patterns of the fluid, Fig. 6-14. Some of the ball checks have two seats connected to different pressure paths. In this type of valve the ball is seated by the higher pressure and blocks the lower pressure, Fig. 6-15.

The *poppet check valve* is a flat disc that seals around a hole smaller than the disc. A light

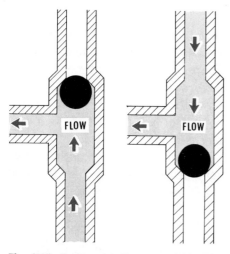

Fig. 6-15. Two seat ball type check valve.

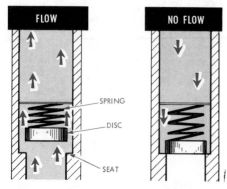

Fig. 6-16. Poppet valves use discs for sealing. (Chrysler Corp.)

spring guides the disc and holds it seated when no pressure is applied, Fig. 6-16. The operation is the same as a simple ball check valve.

Relief Valves

A *relief valve* is a spring loaded, pressure operated valve that bypasses pump delivery to the sump, thereby limiting system pressure to a predetermined maximum value. It is always connected between the pump outlet and sump and it meters pump delivery back to the sump when the desired pressure has been reached in the system.

A simple relief valve, Fig. 6-17, is like a check valve in construction, except that it has a heavier spring to hold it seated against pressure. The spring tension can either be fixed, or adapted to an adjusting screw to vary the spring tension, and thereby vary the pressure at which the valve relieves. Once the spring tension is set it cannot be varied in operation. System pressure will be determined by the spring tension.

In operation, the spring holds the valve seated against pump delivery until system pressure is high enough to overcome the spring. The valve unseats and meters fluid from the pump or main circuit back to the sump. It adjusts itself automatically so just enough fluid is bypassed to the sump that system operating pressure is maintained.

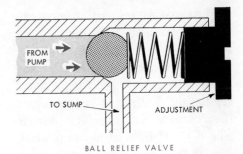

BALL RELIEF VALVE

Fig. 6-17. A relief valve is a check valve with a heavy spring exerting a fixed pressure to one side. (Chrysler Corp.)

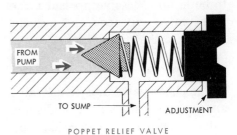

POPPET RELIEF VALVE

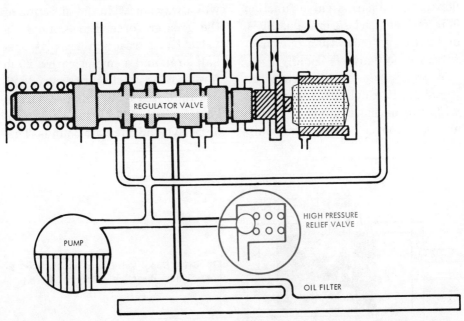

Fig. 6-18. High pressure relief valve used in TorqueFlite to protect against excessive pressures.

135

The pressure regulation in an automatic transmission requires a regulation system capable of giving variable values, and therefore the relief valve is not used for pressure regulation. Rather, it is sometimes incorporated as a safety device, Fig. 6-18. If the normal regulation system fails and permits the pump to build up excessive pressure, the relief valve will open and prevent damage to the transmission.

Spool Valves

The check valve and relief valve are the simplest kinds of hydraulic valves, both in construction and operation. They are limited in means of control and number of flow paths. Where a valve function is to interconnect several passages, or to react to more than one pressure, a spool valve is usually used.

A *spool valve* is illustrated in Fig. 6-19. It is cylindrically shaped with two or more lands and with annular grooves between the lands.

The valve is closely fitted to a round bore and slides in the bore on a pressurized film of fluid. Fluid passages are open or closed to each other depending on the valve land positions. Spool valves can be positioned manually, by springs, or by pressure, Fig. 6-20.

When a valve is acted upon by a spring and by pressure, the spring exerts force in one direction, and the pressure opposes the spring. A pressure that opposes the spring is called a *reaction pressure,* and the area on which it acts is called a *reaction area.*

Pressure can be resolved into *force* by multiplying the pressure and the reaction area. The valve will always move in the direction of the greater force. For example, a valve has a reaction area of one-half sq in and a spring with a 20 lb force. If the reaction pressure is 25 psi, the force from this pressure is 25 psi multiplied by one-half sq in, or twelve and one-half pounds. This

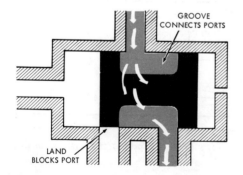

GROOVE
CONNECTS PORTS

LAND
BLOCKS PORT

Fig. 6-19. Spool valves are widely used to control flow direction. (Chrysler Corp.)

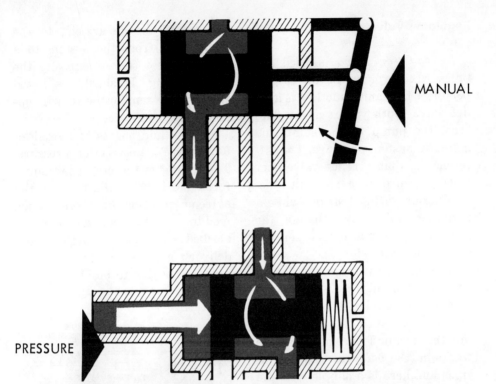

MANUAL

PRESSURE

Fig. 6-20. Spool valves may be operated manually or by pressure. (Chrysler Corp.)

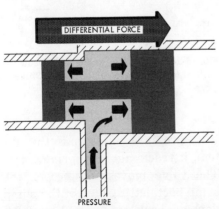

DIFFERENTIAL FORCE

PRESSURE

Fig. 6-21. Spool valves can be made to operate on a differential force. (Chrysler Corp.)

is less than spring force and the spring holds the valve closed. If reaction pressure rises to 50 psi, its force is then 25 pounds. This will overcome the spring and the valve will shift.

When two adjacent lands of a spool valve have different diameters, and pressure is applied between the lands, a *differential force* results, Fig. 6-21. The force on the larger land is greater than on the small land and this results in a differential force in the direction of the large land.

137

Regulator Valve

A *regulator valve* is used for pressure control and in this respect performs the same function as a relief valve. Both valves meter fluid from the pump to the sump and maintain system pressure. The difference is that a relief valve controls pressure at a set value depending on spring tension, while a regulator valve can change the pressure in response to other hydraulic pressure signals.

All regulator valves must have a basic fluid input feed. This input feed is then regulated to a specified working pressure and passed on into the circuit. The regulator valve works on the *balanced valve* principle, and here is a simple example of how it operates when used as a pressure regulator for the pump.

A study of Fig. 6-22 will show that the valve has connections from

the pump, to the system, to the sump, and from the system to a *reaction area* that is opposite the valve spring. It should be noted that the system pressure will oppose the spring force.

Before fluid begins to flow, Fig. 6-23, there is no reaction pressure. The spring is the only positioning force and it holds the valve in the extreme position of a wide open feed to the system and a completely blocked sump port. All the pump delivery goes to the system until pressure begins to build up.

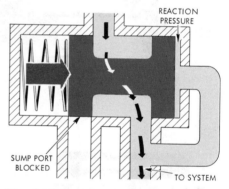

Fig. 6-23. Regulator valve is closed by spring force before fluid flow. (Chrysler Corp.)

As pressure builds up in the system, it reacts against spring force. The valve moves to uncover the sump port, letting part of the pump flow go back to sump, Fig. 6-24. When the pressure tends to decrease, it allows the spring to force

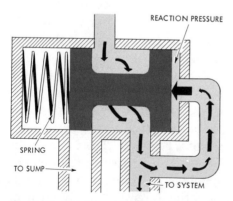

Fig. 6-22. Regular or balanced valve system. (Chrysler Corp.)

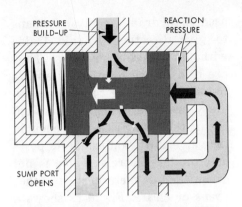

Fig. 6-24. Regulator valve opens when pressure in system builds up and overcomes spring tension. (Chrysler Corp.)

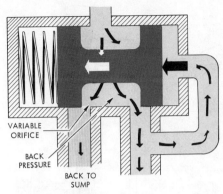

Fig. 6-25. Regulator valve acts as variable orifice. (Chrysler Corp.)

the valve back and cut down the bleed-off to the sump. This permits the system again to very rapidly re-establish or maintain its operating pressure and the cycle continues to repeat itself.

A condition of equilibrium occurs with spring force and reaction pressure balancing one another. The valve is poised between the two forces with the valve land and the sump port acting as a variable orifice which meters or bleeds off the flow back to sump, Fig. 6-25. If the reaction area of the valve was one sq in and a spring force of 90 pounds was used, then the valve would balance or regulate at 90 psi.

The regulator valve just described is really nothing more than a sophisticated relief valve. To become a true regulator valve, another pressure signal must be added to change the system pressure, as

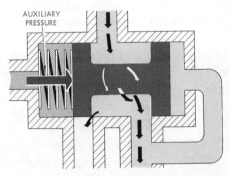

Fig. 6-26. Auxiliary pressure assists the spring to control regulator valve. (Chrysler Corp.)

in Fig. 6-26. If this *auxiliary pressure* opposes the spring, it simply subtracts from the spring's effective force and decreases the regulated pressure. If the auxiliary pressure assists the spring, the regulated pressure is increased.

139

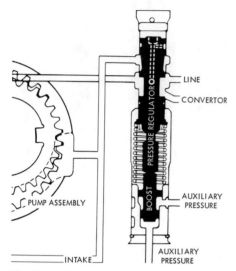

Fig. 6-27. Typical pressure regulator valve system used in automatic transmissions. (Oldsmobile Div., General Motors Corp.)

used in hydraulic control systems to give direction to fluid traffic without changing pressure. They are held in one position by spring force, or by spring force plus auxiliary pressure. When pressure opposing the spring rises high enough, the valve shifts and connects ports or circuits. The relay valve is not designed for metering; it either *opens* or *closes*. Fig. 6-28 shows a relay valve triggered by hydraulic pressure overcoming spring force and the auxiliary pressure.

Illustrated in Fig. 6-27 is a typical pressure regulator valve assembly used in automatic transmissions. Note that the reaction area is on the top end of the valve and that line pressure is regulated according to a fixed spring force and fluid pressure on the boost valve.

Other examples of regulator valve applications in automatic transmissions are the governor and the throttle systems (discussed in the next chapter). A solid understanding of regulator valve operation and the balanced valve principle will be very helpful.

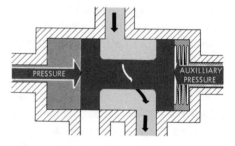

Fig. 6-28. Relay valve position ON or OFF is controlled by opposing forces. (Chrysler Corp.)

Relay Valve

The *relay valve* is another application of the spool valve having two positions, ON and OFF. These are

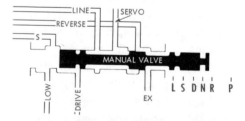

Fig. 6-29. Manual relay valve is used to establish operating range in automatic transmissions. (Oldsmobile Div., General Motors Corp.)

The automatic transmission manual valve and shift valves are classic examples of relay valve applications. Illustrated in Fig. 6-29 is a typical manual valve which establishes the operating range of the transmission. Movement of the manual valve interconnects the line pressure with the various operating range circuits.

Checking On Your Knowledge

The following questions give you the opportunity to check up on yourself. If you have read the chapter carefully, you should be able to answer the questions. If you have any difficulty, read the chapter over once more so that you have the information well in mind before you go on with your reading.

1. What is a hydraulic pump?
2. What drives the front pump in an automatic transmission?
3. Make a brief comment, "The pump is the heart of any pressure hydraulic system."
4. How does a rotary pump create a void? What causes the fluid to move from the sump into the void?
5. How does a rotary pump create pressure?
6. What two types of rotary pumps are popularly used in current automatic transmissions?
7. Explain why IX rotor and IX gear pumps are classified as positive delivery pumps?
8. Name the two general classes of hydraulic valves and briefly describe their function.
9. What is an orifice?
10. When does pressure equalize itself on both sides of an orifice?
11. How are orifices used in the hydraulic system of an automatic transmission?
12. What is a check valve?
13. Name the two most common kinds of check valves.
14. What is a relief valve?
15. What is the purpose of the relief valve spring tension?
16. Why can't a relief valve be used for pressure regulation in an automatic transmission?
17. What is the purpose of using a relief valve in an automatic transmission pressure system?
18. What is a spool valve? Give some examples of their application in a hydraulic system.
19. Name three methods that are used for positioning spool valves.
20. Define *reaction pressure, reaction area,* and *differential force* as it relates to spool valve operation in a hydraulic system.
21. How does a regulator valve differ from a relief valve?
22. In a simple pressure regulator valve system, what determines the value of the regulated output pressure?
23. What is the purpose of a bleed off port in a regulator valve system?
24. How is *auxiliary pressure* used to boost the regulated output of a pressure regulator valve?
25. What is the purpose of a relay valve?
26. Which of the following examples from an automatic transmission hydraulic control system are classified as *regulating valves* or *relay valves:* pressure regulator valve, manual valve, governor valve, throttle valve, and shift valve.

The Automatic Transmission Hydraulic System Fundamentals of Operation

The hydraulic system operation of any automatic transmission can be made as complicated as one would want to make it. Since we're not in the engineering business, our objective is to keep it simple.

As emphasized before, every automatic transmission varies only by its own particular design and construction. The basic operating principles, mechanical and hydraulic, are typically the same. The approach therefore to discussing the subject matter of the automatic transmission hydraulic system will be based on those materials that are common and necessary to the working of all transmissions.

Hydraulic system construction details peculiar to an individual transmission can always be found in the manufacturer's service manual.

The hydraulic system is responsible for the *release* and the *apply* of the band-clutch combinations, the control of automatic shifting, and transmission operational requirements. It includes the pump, clutches, servos, accumulators, and valving whose functions are interrelated.

For discussion purposes let's apply our knowledge of hydraulic fundamentals, Chapters 5 and 6, and gradually build up an automatic transmission hydraulic system using a 2-speed transmission as our prime example.

First, we will introduce the basic assemblies involved in the typical hydraulic system, learn about their job function, and explain how they work. (As a result of your study of Chapters 5 and 6, the write-up on the hydraulic operation of the various assemblies and circuits should not require detail.) With this background, it can be simply illustrated how all units work together and what goes into making up a total system.

The Pressure Supply System

The pressure supply system is responsible for pressure development and control. This system incorporates a *front* or engine-driven pump, and sometimes an additional *rear* or output shaft-driven pump, both of which are controlled by a main regulator system to meet the engineered pressure schedule for transmission operation.

All transmissions require the pressure supply system to perform these duties:

1. Establish and maintain a mainline pressure (a feeder) for operation of all the individual hydraulic circuits.
2. Fill and maintain a charge pressure to the converter.
3. Supply and circulate fluid for cooling.
4. Supply and circulate fluid for lubrication of the gears, bushings, thrust washers, clutch plates, sprag and roller clutches.
5. Supply fluid to a valve control body and a governor for the regulation of apply and release of the clutches and bands.

If a rear pump is used, it would perform three additional functions:

1. Provide a working pressure for the transmission during push starts.
2. At a designed vehicle speed, it cuts into the main regulating circuit and takes over the duties of the front pump.
3. It provides a source of fluid supply to the governor.

The current practice is to eliminate the use of the rear pump in transmissions. This trend started in 1959 and continued until no rear pumps appeared in any transmissions in the production year 1968.

Since the rear pump usage is not too ancient, let's briefly look at a front and rear pump regulating system, Figs. 7-1 and 7-2. The front pump is the larger and is needed to supply the transmission hydraulic demands under the most severe conditions, and during *stall* and *low speed* operation whenever

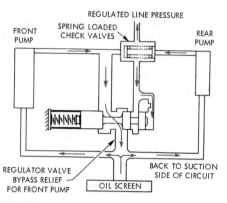

Fig. 7-1. Front pump pressure is regulated by a regulator valve by-pass.

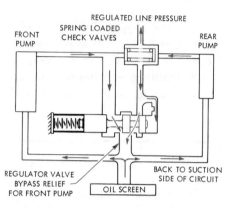

Fig. 7-2. Rear pump regulation. Note the position of the regulator valves and check valves as compared to Fig. 7-1.

pressure requirements are high and the pump speed is low.

Note the position of the check valves and the regulating valve when the front pump is working the system, Fig. 7-1. As the vehicle gains speed the output delivery of the front pump becomes more than adequate and the excess is bled off back through the regulator valve to the suction side of the circuit. Meanwhile, the rear pump is building up its pressure with increased vehicle speed. When its pressure is sufficient to overcome the line pressure, the rear pump check valve is opened and the front pump check valve is closed, Fig. 7-2. The rear pump cuts in at a slightly higher pressure than line pressure because of check valve design—the effective hydraulic area is larger on the check valve spring side.

Note in Fig. 7-2 that the regula-

tor valve has repositioned itself for regulation of the rear pump output and the re-cycling of the entire front pump output back to the suction side of the circuit. Reducing the front pump operating pressure to zero results in increased efficiency—it takes less power to operate the smaller rear pump. If for any reason the rear pump fails to meet the transmission hydraulic demands, the front pump immediately cuts back into the system.

In systems using a rear pump it is common practice to supply the governor feed oil directly from the rear pump output. In cases of a *no shift* or *delayed shift* operational complaint, the technician should be aware that the rear pump circuit may be at fault—no rear pump pressure results in zero governor pressure and a *no upshift* pattern. Low rear pump pressure results in

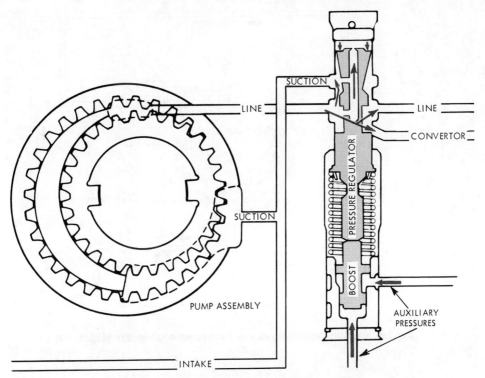

Fig. 7-3. Pressure supply system with single pump.

low governor pressure, and a de-layed upshift and a high closed-throttle downshift pattern.

In a typical single pump pressure supply system, Fig. 7-3, the pump output is sensed by a pressure regu-lator valve. The regulator valve works on the balanced valve princi-ple and regulates the main trans-mission line pressure according to a fixed spring force and auxiliary oil pressure on the *boost valve.* Note in Fig. 7-3 how pressure through a drilled orifice builds up above the regulator valve and

moves the valve against the spring force and boost valve. A bleed-off back to the suction side of the cir-cuit is provided for valve balancing.

In addition to controlling the pump pressure, the regulator valve is usually assigned the extra job of feeding a constant oil supply to the converter when the engine is run-ning and prevents oil from draining back out of the converter through the pressure regulator valve when the engine is stopped, Fig. 7-4. If the converter were to drain when-ever the engine stopped, an unde-

145

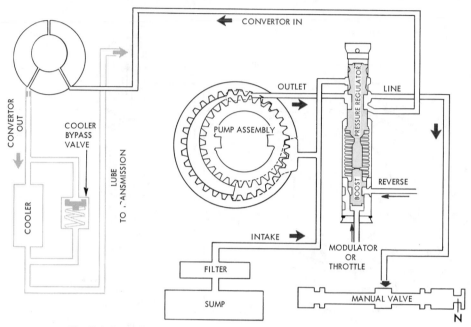

Fig. 7-4. Pressure regulator valve and converter cooling-lube circuit.

sirable delay would be experienced when operation resumed.

When talking about the converter circuit, by necessity the cooling and lubrication circuits must be included because they are all tied together, Fig. 7-4. When the pressure regulator valve is at rest it is bottomed in its bore by the spring, and the converter feed opening is sealed. During operation the regulator valve moves from its *rest* position, and before regulation begins it uncovers a port to feed the converter; thus, oil from the mainline pressure is permitted to flow into the converter circuit. The port opening is sometimes designed with a

metered orifice to assist converter pressure regulation. Converter pressure regulation is concerned with maintaining a minimum of charge pressure to prevent converter *cavitation* and the limitation of maximum charge pressure to prevent converter *ballooning*.

The converter regulation system usually consists of a simple arrangement of restricting orifices, check valves, and a pressure relief valve. The oil flow from the pressure regulator valve to the converter fills and keeps the converter full of oil, Figs. 7-4 and 7-5.

In observing Fig. 7-5, note how oil is directed through the clearance

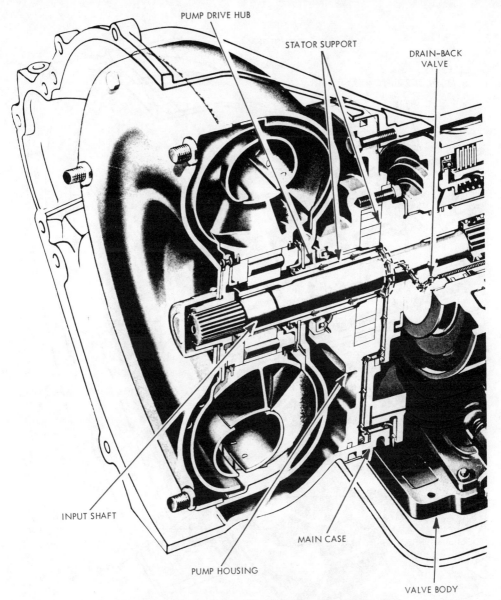

PUMP DRIVE HUB

STATOR SUPPORT

DRAIN–BACK VALVE

INPUT SHAFT

PUMP HOUSING

MAIN CASE

VALVE BODY

Fig. 7-5. Converter-flow-IN circulation. (Ford Motor Co.)

provided between the reactor support and the converter pump drive hub, and finally into the converter

between the converter pump and stator. Not shown in the illustration, but located in the valve body,

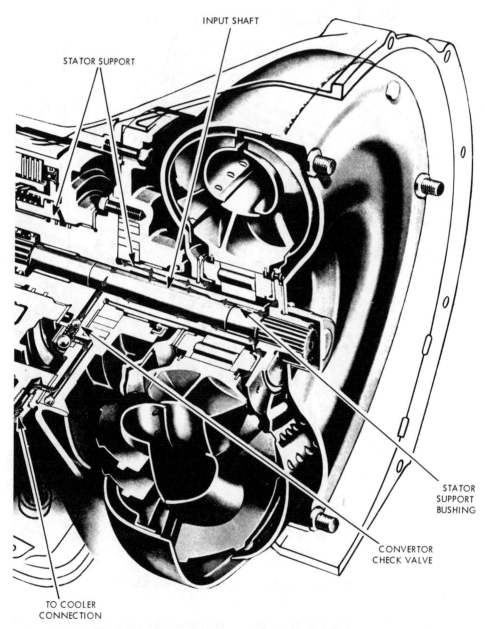

STATOR SUPPORT

INPUT SHAFT

STATOR
SUPPORT
BUSHING

CONVERTOR
CHECK VALVE

TO COOLER
CONNECTION

Fig. 7-6. Converter-flow-OUT circulation. (Ford Motor Co.)

is the main pressure regulator valve and a converter pressure relief valve to limit maximum *converter-in pressure.*

In this particular illustration, Fig. 7-5, a front lube circuit is tapped from the converter in-flow and used for lubrication of the clutch friction plates, bushing supports, and thrust washers located in the forward section of the transmission case. A drain-back valve is incorporated to prevent oil from draining from the converter into the lube circuit when the engine stops. To keep the lube circuit from diverting too much oil from the converter in-flow, the lubrication feed is orificed down-stream.

Getting the oil flow in and out of the converter is quite an engineering stunt. There is an almost constant flow of oil through the converter, through the cooler, to lubrication, and back to sump whenever the engine is running. On occasion, however, this flow is interrupted when severe demands are made on the transmission pump. For example, a manual shift into *reverse* at *engine idle* will usually cause a temporary drop in main line system pressure because of the oil volume demanded to apply the friction elements. To restore the main line pressure back to normal, the pressure regulator valve temporarily cuts off converter feed until the friction elements are applied.

Oil flow out of the converter, Fig. 7-6, goes behind the front bushing into the reactor support and continues to exit between the input

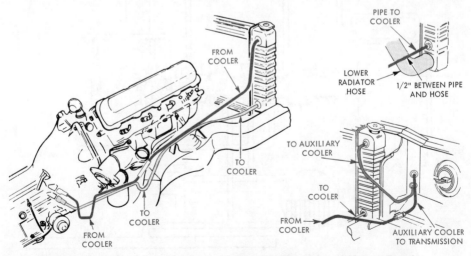

Fig. 7-7. Converter cooler lines. (Oldsmobile Div., General Motors Corp.)

shaft and stator support, through the pump housing, and into the transmission case. The converter out-flow from the transmission case is then piped to and from the cooler through steel tubing, Fig. 7-7. The return line from the cooler is coupled to the transmission case where the oil flow is used for lubrication of the rear transmission sec-

tion which contains the planetary gear train. After the fluid does its job in the front and rear lube circuit, it returns to the sump.

The converter check valve in Fig. 7-6 does two things. It maintains a minimum of pressure in the converter when the engine is operating, and it keeps the converter oil from draining into the sump

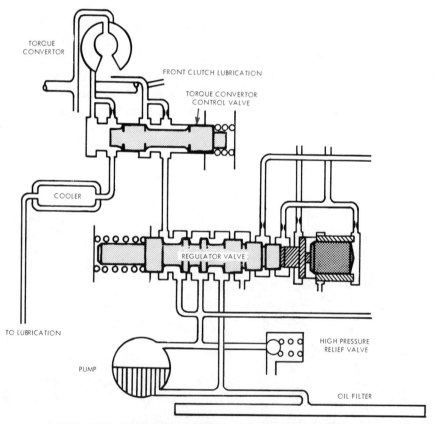

Fig. 7-8. Converter feed circuit using a control valve. (Chrysler Corp.)

through the cooler and rear lube circuits when the engine is stopped.

Most hydraulic systems use the regulator valve as the source of oil feed to the converter, cooling, and lubrication circuits. These circuits are unaffected by the manual valve position and function the same in each operating range of the transmission. Keep in mind that our discussion is based on a typical example and that there are slight circuit design variations between the transmissions.

As an illustration, study the converter feed circuit in Fig. 7-8 and note that the circuit feed and charge pressure is controlled by a regulator valve and torque converter control valve.

If you recall the discussion in Chapter 6, a regulator valve is used

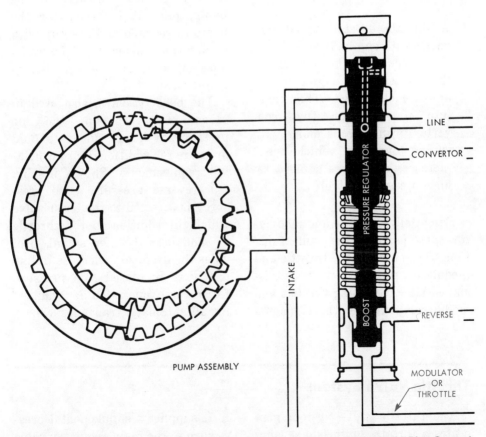

Fig. 7-9. Regulator valve boost system using auxiliary pressures. (Oldsmobile Div., General Motors Corp.)

for pressure control just like a relief valve. The difference is that a relief valve controls pressure at a set value depending on spring tension, but a regulator valve can change the pressure response according to other hydraulic pressure signals. This change of pressure response is typically brought about by use of a booster valve which is sensitive to hydraulic pressure signals, and in effect, varies the pressure regulation, Fig. 7-9, by:

1. A throttle booster signal that varies with engine torque.
2. Or a modulator booster signal that varies with engine torque and vehicle speed. This takes into consideration that converter torque drops along with engine torque as vehicle speed increases and gives a more refined pressure control.

Essentially, throttle and *modulator boost* perform the same function. The source of the throttle and modulator pressures will be discussed later. By using throttle and modulator pressures the transmission line pressure can be feathered between a minimum and a maximum to give the clutch and servo pistons the necessary holding force in relation to engine and converter torque. This means that for power performance the line pressure is high and the shift sequence is aggressive, whereas cruising or light throttle conditions require lower operating pressures. Operating at minimum pressures means less horsepower loss in driving the pump, plus, it is easier for the pump to respond and keep up with the hydraulic demands of the transmission, and soft shift quality is maintained.

The boost valve is also used in reverse for increasing the line pressure to insure adequate fluid pressure for additional torque holding requirements. Shown in Fig. 7-9, reverse pressure (line pressure) is directed to the boost valve which, in addition to the throttle or modulator booster signal, provides the necessary increase in line pressure. Increased line pressure for reverse operation is required for all automatic transmissions.

Throttle Valve System

The throttle valve system generates a throttle or torque sensing signal for the following functions:

1. It supplies a supplemental pressure to the main regulator valve to boost the line pressure for

added holding force of the bands and clutches, Fig. 7-9.

2. In conjunction with governor pressure, it provides for a wide range of automatic shift points.
3. It may be used anywhere in a hydraulic control system to control shift quality. For example, it is typically used to control the accumulator action on a clutch apply.

The throttle valve is another example of a regulating or balanced valve application. Again we will see a hydraulic force balancing against a variable spring force. There are two methods of obtaining a throttle signal in current transmission designs, vacuum and mechanical. Let us consider a vacuum controlled system, one that uses a non-compensated (for altitude) diaphragm unit, Fig. 7-10. The function of the vacuum unit is to sense the *intake manifold vacuum* (same as engine torque) and correspondingly to reflect the manifold vacuum on the throttle valve through spring tension.

There are three forces acting within the vacuum unit. The *absolute pressure* and *spring tension* on the vacuum side of the diaphragm, working *toward* the throttle valve, and the *atmospheric pressure* which acts on the diaphragm *away* from the valve. It is the effective spring tension that determines the throttle pressure. Keep in mind that atmospheric pressure is acting on the diaphragm to decrease the spring force on the valve and that high engine vacuum conditions such as *idle* produces little or no throttle pressure. As the throttle is opened the engine vacuum drops, causing an increase in spring tension and resulting higher throttle pressure.

NOTE, that the atmospheric air pressure must work against the combined efforts of spring tension and the absolute manifold air pressure. As manifold vacuum decreases, the absolute air pressure is increased and approaches atmospheric. This adds to the spring force and increases the throttle signal.

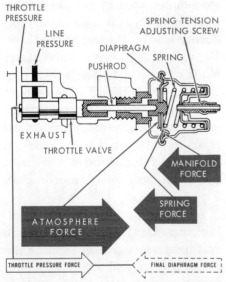

Fig. 7-10. Vacuum diaphragm control unit.

In the non-compensated vacuum throttle unit the effect of altitude must be considered. With an increase in altitude, atmospheric pressure falls while the absolute engine manifold pressure remains relatively unchanged. Referring again to Fig. 7-10, it is apparent that throttle pressure will increase with altitude. The throttle pressure increase, along with the normal loss of power, tends to raise the minimum shift points and to make the shift quality more aggressive (higher throttle pressure produces a higher line pressure for clutch and servo piston apply). To compensate for this latter effect, an altitude-compensated vacuum diaphragm unit is used, Fig. 7-11. This unit incorporates an evacuated bellows that is sensitive to barometric pressure.

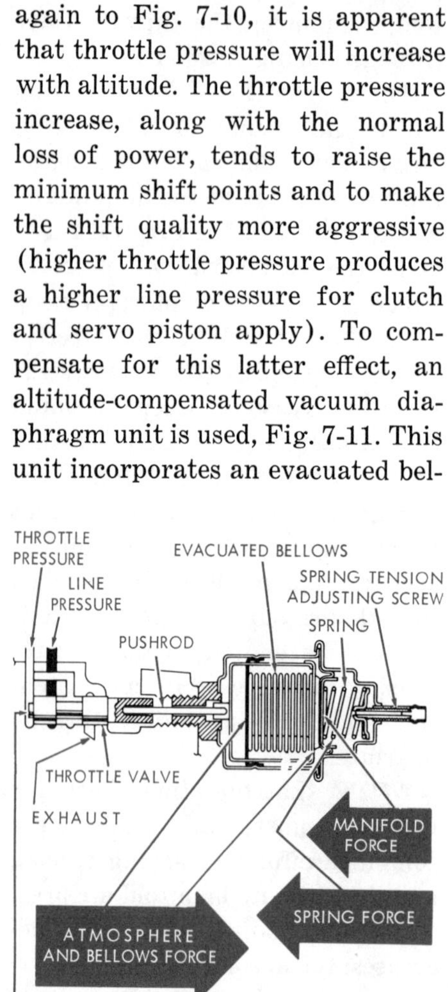

The throttle pressure schedule is the same at sea level for both non-compensated and altitude-compensated vacuum units. However, at higher altitudes the barometric pressure decreases and the *crush effect* on the bellows is less. This permits the bellows to expand and to assist the atmospheric force on the diaphragm to decrease the effective spring force on the throttle valve. In effect, the bellows decreases throttle pressure at higher altitudes to make the shift feel comparable to sea level conditions. The sea-level balance between line pressure and engine output is maintained.

In the mechanical version of throttle pressure control, a linkage system actuated by the accelerator pedal movement is used to vary the spring load on the end of the throttle valve. A throttle valve lever shaft within the transmission is rotated in proportion to the amount of throttle opening of the carburetor. This means that a mechanical hook-up between the transmission and carburetor throttle movement must be accurately coordinated, Fig. 7-12.

As the carburetor throttle opening increases, the throttle valve spring exerts a greater force on the throttle valve and a corresponding increase in throttle pressure. It is

Fig. 7-11. Compensated vacuum diaphragm control unit.

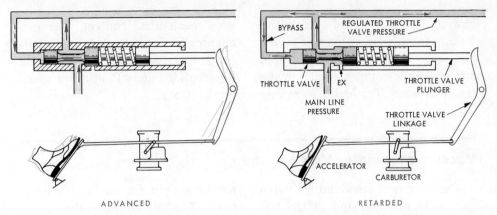

Fig. 7-12. TV pressure, both advanced and retarded throttle positions.

of interest to note that extreme wide open movement of the throttle level will bottom out the throttle valve, and line pressure will pass through the throttle valve unregulated—throttle pressure is equal to line pressure. The same is true with vacuum controlled throttle systems when the manifold vacuum is at zero or near zero.

The vacuum and mechanical throttle systems each offer their own advantages. In the vacuum control, no periodic adjustments are required of the system after the transmission leaves the factory. If the diaphragm fails or the vacuum line develops a leak, high line pressure will result, whereas an incorrect mechanical linkage adjustment can cause low line pressure and permit clutch or band slippage. If not immediately corrected the excessive friction element slippage

leads to transmission failure.

Although the periodic adjustment requirement of mechanical linkage is subject to human error and wear, the vacuum system is not entirely *fail-safe*. A leaky diaphragm will actually permit the manifold vacuum to pull the transmission fluid into the engine for consumption. This loss of fluid is usually not picked up until transmission slippage is evident to the driver and that might be too late. In addition, a pinched vacuum line will cause a temporary delay in line pressure build-up during quick acceleration, resulting in transmission slippage, especially during forced downshifts. The pinched line prevents the vacuum unit from sensing an immediate change in manifold pressure.

Vacuum controlled throttle systems are currently used in the Ford

155

Motor Company and American Motors families of automatic transmissions—both non-compensated and altitude-compensated, while the Chrysler TorqueFlite family uses mechanical control. The mechanically controlled throttle system is also used in Chevrolet Powerglide and Pontiac 2-speed applications.

Vacuum Modulator Valve System

The vacuum modulator valve system is incorporated in the hydraulic control systems of all current General Motors automatic transmissions, Fig. 7-13. In general, it performs some of the same functions as any vacuum controlled throttle valve. The vacuum controlled modulator valve produces a regulated modulator pressure signal that varies the transmission line pressure with the torque input to the transmission (engine plus converter). It is conscious of both engine vacuum and governor pressure, Fig. 7-14.

In observing the illustration, it is shown that line pressure serves as the supply for modulated pressure. The modulator valve itself must balance against spring force in the vacuum unit and is assisted by governor pressure to help move against the spring. Governor pressure at the valve acts to decrease the modulator pressure.

The vacuum modulator unit comes in two designs, noncompensated and altitude-compensated. Both types are similar in design and operate identically to the throttle vacuum units previously described in detail: high vacuum produces a low modulator pressure and a low vacuum produces a high modulator pressure.

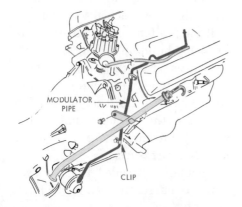

MODULATOR PIPE

CLIP

Fig. 7-13. Modulator unit and vacuum attachment.

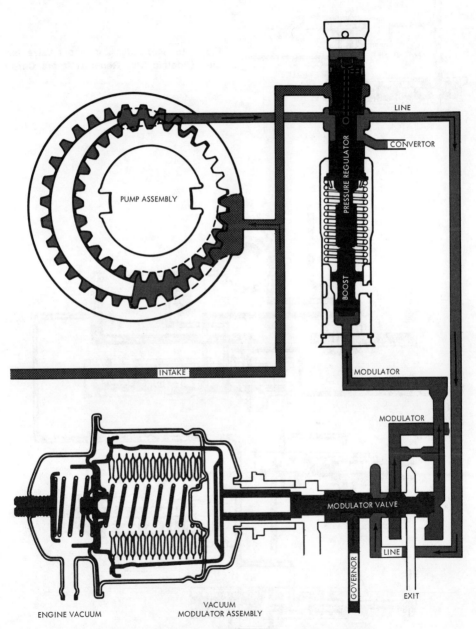

Fig. 7-14. Pressure modulating—line pressure control.

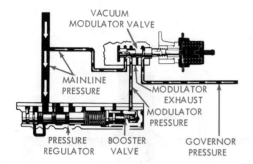

Fig. 7-15. Modulator and boost valve circuit. (Pontiac Div., General Motors Corp.)

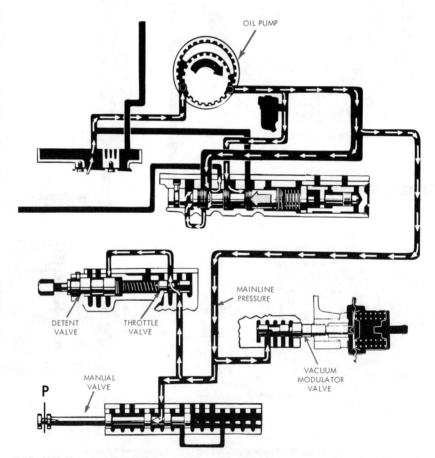

Fig. 7-16. Mainline pressure circuit illustrating separate throttle and modulator systems. (Pontiac Div., General Motors Corp.)

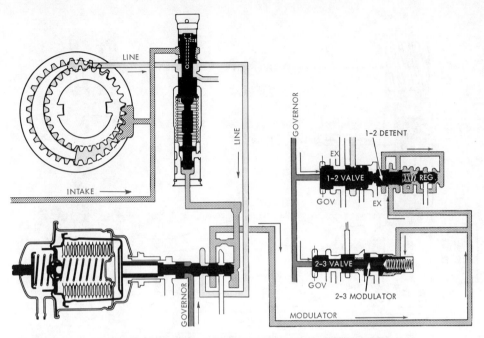

Fig. 7-17. Modulator pressure as feed for shift scheduling.

In some of the G.M. automatic transmissions, the modulator system is used solely for *line pressure boost*, Fig. 7-15. In this case, a separate throttle valve system (mechanically controlled) is added to provide the necessary shift scheduling, Fig. 7-16. This set-up is found in the Chevrolet 2-speed Powerglide and Pontiac 2-speed (M-35) transmissions.

The T-400, T-350, and T-300 transmissions do not have a separate add-on throttle system, but utilize the existing modulator pressure for shift scheduling Fig. 7-17.

Governor Valve System

The governor is a hydraulic speedometer, Fig. 7-18, and is driven by the output shaft of the transmission and is classified as a regulating valve. It transmits a hydraulic pressure signal to the transmission which is proportional to vehicle speed and is primarily

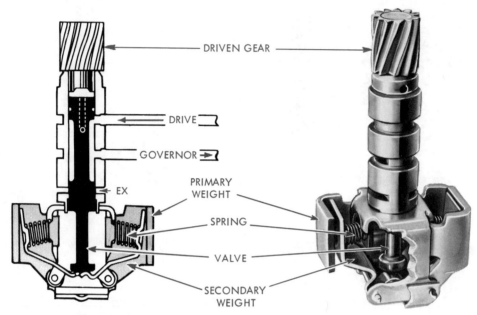

Fig. 7-18. Governor valve. (Oldsmobile Div., General Motors Corp.)

used for scheduling the transmission shifts, along with throttle or modulator pressures. It is also used in some transmissions as a signal for auxiliary or supporting control valves; we will concentrate on its use for *shift scheduling.*

There are several types of governor valve assembly designs in current use today but they all rely on the centrifugal effects of some rotating mass (weights).

When the transmission output shaft drives the governor assembly as in Fig. 7-18, the governor weights fly outward and exert a centrifugal force on the governor valve. *Drive oil,* which is actually

mainline oil from the transmission pump, feeds the governor valve until sufficient pressure build-up on top of the valve balances the centrifugal force of the weights. The greater the vehicle speed the greater is the centrifugal force of the weights, and hence the greater the governor pressure necessary to balance the centrifugal force. Eventually vehicle speed reaches a point where the governor valve cannot balance itself against the centrifugal force of the weights. When this happens, the governor valve is in the open position and governor pressure equals the mainline supply pressure.

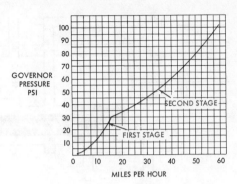

Fig. 7-19. Typical two-stage governor pressure curve.

The governor weight assembly is constructed with two sets of *weights, primary* and *secondary.* This produces a two stage pressure curve, Fig. 7-19, that provides a pressure range which will produce shifts at the desired speeds. At the lower speeds, both weights act together, with the result that small changes in vehicle speed give comparatively large changes in centrifugal force and governor pressure. As vehicle speed becomes greater the primary weights reach a limit and are no longer effective. From this point on the secondary weights and springs remain active on the governor valve only. The single effect of the secondary weights and springs at higher speeds results in small variations in governor pressure with small changes in vehicle speed.

Most current governor assembly designs use primary and secondary weights to produce a two-stage effect as shown in a two-stage governor curve.

Manual Valve

An automatic transmission is not entirely automatic and is dependent upon manual control for driver selection of the transmission operating range (*park, reverse, neutral, drive,* etc.), Fig. 7-20. As should be obvious, the *manual valve* derives its name from the fact that it is manually actuated by the driver.

The manual valve directs regulated line pressure to the shift valves for clutch or band applications during automatic shifts.

161

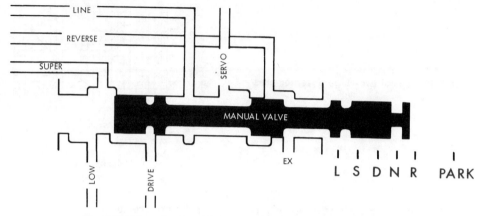

Fig. 7-20. Manual valve. (Oldsmobile Div., General Motors Corp.)

However, it is also used for routing line pressure directly to specific friction elements for the non-automatic gears, first gear (*low*) and *reverse*, for example. The manual valve *sets* operating conditions.

Servo Assemblies

A *servo unit* consists of a piston in a cylinder, or bore, and transforms hydraulic pressure into a mechanical force. In most designs the servo unit is formed as a separate unit bolted to the case, or as

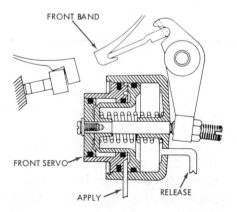

Fig. 7-21. Bolted servo to case.

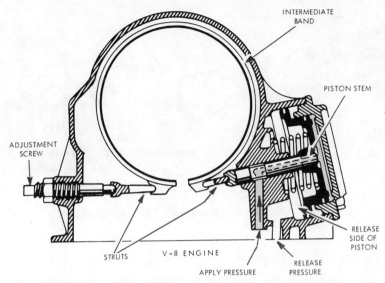

Fig. 7-22. Servo unit as part of case. (Ford Motor Co.)

part of the transmission case, Figs. 7-21 and 7-22. Through suitable linkage and lever action, the servo is connected to the band it operates. Some servo units do not require a lever arm and are direct acting, Fig. 7-22.

The servo unit band application must rigidly hold and ground a planetary gear member to the transmission case for forward or reverse gear reduction. When hydraulic apply pressure is cut off from the servo apply line, spring pressure simply returns the piston to the OFF position and the band is released.

Band application is involved with both manual and automatic shifts.

Clutch Assemblies

Clutches are used in both manual and automatic shifting. The most popular type of clutch unit used in automatic transmissions is the multiple disc clutch. This can be attributed to several factors:

163

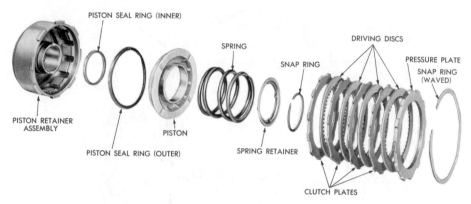

PISTON SEAL RING (INNER)

SPRING

DRIVING DISCS

SNAP RING

PRESSURE PLATE

SNAP RING (WAVED)

PISTON RETAINER ASSEMBLY

PISTON

PISTON SEAL RING (OUTER)

SPRING RETAINER

CLUTCH PLATES

Fig. 7-23. Disc clutch assembly. (Chrysler Corp.)

1. Multiple discs give the clutch a high torque-holding capacity in a small package.
2. Unlike bands, disc clutches can easily be used as rotating engagement members.
3. Once the proper running clearance has been established during factory or field service assembly, there is no adjustment requirement for wear.

Fig. 7-23 is representative of a rotating multiple disc clutch assembly. Note that the piston will squeeze the clutch pack together against the pressure plate and snap ring. The snap ring fits behind the pressure plate and into a snap ring groove in the piston retainer (drum).

In Fig. 7-24 a pair of multiple disc clutch assemblies show a more exact relationship to a transmission power flow. Both clutches are oil-applied and spring-released. With both clutches OFF, there is no power to the gearset, whereas a front clutch apply drives the primary sun gear and a rear clutch apply drives the secondary sun gear. This is how power enters the gearset for forward reductions and *reverse*. For *direct drive* both clutches are applied and both sun gears together are used as an input to the gearset.

Notice the disc spring in the front clutch, Fig. 7-24. It has a dual purpose. It serves as a piston return, and also as a lever arm to multiply the *apply force* of the piston. Fig. 7-25 shows a disc spring installation as it appears in a clutch assembly.

In rotating clutch units, a problem is usually inherited when the clutch is not engaged. With the clutch OFF, the clutch drum or

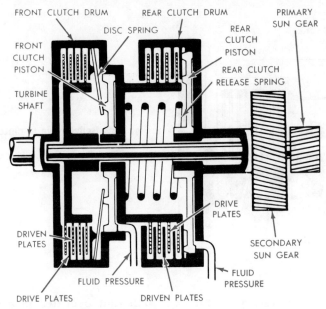

Fig. 7-24. Gear train power flow using front and rear disc clutch assemblies; bands not shown. (Ford Motor Co.)

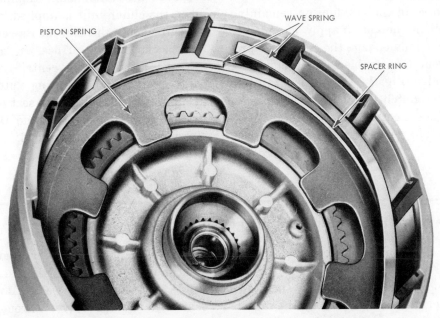

Fig. 7-25. Disc spring installation. (Chrysler Corp.)

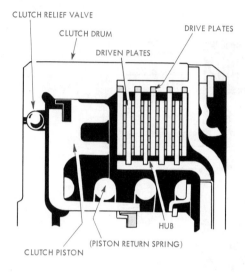

Fig. 7-26. Relief valve in clutch drum.

housing still spins; as a matter of fact, the *spin-up* may be at an overdrive speed. The high rotation could create sufficient centrifugal force in the residual or remaining oil in the clutch-apply cylinder to partially engage the clutch. To prevent this problem, a clutch relief valve, Fig. 7-26, is incorporated in the clutch drum or sometimes in the clutch piston.

The relief valve is a steel check ball that operates in a cavity and on a seat. A small hole or orifice is tapped from the seat for pressure relief. In the clutch drum example, when the clutch unit is applied, oil pressure holds the ball on its seat and blocks off the orifice. In the released position, the centrifugal force created by the rotating clutch drum moves the ball off its seat allowing the trapped oil behind the clutch piston to be discharged.

Automatic and Manual Shift Systems

The job of the shift system is to program a gear ratio change that is compatible to the vehicle speed and performance desired by the driver. If these changes are to occur automatically, a shift valve arrangement must be provided. Otherwise, single speed operating ranges are controlled by the driver through the range selector and manual valve. The current semi-automatic transmissions used in small size passenger cars, for example, do not have automatic shift systems and individual gear ratios are selected solely by the driver. Automatic shifting, however, offers a more discriminating choice of gear selection.

The essential hydraulic support systems for transmission operation have already been discussed: the pressure supply system, throttle or modulator system, and governor system. Add to this the manual valve, servos and bands, and clutches. If you're still a little fuzzy on how these systems and units operate, that's all right; you can still understand automatic and manual

shifting if you know what each system must do.

We are going to correlate our shift system operation, automatic and manual, with a typical 2-speed transmission in current use. Let us examine Fig. 7-27, which is no stranger to you, and be positive about the friction elements that must be controlled. In P and N, the friction elements are not applied. The low band is engaged for *automatic drive range—low gear and manual low gear*, the forward or direct clutch for *automatic drive range-high gear*, and the reverse clutch for *reverse*.

We start our shift system discussion with a quick inspection of the pressure supply system since it

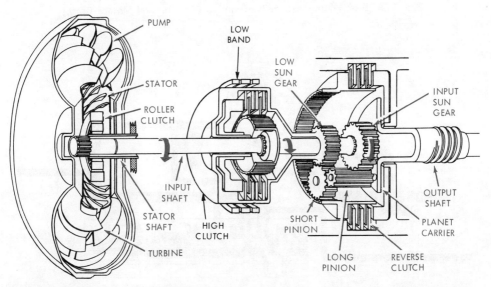

Fig. 7-27. Note the friction elements of 2-speed transmission. (Pontiac Div., General Motors Corp.)

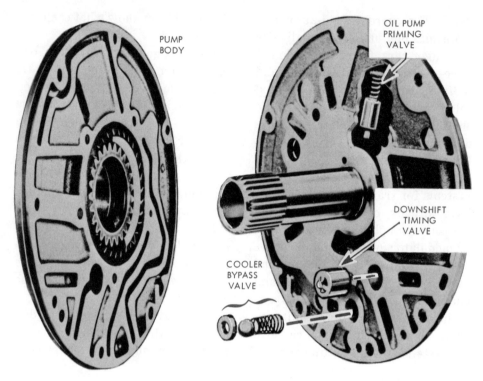

Fig. 7-28. Front pump assembly. (Pontiac Div., General Motors Corp.)

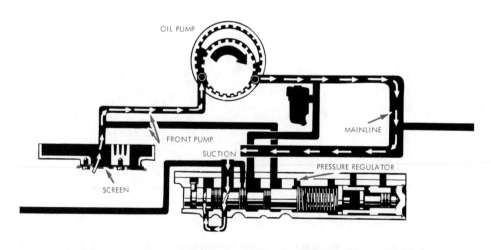

Fig. 7-29. Oil pump circuit. (Pontiac Div., General Motors Corp.)

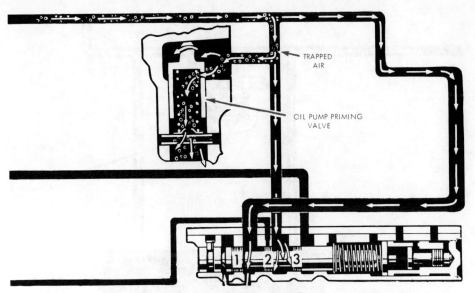

Fig. 7-30. Oil pump priming valve circuit. (Pontiac Div., General Motors Corp.)

Fig. 7-31. Converter charging circuit. (Pontiac Div., General Motors Corp.)

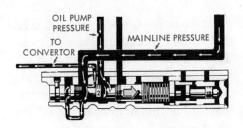

is basic to the life support of the transmission and directly related to the shift system itself. Figs. 7-28, 7-29, 7-30, 7-31, 7-32, 7-33, and 7-34 review the basic functions of the pressure supply system.

The oil pump priming valve viewed in Figs. 7-28 and 7-30 simply provides for a purging of air that might be trapped in the sys-

tem. A spring holds the valve in the open position, allowing for an air exhaust until system pressure begins to build up in the pump circuit. Once the pump pressure begins to build up, the priming valve is seated in its bore, closing the bleed hole.

Also notice the mainline pressure circuit in Fig. 7-33 and the modu-

169

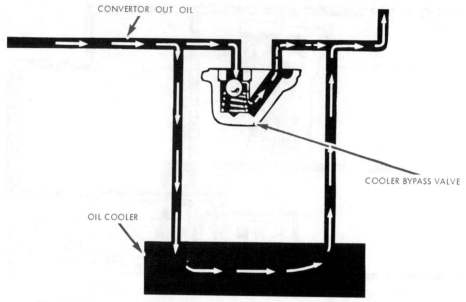

CONVERTOR OUT OIL

COOLER BYPASS VALVE

OIL COOLER

Fig. 7-32. Oil cooler and lubrication circuit. (Pontiac Div., General Motors Corp.)

lator-booster valve circuit in Fig. 7-34. The modulator is used for one function only, to modulate or vary mainline pressure. A separate mechanical throttle system is incorporated in this hydraulic circuit for shift scheduling purposes.

Neutral and Park

A line diagram, Fig. 7-35, shows the simplicity of the *neutral* and *park* ranges. The only part of the entire hydraulic control system that is actually functional is the pressure supply system which satisfies the requirements of establishing a mainline operating pressure, a converter feed, cooling, and lubrication.

The manual valve blocks the oil pressure to the apply lines of the band and clutches.

Automatic Drive Range— Low Gear

When the manual valve is positioned in D, mainline pressure is directed to the low servo and the low band is applied, holding the low sun gear stationary, Fig. 7-36.

The low band-apply is a manual valve function and is not caused by any automatic shift control.

Automatic Drive Range— High Gear

While the vehicle is operating in low gear, the transmission auto-

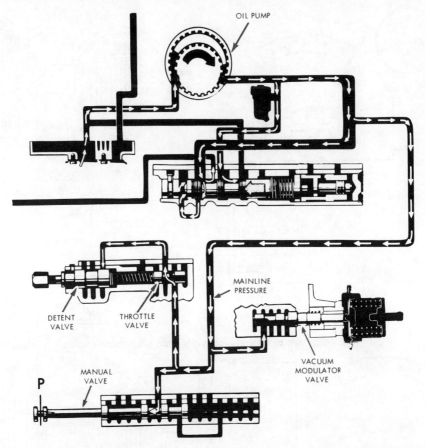

Fig. 7-33. Mainline pressure circuit. (Pontiac Div., General Motors Corp.)

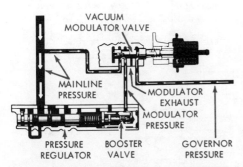

Fig. 7-34. Modulator booster valve circuit. (Pontiac Div., General Motors Corp.)

matic shift controls are preparing for the *low* to *high* shift.

Any transmission that provides for automatic shifting must have one or more shift valves (in this case only one shift valve), a governor circuit, Fig. 7-37, and a throttle valve circuit, Fig. 7-38. (Sometimes a modulator system is used as the throttle sensitive pressure to the shift valve.)

171

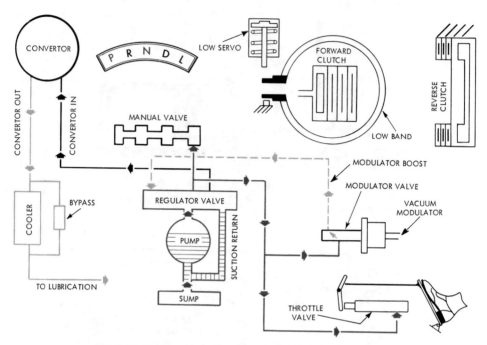

Fig. 7-35. Park or neutral—converter and lubrication circuit.

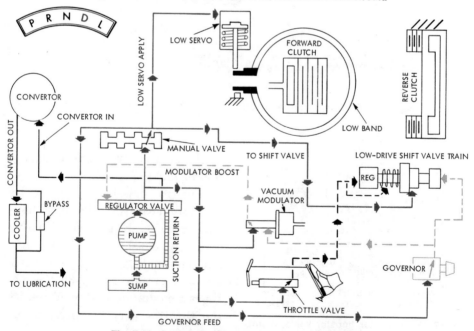

Fig. 7-36. Automatic drive range—low gear circuit.

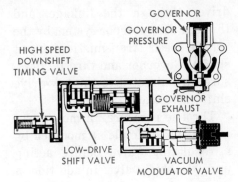

Fig. 7-37. Governor circuit. (Pontiac Div., General Motors Corp.)

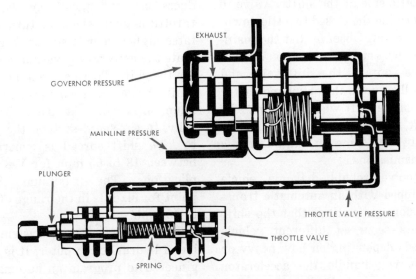

Fig. 7-38. Throttle valve circuit. (Pontiac Div., General Motors Corp.)

The shift valve can be classified as a *flow control* or *relay valve*, it causes the shift to occur. Its movement or position is determined by pressures from its supporting controls, the governor and throttle circuits. Governor pressure, a vehicle speed sensitive signal, acts on the shift valve to push it into an *open* or *upshift* direction. Whereas, throttle pressure which is an engine torque sensitive signal, tends to prevent the upshift movement of the valve and keep it closed.

In Fig. 7-38, the throttle system is activated mechanically by the driver through the linkage, and through the governor system by the vehicle speed (transmission output shaft). Governor and throttle pressures are directed to the low-drive shift valve train.

Throttle pressure, in most cases and in this example, is modified by a regulating valve before acting upon the shift valve. In addition, a fixed spring load is used on the throttle side of the shifter valve to determine the closed throttle downshift point. Observe that the mainline pressure from the manual valve waits at the shift valve and it will serve as the prime mover for the entire shift when it occurs. The shift system just described is typically the same in all automatic transmissions.

You've probably driven a vehicle equipped with an automatic transmission and noticed that the shift points occur at different vehicle speeds depending on how heavy or light you handle the accelerator with your foot. Perhaps you wondered how this happened. The answer is very simple. A light throttle opening produces a small throttle signal to the shift valve and only a low vehicle speed is needed to generate a sufficient governor signal to overpower the forces of throttle and spring pressures.

If the driver requires added performance, the throttle opening produces a correspondingly larger throttle signal which in turn dictates higher vehicle speeds to generate the necessary governor signal for the shift. There are engineered limits, however, at which the maximum shift can take place. Typically, in a 2-speed system, the *low* to *high* shift spread is generally between 18 to 65 mph for V-8 applications. The maximum shift point for sixes is in the range of 38 to 45 mph.

The automatic shift system is like a hydraulic computer. It is engineered to program an automatic shift at an appropriate throttle

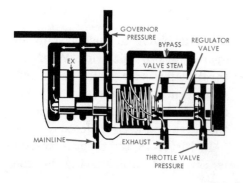

Fig. 7-39. Governor and throttle signals programming the automatic shift. (Pontiac Div., General Motors Corp.)

opening and vehicle speed by accepting and evaluating information sent by a throttle and a governor signal. Finally, the governor signal triggers the shift valve for a gear ratio change, Fig. 7-39.

With the shift valve now *open*, in our diagram, Fig. 7-40, mainline pressure enters the clutch apply line and acts on both the high and low servo pistons, Fig. 7-41. Engagement of the clutch plates locks the low sun gear to the input shaft. With two sun gears acting as inputs, the planetary carrier assembly is locked at a 1:1 ratio (Fig. 7-27).

The low servo release shares a common pressure supply with the forward clutch. There is now mainline pressure acting on both sides and equal areas of the servo piston; therefore, the force of the return spring is left to move the piston to the release position, the band is now OFF.

In reviewing Fig. 7-40 you will notice that when the shift valve is opened, the TV pressure is exhausted between the shift valve and regulator valve. This sudden exhaust of TV pressure gives the shift valve a snap action on the upshift and eliminates any *hunting* or indecision of the valve to shift and stay shifted, especially if the vehicle speed is maintained at or near the shift point. Once the shift

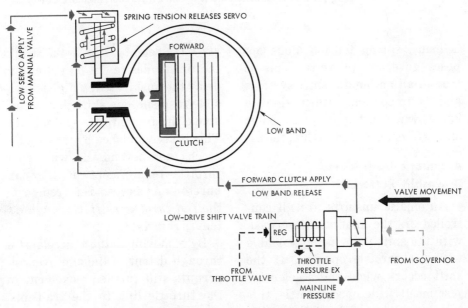

Fig. 7-40. Automatic drive range—high gear circuit.

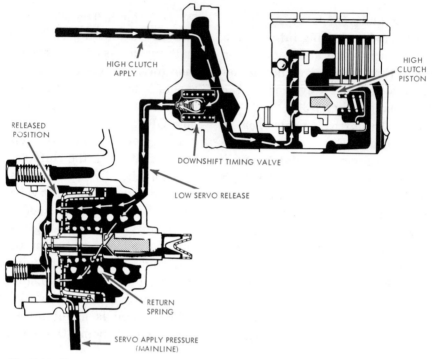

HIGH CLUTCH
APPLY

HIGH
CLUTCH
PISTON

RELEASED
POSITION

DOWNSHIFT TIMING VALVE

LOW SERVO RELEASE

RETURN
SPRING

SERVO APPLY PRESSURE
(MAINLINE)

Fig. 7-41. Clutch-apply/servo-release circuit. (Pontiac Div., General Motors Corp.)

is made, spring tension alone opposes governor pressure. This is true in all automatic shift systems and is important information to know when attempting to solve shift system problems (Chapter 8).

Automatic Upshift and Downshift Patterns

Automatic upshifts are all controlled in the manner described, with the shift point being variable with the throttle opening. If the shift occurs when the accelerator just meets wide open throttle, this is referred to as the *full throttle*

shift (*to* detent), Fig. 7-42. Should the driver desire, he may want to delay the upshift to the highest possible road speed, a shift that occurs above the full throttle (*to* detent). This is accomplished by moving the accelerator beyond the wide open throttle requirement of the carburetor and is also referred to as the *full throttle shift* (*through* detent), Fig. 7-43.

By moving the accelerator through detent, a linkage override permits still further movement of the throttle link to the transmission. This extra movement me-

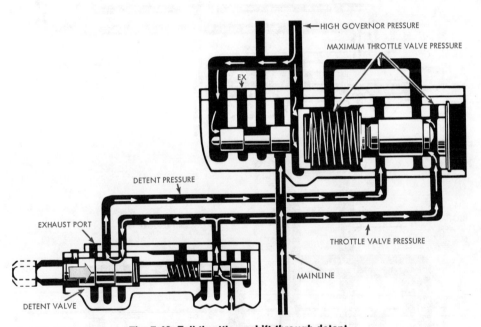

Fig. 7-42. Full throttle upshift *to* detent.

GOVERNOR
PRESSURE

TO
DETENT

THROTTLE VALVE
PRESSURE

MAINLINE PRESSURE

HIGH GOVERNOR PRESSURE

MAXIMUM THROTTLE VALVE PRESSURE

EX

DETENT PRESSURE

EXHAUST PORT

THROTTLE VALVE PRESSURE

MAINLINE

DETENT VALVE

Fig. 7-43. Full throttle upshift *through* detent.

chanically triggers a detent valve in the throttle valve assembly that allows mainline supply oil to pass through the throttle valve unregulated and into a detent passage to the shift valve.

In Fig. 7-42, the detent valve is shown in a position that blocks pas- sage of throttle valve (TV) fluid. The through detent travel, how- ever, moves the detent valve to the right, Fig. 7-43, and TV fluid, which is equal to mainline pressure at this time, can now route itself to the shift valve via the detent cir- cuit, Fig. 7-44. With TV and detent

177

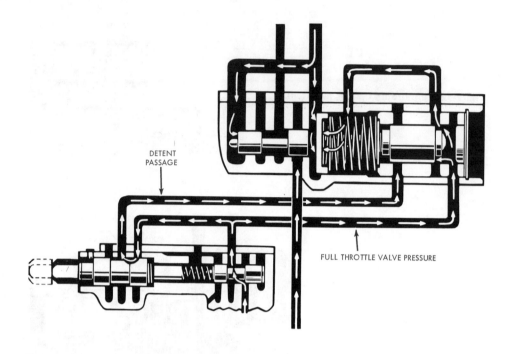

DETENT PASSAGE

FULL THROTTLE VALVE PRESSURE

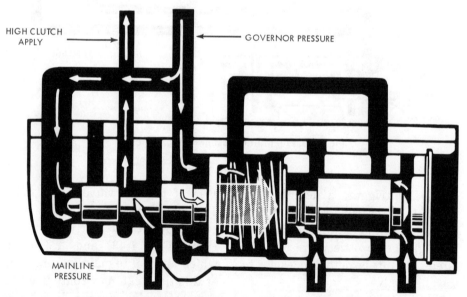

HIGH CLUTCH APPLY

GOVERNOR PRESSURE

MAINLINE PRESSURE

Fig. 7-44. Upshift through detent. Note that detent by-pass is not used although it has been triggered.

pressures equal to mainline pressure, it should be obvious why this combination gives the maximum shift delay. Figs. 7-39 and 7-44 compare the action on the throttle side of the shift valve between *to detent* and *through detent*. The exhaust in Fig. 7-39 is actually the detent line with the detent valve providing an open port.

In some mechanically controlled throttle valve assemblies, the detent valve is called the kickdown valve and the action is the same (TorqueFlite). The Ford Cruise-O-Matic family, which uses a vacuum controlled throttle system, incorporates a separate downshift valve assembly which is mechanically controlled by a throttle link and which accomplishes the same job. The *downshift valve* could be correctly called a *detent valve*.

In the G.M. Hydra-Matic 400 and 350 and the Turbine 300 transmissions, the detent system is separate from the vacuum modulator valve assembly. The 350 detent system is triggered mechanically, whereas the 400 and 300 detent systems are triggered from an electrical switch acted upon by accelerator linkage. This excites an electrical solenoid mounted on the valve body assembly and causes a detent shift action. This same technique is used in the American Motors Shift-Command and in later versions of the Flash-O-Matic.

Whatever system is used, the driver is always in control with the accelerator.

Automatic downshifts are divided into three types: *coast* or *closed throttle downshift, forced downshift* (*to* detent), and *forced downshift* (*through* detent). The control for these downshifts is provided by the pressure variables acting on the individual shifter valve trains. These pressures (governor, TV or modulator, and detent) are the same ones previously discussed.

In the case of our 2-speed system, the downshift of the low-drive shift valve shuts off the mainline pressure feed to the clutch apply passage. The conditions that cause the various downshifts are: reduced road speed, increased pressure on the accelerator, or both.

Coast or Closed Throttle Downshift. As the vehicle slows down, governor pressure holding the low-drive shift valve is being reduced. At approximately 15 mph governor pressure is less than the opposing spring force on the throttle side of the shift valve. When this occurs, the spring force snaps the valve closed and provides for an exhaust of the high clutch apply-oil, Fig. 7-45. Keep in mind that it is the spring force that determines the coast or closed throttle downshift point. TV pressure is zero at closed throttle and has no effect on the end of the regulating valve.

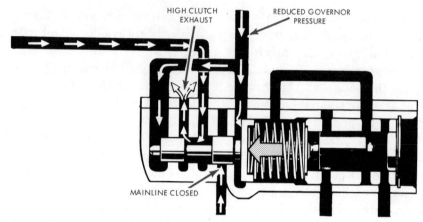

Fig. 7-45. Coast or closed throttle downshift. (Pontiac Div., General Motors Corp.)

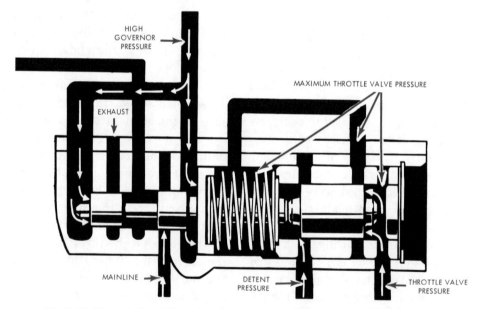

Fig. 7-46. Through detent forced downshift. (Pontiac Div., General Motors Corp.)

Forced Downshift—To Detent. At low to moderate road speeds, increased pressure on the accelerator will result in an increased TV signal acting on the end of the TV regulating valve. This pressure overcomes the governor pressure and moves the low-drive shift valve back in its low gear position. The shift valve remains in its low gear position until the vehicle speed and resultant governor pressure overpower the TV pressure.

Forced Downshift—Through Detent. The detent system is activated as previously described and the transmission can be automatically shifted to low gear; review Fig. 7-46. The vehicle speed, however, must be below the maximum speed at which the detent upshift occurs. The transmission remains in low gear until the driver relaxes the accelerator pedal or until the vehicle speed reaches the maximum shift point. In essence, the detent operation temporarily overrules the

shift valve. Eventually, the vehicle speed and governor pressure reach a value that will keep the transmission in high gear regardless of accelerator position.

Low Range

Low range is a manual valve function and is non-automatic. When the manual valve is moved into the L position, mainline oil is directed into the low servo apply line and to the modulator exhaust circuit, but not to the shift valve; therefore, regardless of shift valve position, mainline oil cannot charge the high clutch apply line, Fig. 7-47. Since the low-drive shift

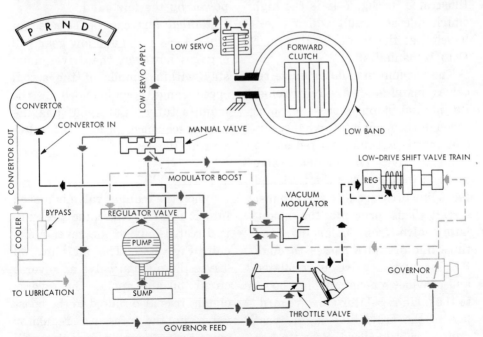

Fig. 7-47. Manual low circuit; etc.

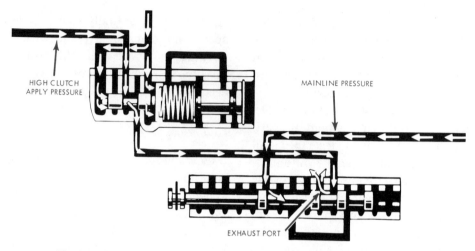

Fig. 7-48. Downshift to low range. (Pontiac Div., General Motors Corp.)

valve has no affect on the transmission operation, low gear remains throughout the L range operation. Illustrated in Fig. 7-48 is the high clutch release circuit which is exhausted at the manual valve on a D to L manual shift.

The vacuum modulator valve receives mainline pressure through its normal supply passage, plus through the modulator exhaust circuit that is normally ported at the manual valve. The manual valve position in *low* closes the port and feeds line pressure into the exhaust circuit. This prevents the modulator valve from balancing, and thus, line pressure passes through the modulator valve unregulated and provides a constant high boost to the main regulator valve regardless of the prevailing engine vacuum or vehicle speed. Because *low*

range is used for braking or heavy duty pulling, this boost arrangement is needed for extra holding power by the low band.

Manual low can be selected at any vehicle speed and low gear will engage; however, the driver must stay within bounds of the actual speed range recommended by the manufacturer. Can you imagine the consequences of a D to L selection at 100 mph?

Reverse Range

When the manual valve is moved into R position, mainline pressure is directed only to the reverse circuit, Fig. 7-49. The mainline oil leaves the manual valve as reverse circuit oil and applies the reverse clutch. It is also routed to the boost valve in the pressure regulator valve train assembly. Modulator oil

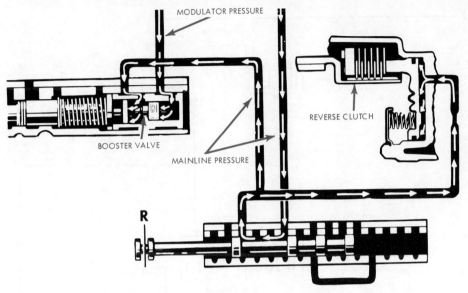

Fig. 7-49. Reverse circuit. (Pontiac Div., General Motors Corp.)

also provides its normal action on the boost valve and in combination with reverse boost oil, it doubles the regulated line pressure in comparison to the maximum available in *drive*.

The low servo and high clutch apply-circuits are all open to exhaust at the manual valve and cut off from any mainline oil feed.

Automatic Shift System In A 3-Speed Transmission

The automatic shift system in a 3-speed transmission fundamentally works the same as the automatic shift system in a 2-speed transmission. The 3-speed transmission, of course, incorporates two shift valves in the system, Fig. 7-50.

The 1-2 and 2-3 shift valve train assemblies must be designed to give an appropriate shift point spread for vehicle performance, the shift valves must not open and close together although some systems do have the shift valves close together on closed throttle downshifts for a 3-1 effect.

The shift valves can easily be tuned for their individual shift point control when we compare the shift valves in Fig. 7-50. The shift valves are shown in their *closed* position. Notice that the governor pressure will be able to easily overcome the light spring tension and low regulated throttle pressure at the 1-2 shift valve before overcoming the more powerful spring force and higher regulated throttle pres-

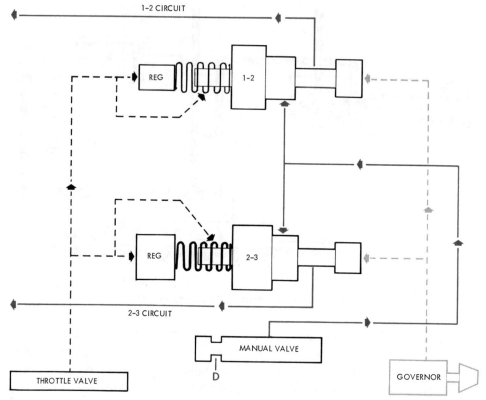

Fig. 7-50. Representative automatic shift valve arrangement—3-speed transmission.

sure acting on the 2-3 shift valve. It should be evident that a higher vehicle speed is necessary to generate the extra governor pressure to overcome the 2-3 shift valve.

On closed throttle downshifts, the heavier 2-3 spring will close the 2-3 shift valve before the lighter 1-2 spring can close the 1-2 shift valve. Forced downshift (to detent) and (through detent) are available 3-1 and 3-2 depending on the throttle opening and vehicle speed. This action is not illustrated,

however it typically works off of a detent or kickdown system that overrules the shift valve and forces the downshift.

In addition to varying the regulated throttle pressure and spring force, differences in valve spool reaction areas on the throttle and governor sides of the shifter valves are used to assist in establishing the desired shift point spread.

To block out the shifter valve action in manual low, mainline pressure from the manual valve is

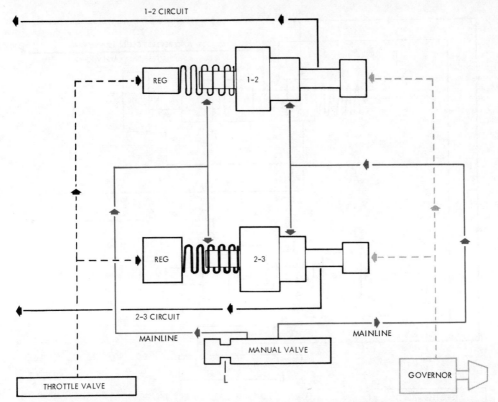

Fig. 7-51. Shift valve arrangement with block-out circuit for manual low—3-speed transmission.

usually applied and directed to the throttle side of the shift valves, Fig. 7-51. The high value of the mainline pressure, plus the reaction area advantage on the shift valves, makes it impossible for governor pressure to upshift the valves regardless of throttle opening and vehicle speed. Since the transmission cannot shift, it remains in low gear.

For an intermediate range operation when the transmission will shift 1-2, but remain in second gear, the 2-3 shift valve would be simply blocked out by mainline oil from the manual valve.

In the Select-Shift (P-R-N-D-2-1) used by Ford Motor Company in the C-6 and C-4, a slightly different arrangement is made at the shift valves for operation in the 2 and 1 positions.

In Fig. 7-52, the *manual low (1)* position is illustrated. Mainline oil from the manual valve is cycled

185

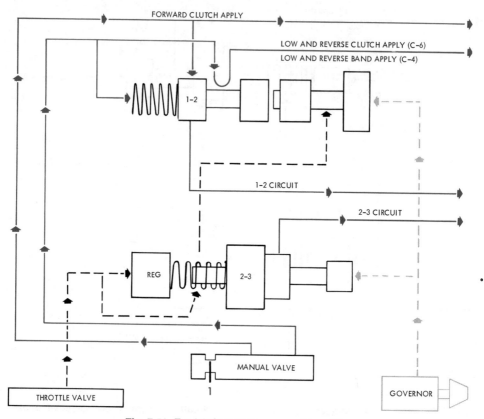

Fig. 7-52. Ford Select-Shift—manual low (1).

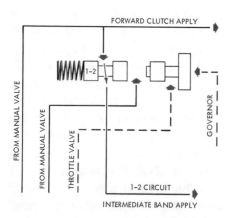

Fig. 7-53. Ford Select-Shift—second gear (2).

through the 1-2 shift valve to apply the low-reverse clutch and at the same time it is routed to the spring side of the shift valve train. Low-reverse apply oil, plus spring tension, plus throttle pressure prevent movement of the 1-2 shift valve by governor pressure. The manual valve does not send supply oil to the 2-3 shift valve and no attempt is made to block valve movement. Without a supply oil, the 2-3 cir-

cuit is not functional when the shift valve opens.

For *manual second gear*, the (*2*) position, the 1-2 shift valve is blocked open by mainline oil from the manual valve, Fig. 7-53. The 1-2 circuit is charged with apply oil to the intermediate band and the transmission starts and stays in second gear. The 2-3 shift valve train operates the same as in *manual low* and is not functional.

Semi-Automatic Shifting

This simply means that the transmission has been stripped of its automatic shift controls and the manual valve is used for individual gear selection. A clutch pedal is not needed because the torque converter is still part of the power flow. Essentially, the transmission operation remains the same with the driver in full control. Changing gears is a matter of moving the

selector lever to desired position.

For example, the basic 2-speed automatic transmission used by General Motors and the C-4 used by Ford have been converted for semi-automatic operation and use in the small size cars. These semi-automatics are respectively referred to as the Chevrolet Torque Drive (P-R-N-H$_i$-L) and Ford Semi-Automatic (P-R-N-H$_i$-2-1).

Accumulator Units

Accumulators are popularly used in automatic transmission hydraulic control systems for shift quality purposes. It is a spring loaded piston device and acts as a timing control to cushion shifts according to engine torque output by absorbing

a certain amount of fluid flow in the process of a band or clutch application. They are mostly designed and housed within a servo unit, or separately in an individual housing. In some applications, however, the accumulator system is made up

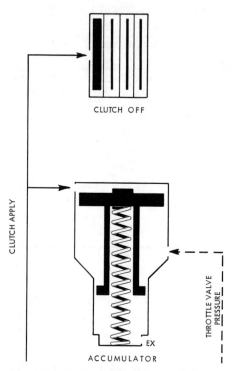

Fig. 7-54. Typical accumulator assembly with piston position before stroking.

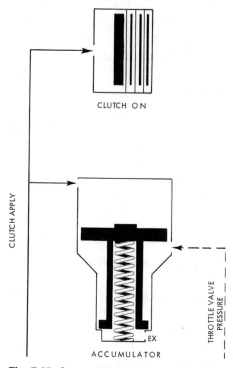

Fig. 7-55. Accumulator piston position after stroking.

of valving and incorporated in the valve body assembly.

A typical accumulator set-up and action is shown in Figs. 7-54 and 7-55 in conjunction with a *clutch unit apply*. Note that the same TV pressure used at the shift valves is added to the accumulator to make it torque sensitive and to vary the effect of the spring tension and accumulator action. In some cases a modified TV pressure is used to get the best possible shift feel.

By inserting an accumulator in parallel to the clutch-apply line, this means that the clutch will not inherit a sudden engagement, but it is delayed to some point in time during the accumulator piston stroke. In effect, the accumulator is controlling the build-up of clutch-apply pressure. The clutch is actually fully applied before the clutch oil builds up to full line pressure when the accumulator piston completes its stroke.

With light throttle shifts, the accumulator action stretches out the time interval to allow full pressure build-up to apply the clutch, and this results in a *soft shift* feel. Under heavy throttle, when quick apply action is needed, the increased TV pressure insures that the accumulator piston will take a shorter stroke (build-up time) to produce the necessary apply pressure. The clutch apply under heavy throttle is still delayed; however, the apply action is quicker and the shift feel is more firm.

Checking On Your Knowledge

The following questions give you the opportunity to check up on yourself. If you have read the chapter carefully, you should be able to answer the questions. If you have any difficulty, read the chapter over once more so that you have the information well in mind before you go on with your reading.

1. The Pressure Supply System:
   a. State the duties of the pressure supply system.
   b. If a rear pump is used in a pressure supply system, state its duties.
   c. How is the front pump driven? The rear pump?
   d. Are rear pumps used in any of the current automatic transmissions?
   e. What is the purpose of the pressure regulator valve?
   f. Briefly explain the regulating or balancing action of a typical pressure regulator valve?
   g. What is the relationship of the pressure regulator valve to the converter feed circuit?
   h. What is the purpose of converter pressure regulation?
   i. What are the two circuits that tie into the converter circuit?
   j. What happens to the fluid when it cycles out of the converter?
   k. What happens to the fluid after it is used for lubrication.
   l. Under what type of operating condition would the fluid flow to the converter get interrupted?

   m. What is the purpose of using a booster valve in the pressure regulator valve train?
   n. What is the purpose of using a throttle or modulator pressure signal at the boost valve?
   o. What additional pressure signal must be added to the boost valve to satisfy increased line pressure requirements for reverse operation?
   p. Name the forces (mechanical or hydraulic) against which the regulated line pressure must balance itself within the regulator valve train both in automatic drive and in reverse.

2. Throttle Valve System And Vacuum Modulator Valve System:
   a. What are the three basic functions of a throttle valve system?
   b. What are the two methods used for obtaining an input signal to the throttle valve system?
   c. Whether the throttle system is vacuum or mechanically controlled, what is the one force against which regulated throttle pressure must balance itself?
   d. Name the source of supply of feed

oil to the throttle valve that is used in all automatic transmissions.

e. In a vacuum controlled throttle system, what effect does a drop in manifold vacuum have on the throttle pressure?

f. In a vacuum controlled throttle system, what effect does atmospheric pressure have on the diaphragm spring force?

g. Explain how, for a given engine vacuum, the non-compensated vacuum throttle unit will produce a higher throttle signal in Denver than it will in Chicago or Detroit.

h. In an altitude-compensated throttle vacuum unit, how does the evacuated bellows assist the atmospheric pressure in producing a throttle pressure schedule that is more nearly the same for all altitudes?

i. In an altitude-compensated throttle vacuum unit, what effect does the bellows have on the throttle pressure schedule at sea level?

j. What effect would a punctured bellows have on the throttle pressure schedule at sea level and at higher altitudes?

k. In a vacuum controlled throttle system, what is the value of throttle pressure in relation to transmission line pressure at zero inches of vacuum?

l. In a mechanically controlled throttle system, what is the value of throttle pressure in relation to transmission pressure at wide open throttle?

m. In a vacuum controlled throttle system, what would happen to the transmission line pressure if the operating diaphragm were punctured?

n. How does a pinched or restricted vacuum line to a vacuum controlled throttle system affect line pressure?

o. How could a vacuum controlled throttle system be responsible for loss of transmission fluid?

p. Explain how a vacuum modulator valve system basically performs the same functions as any vacuum controlled throttle system.

q. What makes a vacuum modulator valve system different from a vacuum throttle valve system?

r. In automatic transmissions that use both a throttle system and modulator system, what are the independent functions of each?

3. Governor Valve System:
a. What is the function of the governor valve system?

b. How does the governor receive its speed signal? How is this speed signal transmitted to the governor valve?

c. Name the source of supply of feed oil to the governor valve.

d. Name the one force against which regulated governor pressure must balance itself.

e. What is the value of governor pressure in relation to transmission line pressure at higher vehicle speeds?

f. Why are most governor weight assemblies equipped with two sets of weights, primary and secondary?

4. What is the function of the manual valve?

5. Explain: the manual valve is a relay valve.

6. What is a servo unit and what is its job function in an automatic transmission?

7. Why are multiple disc clutches popularly used in automatic transmissions?

8. What returns the clutch piston to its "off" position once the oil apply pressure has been exhausted from the clutch-apply circuit?

9. What is the dual role of a disc type clutch spring?

10. What is the purpose of using a steel ball check relief in either the clutch drum or clutch piston?

11. 2-Speed Shift System:
   a. What part of the hydraulic control system is functioning in N and P?
   b. What is the function of the manual valve in N and P?
   c. Explain how automatic drive range-low gear is a manual valve function.
   d. Name the reactionary planet member held by the low band for low gear operation.
   e. To design an automatic shift control system, it must have a shift valve and supporting controls? Name the supporting controls.
   f. Name the hydraulic system responsible for delaying the automatic upshift.
   g. Name the hydraulic system responsible for causing the automatic upshift.
   h. Explain how the automatic shift system is like a hydraulic computer.
   i. When the automatic upshift occurs, where does the shift valve route the mainline pressure?
   j. Name the force that actually returns the low servo piston to the "off" position when the forward clutch is applied.
   k. What usually happens to the throttle pressure at the shift valve once the upshift occurs? Give the reason for your answer.
   l. What is the difference between a *full throttle shift* (to detent) and a *full throttle shift* (thorugh detent)?
   m. Why is the full throttle shift (through detent) always slightly higher than the full throttle shift (to detent)?
   n. What are two current techniques for triggering detent systems?
   o. Briefly describe what is meant by a *coast* or *closed throttle downshift*, *forced downshift* (to detent), and *forced downshift* (through detent).

   p. What determines the closed throttle downshift point of the shift valve?
   q. Explain how *low range* is a manual valve function.
   r. Briefly explain how mainline pressure is boosted for *low range* operation?
   s. Explain how *reverse* is a manual valve function.
   t. Briefly explain how mainline pressure is boosted for *reverse* operation.
   u. Name the reactionary planet member held by the reverse clutch for reverse speed.

12. 3-Speed Shift System:
   a. How many shift valves are used in a 3-speed shift system?
   b. What design features are built into the shift valves to give the appropriate shift point spread for vehicle performance?
   c. How are the shift valves prevented from opening in *manual low?*
   d. How is the 2-3 shift valve prevented from opening in *intermediate range?*
   e. Ford Select-Shift: How are 1-2 and 2-3 shift valves made ineffective for *manual low* (1)?
   f. Ford Select-Shift: How is the 2-3 shift valve made ineffective for *manual second* (2)?

13. What is the basic difference between a semi-automatic and fully automatic transmission?

14. Name two semi-automatic drive transmissions that are currently used in American small size cars?

15. What is an accumulator and what is its job function in an automatic transmission?

16. What type of apply characteristic does an accumulator give a band or clutch during heavy throttle upshifts?

17. Explain how a band or clutch cannot realize full apply-pressure until the accumulator piston has completed its stroke.

191

Automatic Transmission Fluids and Seals

Chapter

8

The Fluid

The hydraulic fluid used in automatic transmissions is a special fluid because it is required to do more things than ordinary lubricating oil does.

The term *fluid* is applied to the liquids used in hydraulics to avoid confusion with ordinary engine and lubricating oils. The most important job of any hydraulic fluid is to transmit force and do it immediately. Therefore, a liquid is used because it is non-compressible.

The automatic transmission fluid mixture performs four main functions:

1. It transfers power from the engine to the drive line via the torque converter.

2. It transmits heat from the transmission to the cooler. Even in air cooled automatic transmissions the fluid acts as a heat-transmitting medium.

3. It transmits hydraulic pressure through a hydraulic control system which utilizes the fluid in the complex pumps, valves, lines, servos, and clutch cylinders.

4. It is a multi-purpose lubricant for the gears, thrust bearings, bushing supports, clutches, bands, etc. Like an engine oil it must lubricate, cool, seal, and clean; however, it is subject to more severe service.

To meet the above requirements automatic transmission fluids (ATF) use a selected mineral oil fortified with a precise blend of additives. These additives, as many as 10 different types and comprising approximately 10 percent of the volume of the ATF, give necessary additional properties needed for transmission operation such as:

Oxidation Stability. It has high resistance to varnish and sludge build-up that occurs from excessive heat. Local temperature as high as 600° F can occur at the clutch plates during engagement. If the fluid cannot withstand the heat, it burns or oxidizes resulting in an almost immediate destruction of friction materials, clogged hydraulic passages, and sticky valves in the transmission.

Viscosity Index Improvers. By using *viscosity index improvers* it keeps the viscosity more nearly constant with changes in temperature. This is especially important at low temperatures where the oil needs to be thin to aid in shifting and for cold weather starting. Yet it must not be so thin at high temperatures as to cause excessive hydraulic leakage so that pumps are unable to maintain the proper pressures.

Compatibility. It must be compatible with the materials used in the transmission. It cannot react chemically with the metals, seal materials, or friction materials.

Other Properties. Other chemical properties reduce wear and corrosion, prevent foaming, and act to slightly swell the seals and keep them from leaking.

Development of Transmission Fluids

A great quantity of fluids of various kinds has been poured into automatic transmissions since they were introduced to American passenger cars in 1939. Over the years much research has gone into the development and improvement of these hydraulic fluids to meet the changing requirements of the various transmission designs and the types of operational service encountered.

For example, a particular model car in 1946 with a 150 hp engine was coupled with an automatic transmission that had a fluid capacity of 13.5 qts. This meant that each quart of fluid had to handle 11 hp. In 1970, on the very same model car, horsepower had been upped to 375 hp and the transmission fluid capacity cut to 11.5 quarts. Each quart of fluid must now handle 33 hp or carry three times the load it did over 20 years ago. It is obvious that the transmission fluid had to continuously change character, especially in oxidation inhibitors, to keep from breaking down and also to accommodate transmission design changes.

In the beginning automatic transmissions were generally fed straight mineral oil, exactly the same type used in the engines. In some cases an oxidation inhibitor was added to the motor oils. As automatics took hold with the motoring public, service experience soon indicated that these oils had definite shortcomings. It became necessary to develop an oil with properties more compatible with actual automatic transmission needs.

An automatic transmission fluid specification was first developed by General Motors in 1949 and labeled *Type A Specification,* for automatic transmission fluid (ATF). This fluid was adopted industry-wide for automatic transmissions with policing of the specification assigned to the Armour Research Foundation, Illinois Institute of Technology (Now I.I.T. Research Institute). If the individual petroleum supplies met the Type A Specification they were approved and given an *AQ* (Armour Qualification) number.

The approved suppliers were licensed to carry the *AQ-ATF* General Motors trademark. These letters, along with the suppliers' numbers and brand names appeared on the containers they sold on the market.

Since the original 1949 formula the fluid specifications have been revised several times to accommodate changes in transmission design and the increased size of engines and cars. The use of options

such as air conditioning and the rise in the number of recreational trailers and the increase in city traffic have imposed additional thermal loads on automatic transmission fluids.

In 1957 field reports, especially with respect to varnish build-up, dictated the first modification of *Type A* fluid. The new specification was simply re-tabbed *Type A Suffix A* and replaced the original *Type A*. It was adopted for use by all the major car manufacturers in their automatic transmissions.

Ford Motor Company, however, developed its own *Type F* fluid under Ford Specification (M-2C33-D) in 1961 for the initial factory fill. In 1964 Ford specified that Type F must also be used for all refills in their automatics. Other car manufacturers continued to use *Type A Suffix A* fluid.

1968 brought about the latest changes in automatic transmission fluids, and it is these newer fluids which are of main concern. Ford Motor Company developed an improved *Type F* fluid (M-2C33-F) for all its transmissions and General Motors introduced a new formula, *Dexron*, Fig. 8-1. The Dexron formula was also adopted by Chrysler and American Motors. Table 8-1 summarizes the latest factory service recommendations regarding the use of ATF. (I. I. T. Research Foundation no longer certifies auto-

Fig. 8-1. Automatic transmission fluid recommendations. (attached chart)

TABLE 8-1. AUTOMATIC TRANSMISSION FLUID

FACTORY SERVICE RECOMMENDATIONS	
AMERICAN MOTORS	DEXRON OR AQ-A AQ-A OR DEXRON
CHRYSLER	DEXRON OR AQ-A DEXRON OR AQ-A
FORD	TYPE F–M2C33F TYPE F–M2C33D OR F
GENERAL MOTORS	DEXRON DEXRON OR AQ-A

AFTER 1968 MODELS IN RED

coefficient of friction and with particular characteristics under the various conditions to be met when that particular transmission functions. While uniformity of transmission fluids is desirable, transmission design goes on; new demands must be met by improved formulations.

Coefficient of Friction. *The force required to stop or prevent motion between two adjacent ob-*

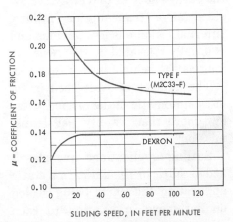

Fig. 8-2. Coefficient of friction (slip curve) for Type F and Dexron transmission fluids.

matic transmission fluids marketed by major oil companies. Ford Motor Company and General Motors Corporation are their own authorizing agents for Type F and Dexron.)

By the nature of its design, any particular automatic transmission will require a fluid with a specific

195

jects (*band and clutch activation in the case of automatic transmissions*).

Ford requires a coefficient of friction increase as sliding speed on clutch or band surface decreases; with Dexron, the fluid's *grab* is reduced as sliding speed of clutch or band surface slows. Ford and G.M. automatic transmission fluid characteristics are compared in Fig.

8-2. Both fluids have substantially increased oxidation stability.

WARNING: Type F *fluid and* Dexron *must be used in the transmission for which they are intended if the clutches and bands are to operate smoothly. The fluids cannot even be slightly mixed without causing shift quality problems and destruction of clutch and band friction materials.*

Sealing the Fluid

The job of the transmission seals is to control the external and internal bleeding of the fluid. The many uses of the fluid and the number of places to which it must travel make an enormous sealing task—especially so when external bleeding is obvious and annoying to the car owner. Any fluid spill on the garage floor or driveway is classified as a transmission failure. Internal leakage is less obvious and is usually tolerated by the owner as long as the vehicle moves forward.

The number of seals used in today's automatic transmission average more than twenty per transmission.

Sealing applications are classified as *static* or *dynamic*. In a static application the parts being sealed do not move in relation to each other. In dynamic applications there is rotating or reciprocating

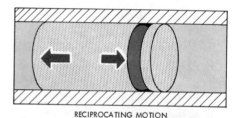

RECIPROCATING MOTION

ROTATING MOTION

DYNAMIC SEALS

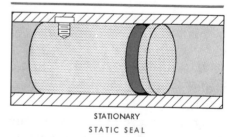

STATIONARY

STATIC SEAL

Fig. 8-3. Sealing applications, static and dynamic.

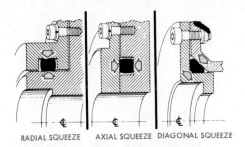

Fig. 8-4. Static seal application for sealing case to cover. (SAE)

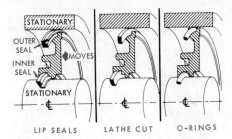

Fig. 8-7. Dynamic seal application to pistons. (SAE)

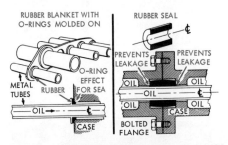

Fig. 8-5. Static seal applications for fluid transfer passages. (SAE).

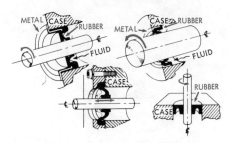

Fig. 8-6. Dynamic seal application to rods. (SAE)

static and dynamic applications used in modern automatic transmissions.

Synthetic Rubber Seals

Today, all modern automatic transmissions use synthetic rubber seals, especially where positive sealing is required. Synthetic rubber seals are used for either static or dynamic applications.

Positive Sealing. The sealing method completely prevents leakage.

Non-Positive Sealing. The sealing method allows some leakage for lubrication.

Probably the most widespread use of synthetic rubber seals has been on the clutch pistons. This area is the most critical in terms of vehicle operation and sensitivity. There is an inner and an outer seal for each piston, Fig. 8-8. In some transmissions where the clutch pistons has two apply chambers, a third seal or center seal is used, Fig. 8-9.

motion between the parts. Static and dynamic conditions are illustrated in Fig. 8-3. Shown in Figs. 8-4, 8-5, 8-6, and 8-7 are typical

197

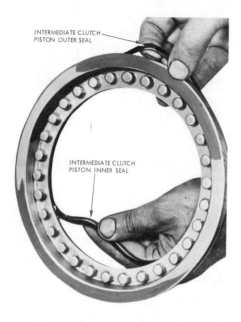

INTERMEDIATE CLUTCH
PISTON OUTER SEAL

INTERMEDIATE CLUTCH
PISTON INNER SEAL

Fig. 8-8. Inner and outer clutch piston seals, Turbo Hydra-Matic 350. (Oldsmobile Div., General Motors Corp.)

OUTER
SEAL

REVERSE
CLUTCH
PISTON

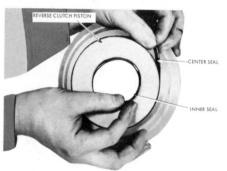

REVERSE CLUTCH PISTON

CENTER SEAL

INNER SEAL

Fig. 8-9. Outer reverse piston seal, and inner and center reverse piston seal, Turbo Hydra-Matic 350. (Oldsmobile Div., General Motors Corp.)

Clutch pistons use three basic designs of synthetic rubber seals; the lip type, lathe cut, and O-rings. These seal designs are not limited to clutch pistons as they are used also on the servo and accumulator pistons. Shown in Fig. 8-10 is a typical servo assembly using a lip seal on the piston.

Lip Seal. The lip seal is used ex-

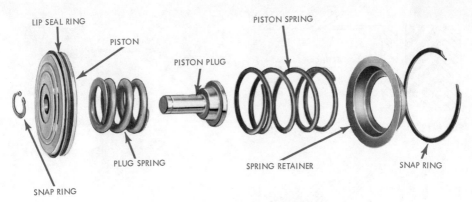

Fig. 8-10. Servo using lip seal.

tensively for dynamic applications. It is a molded seal and works on the deflection principle. Fig. 8-11. The installed lip tip diameter, which is larger than the cylinder bore, is deflected during installation into the cylinder resulting in lip tension against the cylinder wall. The compressing of the free lip position (maximum diameter), thus gives an oil-tight seal. Furthermore, in piston applications, the seal lip is installed toward the pressure source and the piston apply-fluid exerts a pressure against the lip. This balloons the lip out and aids sealing.

In Fig. 8-12, it is interesting to note the flexibility of the lip seal in adapting itself to changes in bore and piston clearances.

Lathe Cut Ring Seal. The lathe cut seal is an "O" type ring that is square in cross-section and used for both dynamic and static applications. The lathe cut seal is gen-

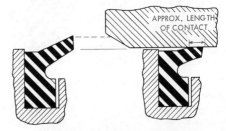

Fig. 8-11. Lip seal. (SAE)

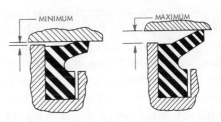

Fig. 8-12. Lip seal provides flexibility. (SAE)

erally extruded or molded in a tube shape, but it is always cut into individual rings on a lathe, Fig. 8-13.

In order to seal, the lathe cut depends on a squeeze when installed in its cylinder bore. Note in Fig.

199

Fig. 8-13. O-ring seal, lathe cut type. (SAE)

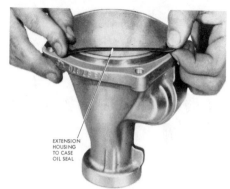

EXTENSION HOUSING TO CASE OIL SEAL

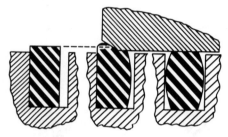

Fig. 8-14. O-ring seal is squeezed into place. (SAE)

REAR BEARING RETAINER

1/2" SOCKET

Fig. 8-15. O-ring lathe cut seal used on extension housing. (Oldsmobile Div., General Motors Corp.)

8-14 how the lathe cut seal is squeezed into the piston groove because its outside diameter is larger than the cylinder bore into which it is installed. Complete installation in the cylinder bore shows that the seal is squeezed and under compression. The reaction force created by the compression tries to return the seal section to its original size and shape, thereby creating a sealing effect on the contact area of the cylinder bore and bottom of the piston groove.

Shown in Figs. 8-15 and 8-16 are static applications of lathe cut seals on an extension housing and a front pump housing assembly.

Lathe cut seals are usually referred to in the trade as square cut seals, but sometimes as "O" ring seals, which leads to confusion with true O-ring seals.

O-Ring Seal. An O-ring seal is molded and has a round circle for a cross sectional area. Like a lathe cut seal it is squeezed and compressed during installation forming a seal against the contacting surface of the bore and bottom of

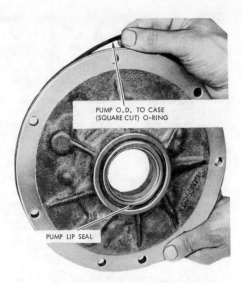

Fig. 8-16. O-ring lathe cut seal used on front pump housing to case. (Oldsmobile Div., General Motors Corp.)

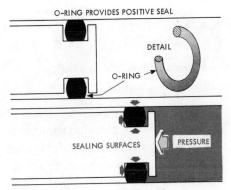

Fig. 8-17. O-ring is compressed on three sides.

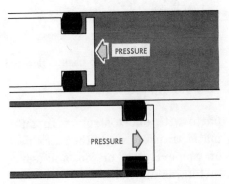

Fig. 8-18. O-ring is forced against walls and seals from either direction.

the piston groove. When pressure is applied it forces the seal against the side of its groove, and in effect, packs it into a corner. The end result is a positive seal on three sides capable of withstanding very high pressure, Fig. 8-17. Of noteworthy mention is the ability of the O-ring to seal from both directions, Fig. 8-18.

An O-ring seal has a tendency to roll or twist in its groove either on installation or while stroking. Therefore its dynamic applications must be limited to reciprocating

201

O-RING SEAL

STRAINER ASSEMBLY

Fig. 8-19. Strainer pipe to case O-ring seal, Jetaway transmission. (Oldsmobile Div., General Motors Corp.)

parts with short strokes. In automatic transmissions they are used on some clutch piston and servo piston installations.

Figs. 8-19 and 8-20 show critical static O-ring applications on a GM Jetaway. O-rings find wide use as tube or pipe seals in addition to their piston sealing use.

Metal Seals

Metal seals do not give positive sealing. They are used to seal rotating shafts that carry fluid under pressure and need some leakage

fluid to lubricate the shaft journals and bushings, Fig. 8-21. Metal seal rings are also used where high temperatures are encountered. The basic metallic ring used in automatic transmissions is designed or shaped like the common piston ring. Depending on the application these piston type rings are made from cast iron or aluminum. Cast iron rings are made from the same kind of piston ring iron used for automotive piston rings or small castings; and where required, are coated with nickel, chrome, or tin.

VACUUM MODULATOR
TO CASE SEAL

Fig. 8-20. Modulator tube to case O-ring seal, Jetaway transmission. (Oldsmobile Div., General Motors Corp.)

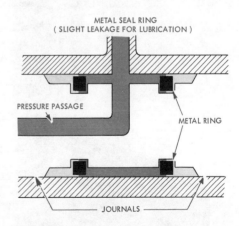

METAL SEAL RING
(SLIGHT LEAKAGE FOR LUBRICATION)

PRESSURE PASSAGE

METAL RING

JOURNALS

Fig. 8-21. Metal seals allow some leakage for lubrication.

Although the metal ring may be used as a static seal, this kind of application is very limited. The largest usage is found in rotary seal applications where some lubrica- tion is useful, and they also have some frequency of use in recipro- cating applications such as servo pistons and accumulator pistons, Figs. 8-22 and 8-23.

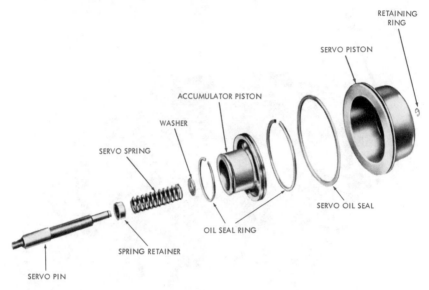

Fig. 8-22. Metal seal application in accumulator for Turbo Hydra-Matic 400. (Oldsmobile Div., General Motors Corp.)

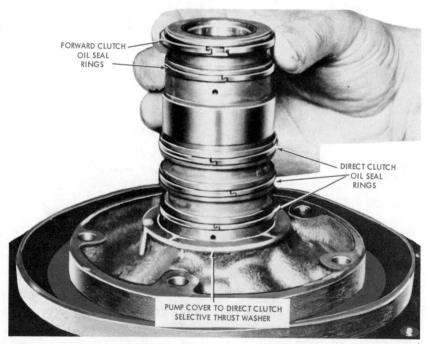

Fig. 8-23. Metal seal oil rings for Turbo Hydra-Matic 350 (Oldsmobile Div., General Motors Corp.)

204

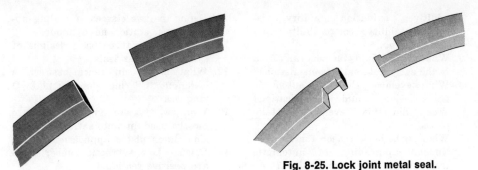

Fig. 8-24. Butt joint metal seal.

Fig. 8-25. Lock joint metal seal.

Transmission oil rings use two distinct types of joint ends. They are (1) butt joint and (2) lock joint, Figs. 8-24 and 8-25. The butt joint is used where small leakage past the joint is not important or where the leakage is utilized for lubrication. A lock joint is used where improved control of fluid leakage is required, and when compression is needed initially to fit the ring to its bore during installation. The lock joint is designed with small tangs which hold the ring in compression.

Teflon Seals

Teflon seals serve the same function as metal seals and are used on a limited basis in some automatic transmissions where rotating shafts are used. Although under present conditions Teflon seals are little used because of their cost, under changed technological conditions Teflon seals could become of greater significance to the transmission repairmen. Their non-binding quality at both relatively high and very low temperatures is quite useful.

Checking On Your Knowledge

The following questions give you the opportunity to check up on yourself. If you have read the chapter carefully, you should be able to answer the questions.

If you have any difficulty, read the chapter over once more so that you have the information well in mind before you go on with your reading.

1. What are the four main functions of an automatic transmission fluid?

2. Discuss the following transmission fluid properties built-in by the use of

additives, oxidation stability, viscosity stability, compatibility, and anti-foaming.

3. What type of fluid was generally used in the early automatic transmissions?

4. Who developed the first automatic transmission fluid specification? When did this development take place?

5. What is the basic reason for the continuous up-grading of automatic transmission fluid specifications?

6. What type of fluid is currently recommended for the automatic transmission families used by Ford, General Motors, Chrysler, and American Motors?

7. Discuss: Dexron and Type F fluids cannot be mixed for purposes of adding fluid or interchanged on fluid re-fills.

8. How would the wrong transmission fluid affect transmission operation?

9. What is the job of the transmission seals?

10. Define the two classes of sealing applications, static and dynamic.

11. What are the three basic designs of synthetic rubber seals?

12. What is the difference between a lathe cut "O" ring seal and plain O ring seal?

13. What two types of synthetic seals are mostly used in automatic transmission clutch piston applications?

14. Discuss how synthetic rubber seals are positive sealing.

15. Discuss how metal seals are non-positive sealing.

16. What are three reasons for using metal seal rings?

17. What type of application does the metal ring find its largest use?

18. Name two automatic transmission reciprocating applications of metal sealing rings?

19. Discuss how you would discover if a can of transmission fluid meets the latest factory requirements.

Principles of Diagnosis

Diagnosis involves a scientific or logical step-by-step plan, an orderly procedure that produces accurate information which the technician can use as clues to pinpoint the most probable cause of trouble. A diagnostic procedure follows a definite sequence of steps that accomplishes the most with the least amount of unnecessary labor. From the technician's viewpoint, diagnosis cannot be a shotgun approach. The procedure must cover the likeliest causes of trouble first and eliminate every possibility that does not require opening the transmission before you start taking things apart.

Accurate diagnosis of transmission problems begins with a rea-sonable understanding of normal transmission operation. Be able to think about what's going on while you're testing it. This doesn't mean that you have to know which way each pinion gear is turning, or what's going on each second in every fluid passage.

From a practical standpoint you are primarily interested in which friction members are applied in different gears and generally what part each hydraulic system component plays in applying the friction clutches. In most cases, this type of information will solve your transmission problem as transmission troubles usually involve slippage, shift quality, or shift timing. If a band or clutch doesn't hold, you have a *slip*. If the valves controlling *shift timing* and *shift quality* do not do their jobs properly, you have shift problems.

Many of the car manufacturers provide a diagnosis procedure guide and suggest problem solutions peculiar to their product. We could easily get very involved with the individual product details of transmission diagnosis. Let's leave the details to the car manufacturers and talk about general guidelines based on proven field experience that can produce results regardless of what transmission has a problem. This is not to say that the car manufacturer is to be ignored. We still need to use product information from the manufacturer dealing with specifications and test procedures as part of any diagnosis.

In the final analysis, it is you who must make the decision as to what is the problem, what caused it, and what must be done to repair it. You will need to depend upon your own good built-in diagnosis tools that nature gave you—your eyes, your ears, your nose, and some common sense. For the novice technician who needs experience it is recommended to stick with the diagnosis sequence and stick with the facts.

STEP 1—Listen to the Customer and Verify the Complaint

An often overlooked, but important aspect of diagnosis is to find out the exact nature of the customer complaint. It is your job to kindly listen to the customer, Fig. 9-1. The customer may not always know what he is talking about with regard to what is really wrong; however, he can relate to you his impression of the car's performance.

It is further recommended that the customer's verbal description be backed up by a short test ride, preferably with the customer along. In some cases, the complaint is simply found to be the customer's misunderstanding of how the transmission should operate, and what he wants corrected is standard and should not be changed.

While your customer is still a captive audience, do some detective work. A trailer hitch can tip you off to the fact that the transmission has been under heavy-duty service. The same is obvious when odometer mileage is higher than average for the age of the car, or an inspection of the right rear or spare tire may tip the hot rodder.

Get the customer to talk about

Fig. 9-1. Listen to the customer for symptoms and clues to malfunctions.

it. You may need to set up a transmission preventive maintenance program with the customer to fit the type of service his transmission encounters.

Some common sense driver education pertaining to transmission life may also need to be included.

This not only adds up to trouble-free miles for the customer, but also protects the reliability of the repair, especially where band and clutch failures have occurred.

The objective of Step I is to avoid the same plight as the dentist who just pulled the wrong tooth.

STEP II—Check the Fluid Level and Fluid Condition

Proper fluid level and fluid condition are basic to the operation of the transmission. A loss of one pint is likely to reflect itself in a transmission malfunction. Checking the dipstick can give the technician some immediate and important clues to the general condition of the transmission. It is here that the diagnosis procedure may provide sufficient evidence, early in the ball game, to dictate an overhaul and further testing is rendered useless.

Fluid Level Check

The fluid level is considered to be okay if it is between the *full* and *add one pint* marks on the dipstick. This inspection is simple, however to get accurate results there are certain conditions that must be right. Often, fluid level is assumed to be incorrect when it is not properly checked. The following procedure will produce the correct fluid level measurement:

1. Make sure the fluid is at operating temperature.
2. With the brake pedal applied, run the transmission through all the operating ranges to be sure the clutch and servo systems are *full*.

3. With the selector in P or N and the engine speed at normal curb *idle*, check the dipstick. Clean any dirt around the dipstick, then pull it out and clean it with a lint-free cloth. Put it back in the filler tube hole all the way, then remove it again and take a reading.

For most dependable checking, the fluid must be at normal operating temperature when it is fully expanded. Cold checking is not reliable, but where it is used, the fluid level must be at, or slightly below the *add* mark on the dipstick. It may not always be convenient to wait for a transmission warm-up. Fig. 9-2 shows the effect

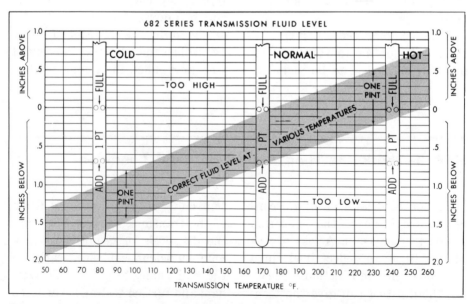

Fig. 9-2. Effect of temperature on fluid level. (Cadillac Div., General Motors Corp.)

of temperature on a transmission fluid level.

Fluid temperature is usually high enough for accurate checking if the car was driven for a short period of time prior to the actual check. If the car has been standing overnight, or long enough to cool off, the better practice is to warm up the fluid before you check the level. On a cold transmission, a warm-up period of ten to fifteen minutes at engine fast idle and the selector in P or N is usually adequate. If the temperature gage on the dash is at its normal range and the fluid is a little hot to touch on the dipstick you know that temperature conditions are right.

There are some other fine points to remember when checking fluid level. When a car is parked twelve hours or more, normal drain-back from the converter will raise the fluid level higher than normal. This means that a cold dipstick check, which is made before the converter has had a chance to refill, will be inaccurate. As a final checking precaution, especially after the transmission is drained and refilled, slowly move the selector through all the ranges and back to neutral to make sure the operating circuits are completely filled.

If the fluid level is down, the low level may be the result of an external leak, a leaky vacuum modulator diaphragm, or improper fill-

ing. If there is no evidence of an external leak which is typically indicated by fluid on the floor, or inspection and testing of the vacuum modulator shows no sign of a leaky diaphragm, then in all probability someone failed to refill. If the fluid condition looks normal, simply add enough fluid to reach the *full* mark and it is a good bet that the transmission will be back to normal. Don't forget to perform a road test before giving the final OK.

Improper filling may raise the fluid too high. Needless fluid may be added by mistake, or an incorrect filling procedure may have been used after the transmission is drained. For example, some transmissions still provide for both a sump and a converter drain. If the converter is not drained, a real mess is in the making. *The manufacturer refill recommendations are usually based on converter plus sump refill requirements.*

If you failed to drain the converter, you are going to have problems stuffing a ten quart recommendation into a four quart sump.

When talking about refills, let's look at another fine point so we don't overfill the transmission. The refill capacity given by the manufacturer is only a *guideline*. It is impossible to determine how much oil did not drain out and therefore remained in the transmission. Therefore, always stop at least one quart short of the total recommended refill and check the dipstick. If you need to add fluid, bring it to the *add* mark. Remember, you are dealing with a cold check. Keep in mind that the *add* mark means add one *pint* of fluid and not one *quart*—another cause of overfilling.

Low Level. Low fluid level can result in the oil pump taking in air along with the fluid. In any hydraulic system, air bubbles will make the fluid spongy and compressible. This can result in a slow build-up of pressure in the transmission hydraulic system.

Low fluid level will cause delayed engagement in *drive* and *reverse,* and slipping on upshifts. You may also get disturbing noises such as pump whine and governor buzz. The slipping action adds to the troubles by causing overheating and rapid wear of clutches and bands. With air in the fluid, the pump can't provide an adequate supply of fluid for converter feed and lubrication, so more overheating is generated and other transmission parts will wear to destruction.

High Level. When the fluid level is too high, transmission gears can raise an air bubble foam and develop similar slipping and overheating problems to those caused by low fluid level. The combination of foam and overheating causes a rapid oxidation of the fluid which leads to

varnish formation and sticky valving. Overfilling, therefore, doesn't exactly "treat" the transmission.

Fluid Condition

Today's transmission fluids all have a red dye. The fluid is considered to be in acceptable condition only if it appears as it did when poured out of the can. It should be clear and red. If the fluid is discolored, or shows signs of foreign material, the transmission may need an overhaul or possibly a transmission tune-up. Watch for these abnormal fluid conditions that can be found on the dipstick.

Dark or Black Fluid. When the fluid is dark or black with the odor of a burned electrical coil and friction material is in the fluid, overheating has occurred and a clutch or band has burned out. The transmission may sometimes work reasonably well in this condition, but the color and smell usually means that an overhaul will be needed to replace worn friction material, plus a complete cleanout to remove any varnish formation.

If the fluid is dark, but doesn't smell burned, the discoloration may be caused by ethylene glycol antifreeze. When the engine coolant leaks into the transmission cooling system, the transmission fluid usually becomes milky pink. However, if the leak is slight, and high temperature causes the water to boil off, the glycol that remains will cause the fluid to appear dark.

Milky Fluid. Milky pink fluid means that there is water in the fluid, either from the oil cooler unit in the radiator, or rain water from road splash that found its way past a raised dipstick sealing cap. (Always make sure the dipstick cap is fully seated.)

Any engine coolant or any moisture mixed with transmission fluid will swell transmission seals and soften friction material. If this condition is discovered early, the problem can be solved by fixing the cooler leak and changing the fluid. However, if the coolant or water has been in the fluid for some time, an overhaul is needed. You can usually judge what's needed by how the transmission acts when you drive it and what you find in the pan.

Varnished Fluid. It gives the fluid a light to dark brown color—the fluid no longer has its clear and red appearance. Not only does the color of the fluid change, but the varnish also tacks itself on the dipstick to leave another clue.

Once varnish starts forming, it builds up in all the valves, servos, and clutches and causes sticking and hardened seals. Eventually it will clog the filter and pump pressure will drop. When this happens, the torque converter will not fill, nor will there be enough apply pressure for clutch or band holding torque, and the transmission cannot operate. The extent of varnish contamination as determined by a pan inspection will show whether a fluid change or an overhaul is needed.

Note: When the fluid condition indicates a burned clutch or band, it is obvious that an overhaul is the sure cure. What to do in case of varnished fluid or milky fluid requires some common sense judgment. In either of the cases, the transmission pan should be dropped for inspection and an evaluation made of pan deposits. Any signs of clutch or band, or metallic deposits, or a burned smell call for an overhaul. If the fluid in the pan reveals no signs of unusual deposits and it looks like the coolant or varnish content hasn't attacked the transmission extensively, then a transmission tune-up is likely to produce successful results. This means a complete oil change (converter plus sump), clearing the cooler lines with air, valve body overhaul, band and external linkage adjustments. In cases where the converter has no drain provision, the transmission will need to be pulled for a converter drain and flush.

Use Approved Fluids

Use only approved fluids that meet the manufacturer's specification. All Ford Motor Company automatic transmissions use *Type F* fluid with specification number *M-2C33-F*. *Dexron* fluid is the recommendation for G.M., Chrysler, and American Motors automatic transmissions.

CAUTION: Type F and Dexron Fluids are not compatible and cannot be mixed or substituted without causing a rapid wear out of friction materials within an automatic transmission.

STEP III—Quick Check of Linkage and Engine Idle

In keeping with the diagnosis objective of reaching the end result with the least amount of effort, we're going to use our eyes and ears for some quick checks in preparation for a road test. It is assumed that the transmission fluid is at the correct level and fluid condition is normal, and we are in need of further testing.

Engine Idle

Set the engine *idle* to manufacturer's specifications using a reliable tachometer, Fig. 9-3.

When the engine *idle* is too high, you get more than normal idle

mainline pressure applying the friction units which causes a rough or harsh initial engagement in the transmission. It is the same kind of feel that you get when you pop a pedal-operated clutch.

Dropping the *idle* 25 rpm can sometimes make a noticeable difference in engagement quality.

Throttle Linkage and Vacuum Line Connections

This is another quick check item requiring mostly visual inspection simply to verify that the connections between the transmission and engine are properly attached and there is no evidence of tampering.

On vacuum lines leading to throttle or modulator diaphragm units, be sure to look for pinched tubing or hose leaks.

The throttle linkage inspection should include a check on the carburetor throttle valve opening as well as any linkage going to the transmission, Fig. 9-4. The accelerator pedal must move the throttle

Fig. 9-3. Setting idle with tachometer, a part of all automatic transmission testing.

Fig. 9-4. Carburetor inspection for full throttle travel.

any of the transmission throttle linkage needs adjustment, Fig. 9-5. The thinking here is to save time and to keep away from detailed throttle linkage adjustment checks unless absolutely necessary. Obviously, if the visual inspection reveals that adjustments or repairs are needed, it should be done at this time. On these adjustments, follow the manufacturer's procedure and specifications.

Manual Valve Linkage

The transmission manual linkage must be adjusted so that the pointer on the selector quadrant (or stops) corresponds with the transmission inside manual lever or manual valve detents. This check

valve wide open and still have further travel left to activate the transmission kickdown or detent system. For accurate results, an assistant should move the accelerator pedal with his foot while you make this observation.

The visual inspection is only a rough check before putting the car on the road for testing. The road test will eventually determine if

Fig. 9-5. Inspection of accelerator linkage.

Fig. 9-6. Checking manual linkage for accuracy of selector positions.

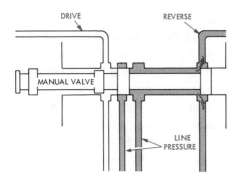

Fig. 9-7. Creep test indicates if manual valve is centered.

takes place from the driver's seat and is a matter of feel of the spring loaded detent plunger dropping into the notches on the manual lever or a manual valve, Fig. 9-6. If the detents are synchronized with the selector positions and the safety switch works in *park* and *neutral,* the manual valve linkage is correct.

Should corrections be necessary, refer to the car manufacturer's procedure for manual linkage adjustment.

If the linkage adjustment is off far enough, and with the selector on N, the manual valve will be off center and admit line pressure into the drive or reverse passages. This causes a full clutch or band apply and the result is car creep in N, either forward or reverse, Fig. 9-7.

Inaccurate positioning of the manual valve in the forward and reverse operating ranges can also result in subsequent clutch and band failures. The manual valve is partly open to an exhaust and the clutch or band circuit fails to realize the fully apply pressure.

STEP IV—Stall Test (Optional)

The stall test is used to check for band and clutch holding ability in the transmission, torque converter reactor (stator) clutch operation, and engine performance. The stall test consists of checking the maximum engine rpm at stall in the forward and reverse ranges.

CAUTION: This test is not to be performed unless recommended by the manufacturer; otherwise, the severe twisting imposed on the transmission case from the torque reaction could damage or distort the case. The stall test is currently approved for diagnosis testing in

Chrysler and Ford transmissions. This should be checked, however, with the service manual on a year to year basis.

Stall Test Procedure

The engine coolant, engine oil, and transmission fluid levels must be correct and at normal operating temperatures.

CAUTION: NO PERSON is to stand in front of the vehicle during the test.

PROCEDURE

1. Connect the tachometer and position it so you can read it from the driver's seat.
2. Apply the parking brake and service brakes firmly.
3. Shift the selector lever to the range being tested.
4. Push the accelerator pedal steadily to the floor and hold it just long enough for the tachometer reading to stabilize. Take the

Fig. 9-8. Stall tests using tachometer.

tachometer reading for recording and back off the accelerator.

CAUTION: This operation must not take over five seconds or severe overheating and damage to the transmission will result, Fig. 9-8.

5. Return the selector lever to *neutral* and operate the engine at 1000 rpm for a minimum of one minute for cooling.
6. Repeat the above procedure in each driving range or test run.

If engine speed exceeds the maximum limits of the stall specification, release the accelerator immediately since slippage is indicated and further damage to the transmission must be avoided.

Stall Test Interpretation

We will use the Chrysler Torque-Flite for an example to explain exactly what a test outcome could predict. Shown below are typical stall speed specifications, a data summary chart, and friction element summary that serves to give the necessary information for interpretation of test results, Tables 9-1 to 9-3.

Stall RPM Meets Specifications. If you have a good stall test reading in any range or ranges, the holding members in that range are okay, but you'll need to know your transmission to catch any exceptions to the rule. The low-reverse

TABLE 9-1. STALL SPEED TEST

STALL SPEED SPECIFICATION CHART		
ENGINE MODEL (CID)	TRANSMISSION TYPE	ENGINE SPEED (RPM)
170	A904–G	1500–1700
225	A904–G	1800–2000
225	A727–RG	1450–1650
273	A904–A	1950–2150
318	A904–LA	2100–2320
318	A727–A	1750–1950
340–4 BBL	A727–A	2250–2450
383–2 BBL	A727–B	1850–2100
383–4 BBL	A727–B	2350–2650
440–4 BBL	A727–B	2000–2300
426–2,4 BBL	A727–B	2650–2850

band in the TorqueFlite, for example, might be slipping in reverse, but you wouldn't know if it slips in *manual* (1) because the one-way clutch holds. Also note that the kickdown band is not used and must be road tested along with the low-reverse band. The stall test on the TorqueFlite is limited in its ability to test the holding power of all the friction elements.

For sure, a good stall test rpm in any range means the engine performance is okay and the torque converter one-way clutch is doing its job.

Stall RPM High. Keep in mind that during the stall test the rear wheels are stationary and the transmission cannot upshift. Here are some possibilities:

1. Slips in all ranges—Line pressure is completely lost or low; proceed to pressure testing and drop the pan for inspection
2. Slips in D and 2—One-way clutch
3. Slips in D, 2, and 1—rear clutch
4. Slips in Reverse—Could be either front clutch or low-reverse band

The holding power of the low-reverse band, kickdown band, and front clutch must be proven on a road test.

Stall RPM Low. Low stall speeds indicate either poor engine performance or that the converter stator one-way clutch isn't holding. A road test will be necessary to identify the exact problem.

If the one-way clutch doesn't lock the reactor, any through gear acceleration to approximately 30 mph will lack pep. Above 30 mph, however, the acceleration will be normal. Poor performance at all speeds is an indication that the engine needs attention.

If stall speed and acceleration are normal, but abnormally high throttle opening is required to maintain a highway speed, then the stator is seized. As a matter of fact, top vehicle speed is drastically reduced

TABLE 9-2. TORQUEFLITE STALL TESTS SUMMARY

STALL SPECIFICATION				
		CONDITION AS TESTED		
RANGE	ACTUAL	LOW	NORMAL	HIGH
DRIVE				
(2)				
(1)				
REVERSE				
OPERATING RANGE	HOLDING MEMBERS APPLIED			
D	REAR CLUTCH AND ONE-WAY CLUTCH			
2	REAR CLUTCH AND ONE-WAY CLUTCH			
1	REAR CLUTCH AND LOW-REVERSE BAND			
R	FRONT CLUTCH AND LOW-REVERSE BAND			
KICKDOWN BAND IS NOT USED DURING STALL TESTS.				

TABLE 9-3. TORQUEFLITE ROAD TESTS

INITIAL CLUTCH AND BAND ENGAGEMENTS					
	ENGAGES		QUALITY		
RANGE	YES	NO	HARSH	DELAYED	NORMAL
DRIVE					
(2)					
(1)					
REVERSE					
NEUTRAL	CAR CREEPS _____		O K _____		

because of the converter's inability to stop multiplying torque. Should this condition be suspected, take another look at the transmission fluid because a lot of heat is generated. This excessive heat generation can actually percolate the fluid and cause a loss of transmission line pressure, resulting in total slip of all friction elements.

STEP V—Road Test

Road testing starts with recognizing normal transmission performance. This is a must before you can give an opinion on abnormal conditions. If you aren't completely familiar with the normal performance, take time to get acquainted. If possible, drive several low mileage, well tuned, current model cars equipped with the same transmission. Drive both six and eight cylinder models.

You can't learn much about normal or abnormal shifting by taking a short joy ride with the selector in D. Try all of the operating ranges. Accelerate and decelerate. Compare shift quality under light, medium, and heavy throttle. Test the kickdown or detent performance. And perhaps most important of all, learn to visualize which band or clutch is applied for each gear.

A properly conducted road test is a valuable diagnostic tool, but only if you know your particular transmission.

On complaints relating to shift quality, don't overlook the condition of the engine, particularly if the stall test was omitted. Idle and engine performance should be up to specifications. The shift pattern and shift quality of the transmission is tailored to normal engine

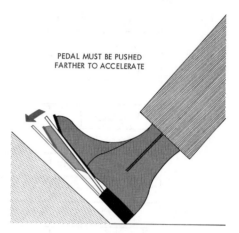

PEDAL MUST BE PUSHED
FARTHER TO ACCELERATE

Fig. 9-9. Poor engine performance requires wider openings and upsets the shift pattern and shift quality.

performance. If the engine is not functioning properly, the transmission has no way of knowing.

When the engine output is low, the driver has to step on the gas harder to accelerate; in effect, the throttle is opened further than normal, Fig. 9-9. If the transmission has a mechanically operated throttle system, the throttle pressure will be too high in relation to actual engine torque because the throttle linkage is advanced too far, Fig. 9-10.

In applications where vacuum modulator or vacuum throttle systems are incorporated, the subnormal engine vacuum will produce

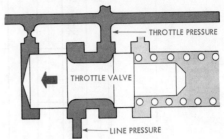

VALVE RAISES THROTTLE AND LINE PRESSURE
HIGHER THAN NORMAL

THROTTLE PRESSURE

THROTTLE VALVE

LINE PRESSURE

Fig. 9-10. Throttle linkage affects throttle pressure.

higher values in these systems in relation to throttle opening. The end result of low engine output in relation to transmission operation is delayed and harsh upshifts—the line pressure is higher for clutch-band application, and it will take more vehicle speed to generate the necessary governor pressure for the upshift pattern.

Always correct an untuned engine condition before the road test starts. More than one shift quality complaint has been corrected by correcting engine performance and not touching the transmission.

The objective of the road test is to gather exact information on transmission performance from which the technician can get more evidence to help pinpoint the transmission problem area. It is the best check-out that you can use for transmission slip and shift quality, and it must be done thoroughly.

Road Test Procedure

The engine coolant, engine oil, and transmission fluid must be cor-

rect and at normal operating temperatures.

The procedure consists of data collecting on road test charts. For our purposes, we are going to use charts applicable to the Chrysler TorqueFlite; however, they could be revised and adapted for any transmission, Tables 9-4 and 9-5.

Because of the many things being tested, it is best to record the test results rather than to depend on memory.

Road Test Interpretation

To be practical, it isn't possible to discuss all the conceivable types of malfunction or shift quality problems that can arise; therefore, let's concentrate on some of the most likely things to give an idea of how to think about the process.

Slipping. If the road test indicates slipping and you have recorded where that slipping occurs, then you can determine which band or clutch is at fault by the process of elimination.

TABLE 9–4. TORQUEFLITE ROAD TEST
ROAD TEST SUMMARY CHART

TORQUEFLITE MODEL _____   ENGINE MODEL _____

NOTE: FULL THROTTLE AND KICKDOWN SHIFTS SHOULD ONLY
BE TESTED ACCORDING TO ROAD AND TRAFFIC CONDITIONS

D RANGE	ACTUAL SHIFT POINTS IN MPH			NONE	SHIFT QUALITY			
	O K	HIGH	LOW		HARSH	MUSHY	SLIP	NORMAL
LIGHT THROTTLE UPSHIFTS								
1-2								
2-3								
CLOSED THROTTLE DOWNSHIFTS								
3-1								
WIDE OPED THROTTLE UPSHIFTS								
1-2								
2-3								
FULL THROTTLE KICKDOWN DOWN-SHIFTS								
3-2								
3-1								
TRAFFIC THROTTLE UPSHIFTS (MODERATE THROTTLE TO OBTAIN 2-3 UPSHIFT AT 30-40)								
(2) RANGE								
LIGHT THROTTLE UPSHIFTS								
1-2								

TABLE 9–4 CONT.

TORQUEFLITE MODEL _____   ENGINE MODEL _____

NOTE: FULL THROTTLE AND KICKDOWN SHIFTS SHOULD ONLY BE TESTED ACCORDING TO ROAD AND TRAFFIC CONDITIONS

	ACTUAL SHIFT POINTS IN MPH				SHIFT QUALITY			
	O K	HIGH	LOW	NONE	HARSH	MUSHY	SLIP	NORMAL
CLOSED THROTTLE DOWNSHIFTS 2–1								
WIDE OPEN THROTTLE UPSHIFTS 1–2								
FULL THROTTLE KICKDOWN DOWN-SHIFTS 2–1								
TRAFFIC THROTTLE UPSHIFTS (MODERATE THROTTLE TO OBTAIN 1–2 UPSHIFT AT 15–25)								

(1) RANGE

UPSHIFTS   YES ____ NO ____

MANUAL DOWNSHIFTS FROM 3RD GEAR AT 25MPH TO TEST BRAKING ACTION   YES ____ NO ____

(R) RANGE

HOLDS	
SLIPS	
CHATTERS	

TABLE 9-5. SPECIFICATIONS FOR TORQUEFLITE EIGHT CYLINDER VEHICLES. (CHRYSLER CORP.) TYPICAL SHIFT PATTERN SUMMARY CHART

CONDITION	VEHICLE SPEED TO AXLE RATIOS						
	273 & 318 CU IN ENGINES		340 & 383 CU IN ENGINES			HIGH PERFORMANCE 426 440	
	2.76:1	3.23:1	2.76:1	3.23:1	3.55:1	3.23:1	3.23:1
CLOSED THROTTLE 1-2 UPSHIFT	7-13	6-11	8-14	6-13	6-10	8-15	7-12
CLOSED THROTTLE 2-3 UPSHIFT	12-18	10-15	13-18	11-17	10-14	13-19	11-16
WIDE OPEN THROTTLE 1-2 UPSHIFT	30-47	25-40	31-49	31-50	28-42	41-58	33-48
WIDE OPEN THROTTLE 2-3 UPSHIFT	70-82	59-71	72-85	62-81	57-67	80-93	68-78
3-2 KICKDOWN LIMIT	60-73	51-63	63-76	55-73	50-60	70-84	60-70
3-1 KICKDOWN LIMIT	27-31	23-27	28-32	23-36	22-35	30-45	25-36
CLOSED THROTTLE DOWNSHIFT	5-12	5-10	6-13	5-12	4-9	6-13	5-11

When Forward Gears Slip = Rear Clutch Problem. In Table 9-6 you will notice that the rear clutch is engaged in *low, second* and *direct drive* ranges. It's obvious from this information that any slipping in all forward gears points to the rear clutch.

If Reverse And Direct Slip = Front Clutch Problem. Since the front clutch is engaged only in *re-*

verse and in *direct* (3rd gear), if there is slipping in these two gear operations, but not in others, the front clutch is probably the cause.

If No Kickdown Apply = 1-3 Upshift. Kickdown band trouble is easy to locate because this band applies only in *second.* When the band does not apply, a 1-3 upshift will occur. This skips second completely. With the kickdown band not apply-

TABLE 9-6. TORQUEFLITE ROAD SLIP TESTS FOR BANDS AND CLUTCHES (CHRYSLER CORP) BAND AND CLUTCH APPLY CHART

LOW (BREAKAWAY)	LOW (MANUAL)	SECOND	DIRECT	REVERSE
REAR CLUTCH	REAR CLUTCH	REAR CLUTCH	REAR CLUTCH	FRONT CLUTCH
OVERRUNNING CLUTCH	LOW AND REVERSE BAND	KICKDOWN BAND	FRONT CLUTCH	LOW AND REVERSE BAND

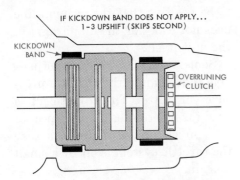

Fig. 9-11. 1-3 upshift skips second if kickdown band does not apply; overrunning clutch replaces kickdown on shift. (Torque-Flite)

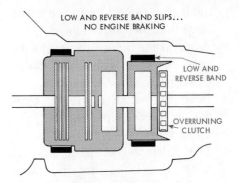

Fig. 9-12. When low and reverse band slips there is no engine braking or reverse.

ing the overrunning clutch will hold in *breakaway* until road speed is reached that is high enough for the shift into *direct,* Fig. 9-11.

Kickdown Slip = Delay And Thump. If the kickdown band slips a little before it is applied, there will often be a short delay and a *thump* as the kickdown band takes over from the overrunning clutch.

If Low And Reverse Slip = No Engine Braking ⏐ *and No Reverse.* Checking out the low and reverse band requires a little different thinking, because when the band slips, the overrunning clutch takes over. This makes it impossible to check the band under power. What you check instead is loss of braking power. You speed up the car to about 25 mph and move the selector from *drive* to *low.* If the low and reverse band slips, you won't feel any engine braking under *coast,* Fig. 9-12.

No Engine Braking In Low Plus No Reverse = Low and Reverse Band Problem. This process of elimination can be used on any automatic transmission.

Shift Timing & Smoothness. Operation of the bands and clutches provides the muscle which makes the upshift, downshift, and reverse actions happen. This muscle depends on having the correct pressure to operate the servos and clutches. Shift timing and smoothness, however, is dependent on several factors, such as healthy clutches and bands, proper clutch and band accumulator action, and shift valve timing.

For shift timing analysis you will need to rely on some of that good old-fashioned theory on automatic shift principles. Let's review the essentials in brief:

1. A throttle or a modulator pressure, plus spring tension, work

225

against a governor pressure to keep the shift valve closed.

2. A governor pressure works to open the shift valve and cause the shift.
3. Once the shift is made, only spring tension opposes the governor force.
4. The shift valve spring determines the closed throttle downshift point against governor force.

If either pressure is out-of-balance, then the upshifts will be delayed or occur too soon. Your job on the road test is to determine which pressure system is at fault, and then it's a matter of isolating the problem within the system.

Let's look at a few tips that we can get from a road test when the shifts are late and harsh, or early and mushy.

Late and Harsh Shifts

Closed Throttle Downshift Speed O.K. = Throttle Or Modulator System Pressure Too High. Should the transmission have mechanically operated throttle system, the first priority check is the throttle linkage adjustment. If the linkage is too long, it moves the transmission throttle valve too far and upshifts are delayed and harsh because the extra travel raises throttle pressure higher than normal.

On vacuum operated throttle systems, the first priority check is to be positive that the vacuum line does not leak nor the diaphragm in the unit itself.

Some vacuum units are adjustable, but change the throttle pressure very little. The adjustment is used for fine tuning. Don't expect to gain much unless it appears that the throttle system is off by a small margin.

The vacuum throttle units may also be removed and bench tested, or checked in the transmission by a fluid pressure test, or by an outside vacuum source from a distributor tester. The manufacturer's procedure must be followed.

A vacuum modulator unit is checked out essentially in the same manner as a vacuum throttle unit.

Should delayed and harsh upshifts occur only at maximum speeds, another suspect is a hung-up kickdown or detent system.

If Closed Throttle Downshift Speed Too High = Governor System Pressure Too Low. The governor valve is venting too much as it tries to balance, and this prevents the normal build-up of pressure in the system. If the valve is stuck permanently in the vented position, then the transmission does not upshift and stays in first gear, Fig. 9-13.

The governor valve can be cleaned and serviced without removing the transmission from the car.

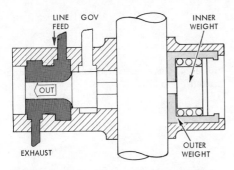

LINE FEED GOV INNER WEIGHT

OUT

EXHAUST OUTER WEIGHT

Fig. 9-13. Vented governor valve means low or no pressure.

If Closed Throttle Downshift Speed Too Low = Sticky Shift Valves. Since the shift valves work like hydraulic relays, sticky valves need more than normal governor pressure to make them move and thus the shifts are delayed. On the closed throttle downshift, the spring tension on the shift valve cannot close the valve until governor pressure drops below normal. Sometimes the vehicle must come to a complete stop before the downshift happens.

Early and Mushy Shifts

If Closed Throttle Downshift Speed O.K. = Throttle Or Modulator System Pressure Too Low. On a mechanically operated throttle system a check on the linkage adjustment is again in order. When the throttle linkage is too short, it does not move the throttle valve far enough and upshifts are early because the throttle pressure is lower than usual. Another obvious indi-cation of short linkage travel is the lack of kickdown or detent action.

Vacuum throttle and vacuum modulator systems should first be checked for vacuum line restrictions and then you can proceed with bench or in-the-transmission checks. Bench testing of the vacuum unit includes a check of the spring tension, which is usually outlined in the manufacturer's service manual. If in doubt about the vacuum unit after testing, re-place it. Vacuum line restrictions can be checked at the transmission with a vacuum gage. Vacuum should vary and respond rapidly to quick changes in throttle openings. Another method is to listen to the rise in engine idle rpm when the vacuum line is disconnected at the vacuum unit.

If Closed Throttle Downshift Speed Too Low = Governor System Pressure Too High. The governor valve is not venting enough as it tries to balance and it thus allows an abnormal build-up of pressure in the system. Typically, when the governor is in this condition, the transmission will not downshift into the last gear until the car is almost or completely stopped. If the valve is stuck permanently and shuts off the vent, Fig. 9-14, then the extreme happens, the shift valves stay in the upshifted posi-tion and the transmission starts in *high.*

227

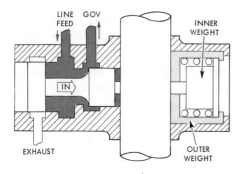

LINE FEED GOV

INNER WEIGHT

IN

EXHAUST

OUTER WEIGHT

Fig. 9-14. Governor valve seals vent means pressure too high.

In checking transmission shift points that seem out of specifications: do not overlook a double check on the axle ratio and tire size that might be the cause of inaccurate speedometer readings.

STEP VI—Pressure Testing

If there is a gear train slip or a shift feel that isn't right and if it cannot be corrected by external service adjustments or repairs, then the next step is to test the hydraulic pressures that control the transmission. Where vacuum throttle and vacuum modulator systems are employed, linkage adjustments are not required.

Pressure tests can be made quickly without dissassembling the transmission, and they help to give you a good idea of where to spot the trouble before you make a move on any disassembly or band adjustment. It would be a waste of time, for example, to adjust the bands if the transmission operating pressures are not correct. Shown in Fig.

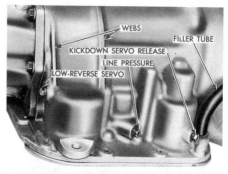

WEBS

FILLER TUBE

KICKDOWN SERVO RELEASE

LINE PRESSURE

LOW-REVERSE SERVO

Fig. 9-15. Pressure taps on transmission case. (Chrysler Corp.)

9-15 are pressure taps on the Chrysler TorqueFlite. Fig. 9-16 shows an additional tap for the governor system.

Pressure testing consists of reading the transmission pressures in

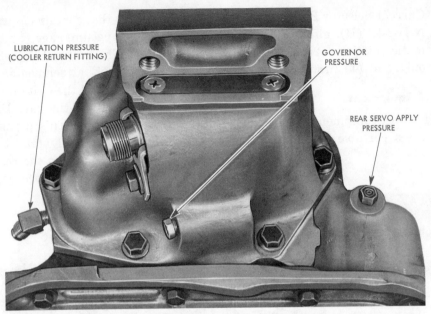

LUBRICATION PRESSURE
(COOLER RETURN FITTING)

GOVERNOR
PRESSURE

REAR SERVO APPLY
PRESSURE

Fig. 9-16. Governor pressure tap. (Chrysler Corp.)

specific operating conditions (on-the-road or shop simulated) and comparing the readings with specifications in the manufacturer's shop manual. Readings that are out-of-specifications will give definite clues for locating the problem in conjunction with other accumulated evidence.

For our discussion purposes, the Ford C-4 transmission is chosen to highlight pressure testing, as it has only one pressure tap and that reads control pressure. Before we proceed, now is a good time to briefly review some things about the C-4 that are important to the understanding and interpreting the pressure test procedure and results:

1. The gear train power flow is identical to the Chrysler Torque-Flite and uses the same band and clutch combinations.

2. A vacuum throttle system is used with the throttle pressure employed as a boost signal for the main pressure regulator valve boost system (do not interpret this as the only job of TV pressure in the C-4).

3. In reverse, line pressure and TV pressure are both used as boost signals at the main pressure regulator valve.

4. Separate external throttle linkage is used to mechanically activate a downshift valve for detent shifts.

229

5. Current Selector Positions, P-R-N-D-2-1. (D) offers full automatic shifting, (2) second gear only, and (1) first gear only.

Test Equipment

For test equipment, we are going to use a portable automatic transmission tester that contains a pressure gage, a vacuum gage, and a tachometer. The tester has extra long instrument attachments to permit mounting of the unit on the front door glass of the car, Fig. 9-17 top and bottom. This permits the technician to easily take test readings with the car on the road, or in the shop. The pressure gage

Fig. 9-18. Pressure gage connection to transmission.

Fig. 9-17. Automatic transmission tester. Shelf holds transmission tester during in-place tests.

connection is shown in Figure 9-18, and in Fig. 9-19. Note that the vacuum connection must be tied into the line at the throttle diaphragm unit. For accurate test results this is done to insure that we are deal-

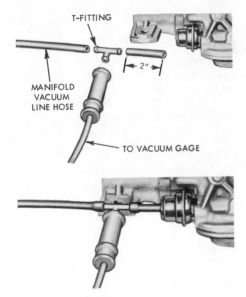

T-FITTING

2"

MANIFOLD
VACUUM
LINE HOSE

TO VACUUM GAGE

Fig. 9-19. T-fitting for vacuum line connection to gage.

ing with the exact working vacuum.

There is only one hydraulic pressure tap on the C-4. It samples the mainline pressure, or as Ford refers to it, control pressure. Since the throttle system has a direct bearing on control pressure, it is important that the vacuum supply and TV diaphragm unit get a quick check to be certain there are no vacuum leaks, that the engine vacuum supply is O.K., and that the diaphragm is functioning. Keep in mind, however, that a functioning diaphragm does not confirm that the throttle vacuum unit is performing with accuracy. The actual pressure test will pick this up.

PROCEDURE

Vacuum Supply and TV Diaphragm Test

1. Check the vacuum gage reading at normal *idle*. It must be a steady 18 inches, or an acceptable reading for the altitude at which you're testing. If it isn't right, check for a vacuum leak or for poor engine vacuum.

2. If the idle vacuum is good, accelerate the engine momentarily and observe the vacuum gage needle. The reading must drop quickly and return immediately to 18 inches as the engine returns to *idle*. If there is no snap action, check the vacuum line for a restriction or an improper connection.

3. To check for a vacuum leak in the diaphragm, use a separate vacuum source from a distributor tester. The diaphragm must be able to hold 18 inches of vacuum or be considered defective.

A defective diaphragm is also indicated by the presence of transmission fluid on the vacuum side. The vacuum source and TV diaphragm must be O.K. before pressure testing starts.

Table 9-7 shows the control pressure test section of the C-4 Diagnosis Guide where pressure readings are recorded for comparison

231

TABLE 9-7. CONTROL PRESSURE TEST SECTION OF AUTOMATIC TRANSMISSION
DIAGNOSIS GUIDE

CONTROL PRESSURE TEST					
(TRANSMISSION FLUID MUST BE NORMAL OPERATING TEMPERATURES)					
ENGINE RPM	MANIFOLD VACUUM (INCHES OF MERCURY)	THROTTLE	RANGE	PSI	
				RECORD ACTUAL	RECORD SPEC
IDLE	ABOVE 18	CLOSED	P	____	52 69
			N	____	52 69
			D	____	52 69
			2	____	80 110
			1	____	80 110
			R	____	100 180
AS REQUIRED	10	AS REQ	D,2,1	____	96 110
AS REQUIRED	BELOW 1	AS REQ	D	____	135 155
			2	____	135 155
			1	____	135 155
			R	____	220 250

with the specifications in Table 9-8. The test procedure follows.

PROCEDURE

1. Be sure the transmission is at normal operating temperature.
2. With a minimum vacuum reading of 18 inches, record the pressure at *idle* in all ranges.
3. Make a control pressure check at 10 inches of vacuum in all forward ranges—D, 2, and 1. With the car brakes applied, advance the throttle until the engine vacuum reading is 10 inches.
4. Make a control pressure check at 1.0 inch of vacuum, or less, in all forward drive ranges and

reverse. With the car brakes applied, advance the throttle until the engine vacuum reading is 1.0 inch or less. This is a stall test condition, and therefore after each test run it is important to move the selector lever to *neutral* and run the engine at 1,000 rpm for one minute to cool the converter.

5. As an alternate method for setting the required vacuum readings, an adjustable vacuum source from a distributor tester can be connected directly to the diaphragm unit. The tests at idle are still made at 18 inches of vacuum. At 10 inches and one

TABLE 9-8. CONTROL PRESSURE AT ZERO GOVERNOR RPM--C4 TRANSMISSION

ENGINE SPEED	THROTTLE	MANIFOLD VACUUM (INCHES OF MERCURY)	RANGE	PSI
IDLE	CLOSED	ABOVE 18[1]	P,N,D	52-69
			2,1	80-110
			R	100-180
AS REQUIRED	AS REQUIRED	10	D,2,1	96-110
AS REQUIRED	WIDE OPEN	BELOW 1.0	D,2,1	135-155
			R	220-250

[1]AT ALTITUDES ABOVE SEA LEVEL, IT MAY NOT BE POSSIBLE TO OBTAIN 18 INCHES OF ENGINE VACUUM AT IDLE. FOR IDLE VACUUMS OF LESS THAN 18 INCHES, REFER TO THE FOLLOWING TABLE TO DETERMINE IDLE SPEED PRESSURE SPECIFICATION IN D DRIVING RANGE:

ENGINE VACUUM	LINE PRESSURE
17 INCHES	52-74
16 INCHES	52-79
15 INCHES	52-84
14 INCHES	52-89
13 INCHES	52-94
12 INCHES	52-99
11 INCHES	52-104

NOTE: Table 9-8 is illustration only. For specification change, always consult the shop manual.

inch, the tests are run at an engine rpm of 1000.

Pressure Test Interpretation

The following charts are furnished by the manufacturer to help you interpret the C-4 pressure test, Table 9-9. The charts are not intended to come up with all the answers. Their main function is to steer you in the right direction and confine the trouble to an area for the problem solution. Chart interpretation and pinpointing the trouble still depends on your knowledge of transmission operation and on your common sense.

Control Pressure. Let's analyze at least one problem area—*low* at idle in all ranges, Table 9-10. You'll notice that many possibilities are listed in the diagnosis guide charts and it may appear confusing. However, always think in terms of the most likely possibilities and what things are easy to check. With this as a guideline, we approach the problem in sequence — starting from the simple and going to the complex.

TABLE 9-9. TROUBLE SHOOTING CHART (FORD MOTOR CO.)

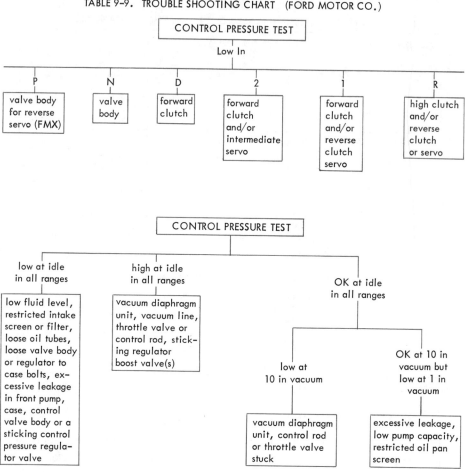

The pressure test indications are that a defect is starting to build up in the pump circuit. The pump circuit has its biggest stress for delivering volume and pressure at *idle,* therefore beginning pump wear or pump circuit leaks are detected under idle or low rpm conditions.

PROCEDURE

1. Check the fluid level again, even though this was done at the very beginning of your diagnosis.
2. Drain the fluid and drop the pan. Examine the pan for metallic deposits which might be coming from a worn front pump. If metallic deposits are found, remove the transmission and get to the front pump.
3. Examine the intake screen for restriction.

TABLE 9-10. CONTROL PRESSURE LOW AT IDLE IN ALL RANGES

				PSI	
				RECORD ACTUAL	RECORD SPEC
CONTROL PRESSURE TEST					
(TRANSMISSION FLUID MUST BE NORMAL OPERATING TEMPERATURES)					
ENGINE RPM	MANIFOLD VACUUM (INCHES OF MERCURY)	THROTTLE	RANGE	RECORD ACTUAL	RECORD SPEC
IDLE	ABOVE 18	CLOSED	P	45	52 69
			N	45	52 69
			D	45	52 69
			2	75	80 110
			1	75	80 110
			R	90	100 180
AS REQUIRED	10	AS REQ	D,2,1	104	96 110
AS REQUIRED	1	AS REQ	D	145	135 155
			2	145	135 155
			1	145	135 155
			R	240	220 250

4. Re-torque the valve body to case bolts to check for looseness. The pump circuit travels between the valve body and case.

5. Remove the valve body and make a complete inspection of the pressure regulator valve train for sticking valves. Although this is not too likely because regulation is O.K. at 10 inches and at 1.0 inch, it is best to double check.

6. If check points 1 through 5 haven't produced any results, then the transmission must be pulled and a visual study made of the front pump assembly and case circuit, especially the intake side of the circuit.

You may be wondering why the throttle system does not enter our discussion since TV pressure is used as a boost signal at the main pressure regulator valve. At *idle* and at normal engine vacuum, TV pressure is zero because of the high vacuum; and therefore the main regulating valve is balancing against spring tension only and TV pressure is not a factor.

If the control pressure is high at *idle* in all ranges then it's a good bet that the vacuum diaphragm unit is at fault, and is not regulating accurately. Secondary considerations should be a sticky throttle valve or sticking boost valves at the main regulator valve. (This is assuming that a leaky diaphragm or vacuum line or untuned engine were eliminated as possibilities before the pressure check.)

The pressure check is a must on any complaint whereby the transmission makes no response to move the car in any of the forward ranges and reverse. Should the pressure read zero, it is most likely that the main pressure regulator valve is stuck in the exhaust position and the zero condition rules out a worn pump.

A worn front pump will always develop a pressure head even if it's low, and obviously, too low a pressure can't furnish the muscle to hold a band or a clutch so the transmission slips. The approach here is to examine the oil level and condition and drop the transmission pan for an analysis of deposits.

On occasion, the pressure is good at *idle* and in all ranges, and you feel the bands and clutches respond and yet the car doesn't move. Look for a sheared input shaft to the transmission or converter turbine part failure. If you have no power input then you can't have a power output.

As a general rule, if transmission pressures meet specifications, if the fluid is healthy, and if the pan inspection shows no unusual metallic or band-clutch deposits, then a band adjustment, an external linkage adjustment, and a fluid change

will usually solve a slip or uncoordinated shift condition. If a band or clutch-apply circuit is designed with an accumulator system, this also may require investigation.

Caution: Pressure tests must follow the manufacturers' procedures. Therefore, always consult with the applicable service manual for the exact procedures and specifications.

In addition to using an oil pressure gage to check pressure readings against manufacturers' specifications, note that the gage can be used to pinpoint malfunctions in particular areas of the transmission. For example, a transmission has a *spin-up* between shifts. The condition may be caused by leakage of the clutch-apply piston seals. If the leakage is severe, that is, if it is greater than the output volume of the pump, then the oil pressure will be below specifications.

But assume that the leakage is not severe. While oil pressures may seem to be normal, since leakage exists it will take a longer time for the clutch-apply chamber to fill and to apply the clutch, thus the spin-up while the shift occurs. With an oil pressure gage the condition can be pinpointed.

Note the action of the needle gage. Usually, when a clutch chamber is filling the oil pressure will drop, then recover as the chamber fills. However, if the clutch seals are leaking it will take longer for the clutch to fill and for the needle gage to return to normal. Thus the time factor for recovery of the needle gage is an important clue to leakage.

To summarize: in normal operation during a shift the needle gage will drop off as the clutch or servo is filling but will snap back after the unit is full. With real leakage, if a seal is defective, as the shift occurs the gage needle will drop, then slowly return as the shift is completed. The greater the leak, the longer the time before the gage reading returns to normal.

Checking On Your Knowledge

The following questions give you the opportunity to check up on yourself. If you have read the chapter carefully, you should be able to answer the questions.

If you have any difficulty, read the chapter over once more so that you have the information well in mind before you go on with your reading.

Define the term, diagnosis:

Step I—Listen to the Customer Complaint

1. Why is it important to listen to the customer on any type of performance complaint?
2. Why is it desireable to road test the car with the customer?
3. What are some tips to indicate that the car is under heavy-duty service?
4. What is the objective of Step I?

Step II—Check the Fluid Level and Fluid Condition

1. How much fluid loss will it take before the transmission begins to malfunction?
2. How much fluid shortage is indicated when the level is on the add mark?
3. Describe the three step procedure that will produce an accurate fluid level measurement.
4. What is an acceptable fluid level when using a cold check?
5. How does the technician know that the fluid is at a normal operating temperature?
6. Explain why the refill capacity given by the manufacturer is only a guideline.
7. State some problems that can be caused by low fluid level.
8. State some problems that can be caused by high fluid level.
9. What is the acceptable fluid color condition?
10. What is indicated by the following fluid conditions: dark or black, milky pink fluid, varnished fluid?
11. Explain why the transmission pan should be dropped, whenever the fluid condition is not proper.

Step III—Quick Check of Linkage and Engine Idle

1. What type of problem is caused by too high an engine idle?
2. Make a list of quick check items on throttle linkage and vacuum line connections.
3. How does the technician quick check the manual linkage?

Step IV—Stall test

1. What is a stall test?
2. What is the purpose of the stall test?
3. The stall test is not a recommended

diagnosis test for all automatic transmissions? Why?

4. What test instrument is used for the stall test?

5. What is the maximum time limit allowed for each test run? Explain.

6. What important step must be taken by the technician between each test run?

7. What must the technician do when the engine speed during a test run starts to exceed stall specifications?

8. What is indicated when the stall rpm is below specifications?

9. Explain why the stall test cannot pick out a one-way stator clutch in the converter that fails to freewheel.

10. Explain why, in the Torqueflite, the holding power of the low-reverse band, kickdown band, and front clutch must be proven on the road.

11. On the Ford C-4, name the clutch and band units that cannot be tested for holding power by a stall test.

12. How is poor engine performance distinguished from a one-way stator clutch that fails to lock?

Step V—Road Test

1. Explain why road testing starts with recognizing normal transmission performance.

2. What effect would a poor performing engine have on the shift quality of the transmission?

3. What is the objective of the road test?

4. Would it be necessary to perform a road test if the transmission fluid was severely varnished or burned? Explain.

5. What kind of transmission engagement quality would result from the following conditions:
   a. abnormally high engine idle
   b. loose engine mounts
   c. worn U-joints
   d. abnormally high fluid operating pressures

6. If the vehicle creeps in neutral what will be the first quick check to make?

7. What effect will a punctured diaphragm in the modulator or throttle vacuum unit have on the upshift pattern of an automatic transmission?

8. What would you suspect if the transmission had a delayed or no upshift condition during warm-up only (atmospheric temperature below 32°F—transmission equipped with vacuum throttle or modulator unit).

9. What effect will a disconnected or loose vacuum line to the throttle or modulator unit have on the upshift pattern of an automatic transmission?

10. Why is a knowledge of the band and clutch applications a valuable asset in diagnosing transmission problems?

11. Name the band or clutch failure that will cause the following problems in a Torqueflite:
   a. Transmission slips in *reverse* and *direct*.
   b. Transmission upshifts 1-3 in D and fails to upshift 1-2 in 2.
   c. Transmission fails to move vehicle forward in both D and 2, but moves it forward in 1. *Reverse* is O.K.

12. Explain the procedure for testing the holding power of the Low & Reverse Band in 1 in a Torqueflite transmission.

13. What would be your prime suspect if the transmission upshift was a delayed 1-3 shift only and the closed throttle downshift 3-1 occurred at normal speed in a Torqueflite transmission?

14. Explain: If the transmission closed throttle downshift speed is O.K., the governor pressure is probably normal and is not the cause of the upshifts being too high or too low.

15. What is the prime suspect in the shift system with the following problems? Explain each.
   a. Transmission starts out in high gear only.
   b. Upshift patern is delayed and the closed throttle downshift pattern is too low.

c. Upshift pattern is too high and closed throttle downshift patern is normal.

d. Transmission stays in first gear and fails to upshift.

16. If the axle ratio number was smaller than the original stock axle ratio, how would this affect the transmission shift points readings?

Step VI—Pressure Testing

1. What is the purpose of pressure testing?

2. What are the three separate instruments needed by the technician for pressure test coverage of automatic transmissions?

3. On those transmissions where the line pressure is affected by the action of a vacuum throttle or modulator unit, why is it a good practice to connect a vacuum gage at the transmission rather than at the engine?

4. A worn front pump will always develop a pressure head even if it is low; explain.

5. If the pressure is zero in all operating ranges, then the pressure regulator is at fault; explain.

Chapter 10

Automatic Transmission Service

Periodic Maintenance

The automatic transmission can be considered as one of the most reliable of the major car components. To maintain its reliability, however, it requires periodic maintenance with the basic standards set by the manufacturer. Periodic maintenance refers to a definite interval in terms of days or mileage for which the transmission is scheduled for a fluid and filter change (or clean-out), and any required band and linkage adjustments. Its objective is to give a long life span to the transmission with a preventive service before major trouble occurs.

The individual car manufacturers have always had a recommended periodic service requirement for their automatic transmissions; however, car owners as a whole have neglected this item because of the lack of emphasis on servicing the transmission. Every car owner in America has been conditioned to change the engine oil and filter, but not the automatic transmission. In recent years this has begun to change. For probably the first time many customers are being educated to the fact that the automatic transmission does require periodic service as part of the car warranty agreement. This service must be performed to keep the warranty in force on the transmission.

When is the proper time to schedule periodic maintenance service? It comes due at the time the transmission fluid needs changing, and this has always been a controversial subject with a long history of changes in thinking.

During the early and mid-1960's, there was a trend by some of the car manufacturers to advertise that the automatic transmission fluid was good for the life of the car. In cases where severe service was the rule of operation, this recommendation did not prove itself. Most car manufacturers now make exception to the "no change needed" rule.

With the introduction of the *Dexron* and *Ford M2C33-F* automatic transmission fluids, a whole new set of periodic maintenance recommendations have been written by the car manufacturers. The recommended line-up for the year 1972, which is also good for all transmissions prior that year, is indicated under each car manufacturer below.

CAUTION: Transmission fluids cannot be substituted or mixed. Use only the ones recommended.

Severe Service Conditions

We've talked about severe service and should give its meaning some attention. Severe service is any driving condition that generates above-normal heat conditions in the transmission, resulting in oxidation of the fluid. The by-product of this oxidation or burning is varnish. Typical severe service conditions are prolonged idling in stop-and-go traffic, especially in hot weather; frequent trailer hauling; wheel spinning on ice and snow or in the mud; driving in mountainous areas; and similar hard usage.

Chrysler Corporation recommends for severe service that the factory fill fluid should be changed initially after 36 months or 36,000 miles, whichever occurs first, and every 12 months or 12,000 miles thereafter, whichever occurs first.

Vehicles equipped with the 426 Hemi engines should have the factory fill changed after 24 months or 24,000 miles, whichever occurs first, and periodically thereafter every 12 months or 12,000 miles.

A filter replacement and band adjustment accompanies every fluid change in the above.

Regular Service Conditions

For all Chrysler car models, except with the 426 Hemi engine, that are operated under normal service conditions, the transmission fluid and filter are considered good for life. Therefore, fluid changes are not required. If for any reason the factory fill fluid is replaced, the new fluid must be changed and bands adjusted every 36 months or 36,000 miles, whichever occurs first in normal service.

NOTE: Use Dexron *for all fluid changes or addition of fluid for Chrysler transmissions.*

General Motors' present recommendation for transmission fluid change is every 24,000 miles or 24 months, whichever occurs first in normal service; every 12,000 miles for severe service.

At the time of fluid change, perform the following:

T-300, Powerglide, Tempest—replace or flush filter screen and adjust low band

T-350—replace or flush filter screen

T-400—install new filter element.

NOTE: Use Dexron *for all fluid changes or additions of fluid to G.M. transmissions.*

The torque converters on G.M. automatic transmissions are not furnished with drain plugs; therefore, the quantity of fluid to add for a pan removal only is considerably less than a full capacity requirement for an overhaul or converter change. On a fluid change, add the following quantities:

T-300, Powerglide, Tempest—2 quarts

T-350 and T-400—3 quarts

T-425—4 quarts

Remember, the end result of any checking and adding procedure is to assure that the fluid level is at the *full* mark when the transmission is at operating temperature, usually reached after over 12 miles of highway driving.

Ford stays with its no-drain recommendation for automatic transmission fluid; however, it does stress adjusting the bands. The band adjustment requirement for normal service is for one time only at 12,000 miles; for severe service, every 12,000 miles.

The C-4 and C-6 adjustments are made externally with no need to remove the pan. On the MX and FMX, the pan needs to be removed to adjust the front band; therefore, it would only be good practice to replenish the sump with fresh fluid, *M2C33-F.*

American Motors is more strict in its required periodic service. It refers to it as a Transmission Tune-Up. This is required every 24,000 miles in normal service. For severe service, the tune-up takes place at the first 6,000 miles, and then every 12,000 miles.

The recommended tune-up includes a fluid change, filter screen replacement, linkage and band adjustment, and control pressure checking and adjustment.

NOTE: Use Dexron *for all fluid changes or addition of fluid to other than Ford products.*

Up to now, we have dwelled on the car makers' intervals for periodic maintenance. The longer intervals are recommended for ideal driving conditions, the shorter for severe service. The independent garage owners directly involved with transmission service have their own opinion about the periodic service interval on automatics, and rightly so. They recommend that in most cases the automatic transmission fluid change, filter service, and band adjustments should occur every 12,000 miles or 12 months, whichever occurs first. In other words, they recommend observing the shorter interval to insure top-notch transmission reliability. The reasoning is very logical. The car owner does not usually know what makes up severe driving conditions, and it is more likely that the transmission has been exposed to at least one severe condition during a 12 month period.

Periodic maintenance of automatic transmissions is a quick service item and is profitable. For the newcomer in automatic transmission service, it offers a grass roots beginning.

Fig. 10-2. Sniff test checks for burned oil.

Fig. 10-3. Draining oil from the converter.

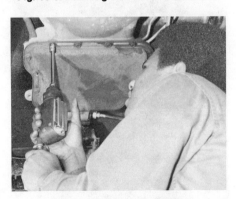

Fig. 10-4. Removing oil pan.

Fig. 10-1. Checking fluid for level, color, and particle contamination.

Illustrated in Figs. 10-1, 10-2, 10-3, 10-4, 10-5, 10-6, 10-7, 10-8, and 10-9, is a sequence of operations showing the simplicity of

Fig. 10-5. When oil pan does not have a drain provision, loosen the front pan bolts and remove the remainder. The oil pan can simply be pried loose and tilted without losing control of the fluid drain.

Fig. 10-6. Filter removal after the oil pan has been taken off.

Fig. 10-7. Band adjustments to be followed by new filter installation.

Fig. 10-8. Sizing new gasket to the clean oil pan before installation.

Fig. 10-9. Putting in new fluid of the approved type.

Fig. 10-10. Remove O-rings and replace oil strainer-to-case O-ring.

automatic transmission periodic maintenance. Filters designed with tubes require a new 0-ring. Before seating the tube in the transmission bore, make sure the old 0-ring has been removed, Fig. 10-10.

External Fluid Leaks

Locating and repairing external fluid leaks is another type of service required for automatic transmissions and in many cases the repair can be made without too much fuss. This is another natural in-

245

volvement for the beginner in automatic transmission repair. In service shops where the facilities are limited in handling detailed automatic transmission repair, external fluid leaks can easily be handled and turned into a profit.

The customer usually becomes aware of an external leak before the technician. This awareness is brought about by the extremely annoying fluid pools spotted on the garage floor or driveway. Sometimes the transmission acts up and the customer is desperate. If severe damage has not already occurred because of a low fluid level, your job is to locate the leak and fix it. Should your observation of the fluid condition reveal transmission damage, stop! The transmission will need to be removed and overhauled.

Locating a leak in service may or may not be an easy problem. Leaks on the outside of the transmission housing are not too difficult to find, although the underbody air currents sometimes blow the fluid around and make the job of locating the leak more difficult. Listed below are some of the more typical outside housing leaks that you could encounter and are common to many automatic transmissions:

Pan gasket
Front pump seal
Cooler lines and fittings

Extension housing seal
Filler tube connection or seal
Speedometer cable connection or seal
Manual shaft seal
Throttle shaft seal
Servo covers

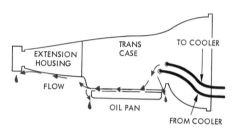

Fig. 10-11. Leak at cooler lines can give false symptoms.

Fig. 10-11, illustrates a simple leak at the transmission cooler line fittings, usually a tricky problem. Note how the fluid leak leads to the bead of the pan and flows off at the rear. Air currents also pick off the fluid and work it against the transmission extension housing. Be careful with this type of leak and don't get caught replacing an extension housing seal or pan gasket only to find out later that the solution to the problem was to tighten the cooler line fittings.

The best policy on external housing leaks is to take a few extra minutes and visually examine all the possibilities.

On extension housing seal leaks, do not overlook the fact that a bad propeller shaft U-joint may have

Fig. 10-12. Some extension housing seals can be removed carefully with a hammer and chisel, or by special tools recommended by the manufacturer.

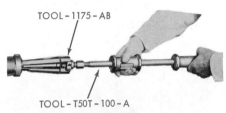

TOOL - 1175 - AB

TOOL - T50T - 100 - A

Fig. 10-13. Using a special seal remover with a knock-out attachment.

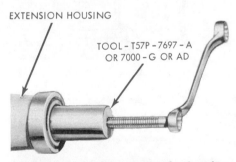

EXTENSION HOUSING

TOOL - T57P - 7697 - A OR 7000 - G OR AD

Fig. 10-14. For in-the-car extension housing bushing removal the threaded bushing remover is essential. (Ford Motor Co.)

wiped out the extension housing bushing along with the seal. The extension housing bushing and seal

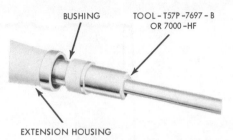

BUSHING   TOOL - T57P - 7697 - B
                 OR 7000 - HF

EXTENSION HOUSING

Fig. 10-15. Installation of extension housing bushing using a special bushing driver.

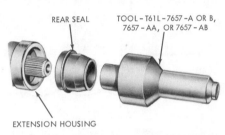

REAR SEAL   TOOL - T61L - 7657 - A OR B,
                7657 - AA, OR 7657 - AB

EXTENSION HOUSING

Fig. 10-16. Installation of extension housing seal using a special tool. (Ford Motor Co.)

can usually be replaced with the transmission still in the vehicle and with the aid of special tooling; Figs. 10-12, 10-13, 10-14, 10-15, and 10-16. Rear seals are often replaced by themselves. An inspection of the rear seal any time a car is on the lift can turn up profitable replacement seal business.

Fluid leakage in the converter area is evidenced by fluid up front around the converter housing. The source of leakage can come from the engine, the converter, or from the front pump. Illustrated in Fig. 10-17 are the paths which these fluid leaks take to reach the bottom of the converter housing.

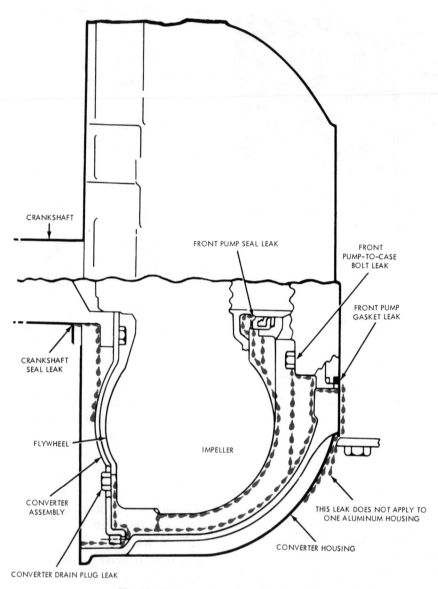

Fig. 10-17. Converter area leak sources.

Engine oil leaks are sometimes improperly diagnosed as transmission front pump seal leaks; however, careful observation will determine if the leakage is from the engine. There are three main sources to check:

1. Leakage from the crankshaft

rear main seal will work back to the front of the flywheel or flex plate and into the converter housing. Fig. 10-17.

2. Leakage from the rear of the rocker arm covers could allow oil to flow over the engine block and converter housing and be present in or at the bottom of the converter housing.

3. Oil galley plug leaks allow oil to work its way down the rear face of the engine block to the bottom of the converter housing.

For additional evidence, check the color of the engine oil against the color of the transmission fluid with a dipstick check. The fluid leakage should match one of the two colors. Transmission fluid is usually dyed red, and this is a definite aid in any leakage check at the converter. As another tip, engine oil leakage wets the face of the flywheel and leaves the area behind the converter dry.

Once the leakage is confirmed to be from the converter or the front pump, and not the engine, make one more quick check before deciding to remove the transmission. Observe the back face of the flywheel for a possible converter plug leak, Fig. 10-17. Should drain plug leakage be suspected, remove the plugs with a six point socket. Coat the threads with a sealing compound and replace.

Front pump leakage wets the area between the back side of the converter and converter housing. Observe in Fig. 10-17, there are three main leak possibilities from the front pump—front pump seal, front pump-to-case bolts, and front pump-to-case gasket or 0-ring body seal. Should it be determined that leakage is coming from the area of the front pump, the transmission must be removed.

Because of the air currents between the converter and housing, front pump leaks are typically sprayed in all directions and it is almost impossible to find the exact source. Although the front pump seal is high on the priority list, it is a good service policy to treat all three main front pump leak areas. Front pump bolts usually require seals and in some instances the threads require a sealing compound. Always include an extension housing rear seal replacement with a front pump seal-up as well as throttle and manual shaft seals.

Shown in Figs. 10-18, 10-19, 10-

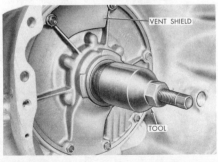

Fig. 10-18. Removing front pump seal with special seal remover.

Fig. 10-19. Some front pump seals can be removed with careful use of hammer and chisel.

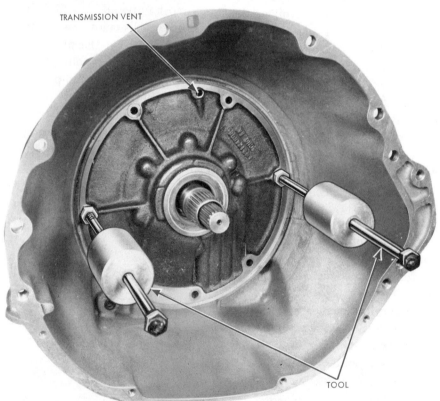

Fig. 10-20. Typical set-up of slide hammers used in removal of front pump.

Fig. 10-21. Installation of new front-pump-to-case gasket, using guide pins.

Fig. 10-24. Torquing front pump to case bolts to complete pump installation.

Fig. 10-22. Treat new pump body O-ring seal with Door-Ease, white lube, or transmission fluid before pump installation.

Fig. 10-25. Seal installation using a seal driver.

20, 10-21, 10-22, 10-23, 10-24, 10-25, and in Fig. 10-26 are typical service operations on a front pump seal-up. Do not neglect to inspect the front pump body bushing for wear; otherwise, your seal-up job is in for trouble. The front pump body bushing is a replaceable item. Figs. 10-27 and 10-28 show a typical bushing replacement.

If for any reason you suspect that the converter itself is leaking from defective welds, an air check can be performed. Using a converter leak checking tool that can be made from standard parts, Fig.

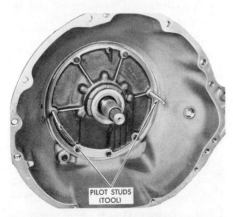

PILOT STUDS (TOOL)

Fig. 10-23. Front pump installation, using guide pins.

Fig. 10-26. Extension housing seal replacement is a good policy to follow on all front pump seal-ups.

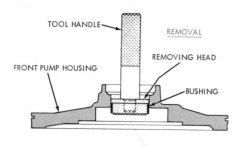

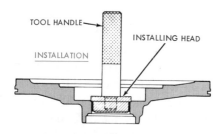

Fig. 10-27. Pump bushing removal and installation. (Chrysler Corp.)

Fig. 10-28. Staking the bushing installation. (Chrysler Corp.)

10-29, pressurize the converter with 20 psi of air, Fig. 10-30, and place the converter in a tank of water. Observe the weld areas for bubbles.

Along with most transmission seal-ups, it is considered good practice to include with the job a fluid and filter change and band adjustment. In many cases you will want to drop the pan as part of the inspection for transmission damage and this additional service is already half finished in terms of extra time.

Although not classified as an external leak source, a defective vacuum modulator diaphragm with a hole or tear will result in engine vacuum pulling the transmission fluid into the engine manifold system for burning in the cylinders. If the transmission fluid level is low with no apparent external

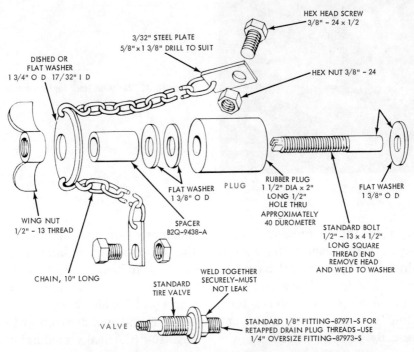

HEX HEAD SCREW
3/8" – 24 x 1/2

3/32" STEEL PLATE
5/8" x 1 3/8" DRILL TO SUIT

DISHED OR
FLAT WASHER
1 3/4" O D 17/32" I D

HEX NUT 3/8" – 24

RUBBER PLUG
1 1/2" DIA x 2"
LONG 1/2"
HOLE THRU
APPROXIMATELY
40 DUROMETER

FLAT WASHER   PLUG
1 3/8" O D

FLAT WASHER
1 3/8" O D

WING NUT
1/2" – 13 THREAD

SPACER
B2Q-9438-A

STANDARD BOLT
1/2" – 13 x 4 1/2"
LONG SQUARE
THREAD END
REMOVE HEAD
AND WELD TO WASHER

CHAIN, 10" LONG

STANDARD
TIRE VALVE

WELD TOGETHER
SECURELY–MUST
NOT LEAK

VALVE

STANDARD 1/8" FITTING–87971–S FOR
RETAPPED DRAIN PLUG THREADS –USE
1/4" OVERSIZE FITTING–87973–S

Fig. 10-29. Leak tool made from standard fittings. (Ford Motor Co.)

Fig. 10-30. Pressure leak test. (Ford Motor Co.)

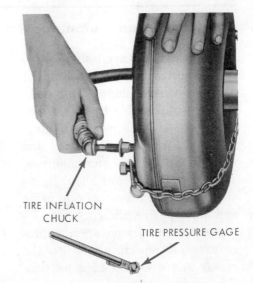

TIRE INFLATION
CHUCK

TIRE PRESSURE GAGE

Fig. 10-31. Vacuum leak test on modulator.

leaks, then the modulator should become a high suspect item. As a reminder, many cars will burn the fluid with little evidence of smoke out the exhaust; therefore, fluid burning in the engine does not necessarily produce a smoker.

For a quick check on a leaky modulator, simply pull the vacuum line off at the modulator and look for any indication of fluid in the vacuum line or modulator itself. For a positive check use the vacuum tester found on a distributor tester, Fig. 10-31. A leaky modulator is a quick replacement item.

Overhauling an Automatic Transmission

Automatic transmission overhaul requires a high standard of reliable workmanship. The technician must be able to give attention to detail, use proper tooling, follow exact specifications, and work in extra clean surroundings. The perfect overhaul should give any technician a sense of real pride and accomplishment.

For the details on specific procedures and specifications on the repair and overhaul of a particular automatic transmission, the best policy is to consult the manufacturer's shop manual. Our job will be to supplement the shop manual instruction with some basic shop practices and to informally get you acquainted with a typical automatic transmission tear-down.

Transmission Removal

The transmission and converter in most cases are removed as an

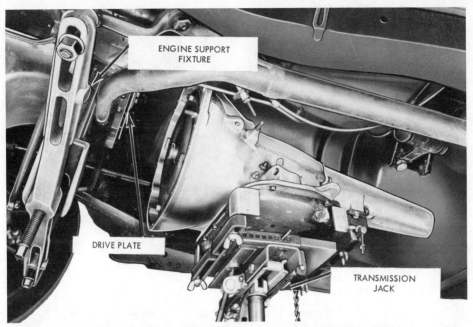

ENGINE SUPPORT
FIXTURE

DRIVE PLATE

TRANSMISSION
JACK

Fig. 10-32. Removal of transmission and converter. (Chrysler Corp.)

assembly, Fig. 10-32. When removing the transmission, here are some important guidelines to follow:

1. Mark the drive plate (also referred to as the flex plate or the flywheel) and converter so they can be installed in the same position for balance purposes. A light paint spray from an aerosol can offers a quick method of marking.

2. Scribe mark or use a light paint spray from an aerosol can for marking the drive shaft and companion flange for correct assembly. This should be standard practice whenever removing the drive shaft to insure that the drive shaft runout is not disturbed for it can cause an unwanted driveline vibration.

3. Remove the converter attaching bolts (or nuts) before removing the transmission to engine block bolts; otherwise, the weight of the transmission will rest on the converter drive plate, resulting in possible damage to the drive plate, front pump bushing, or front pump seal.

Transmission Installation

Installation of the transmission and converter assembly simply requires reversing the removal procedure; however, some key inclusions need to be added.

Fig. 10-33. Installation of converter. (Chrysler Corp.)

DRAIN PLUG

⅛ INCH HOLE

V MARK

Fig. 10-34. Balance marking. (Chrysler Corp.)

When installing the converter in the transmission, make sure that the converter drive hub is fully seated in the front pump drive gear. Fig. 10-33 illustrates the usual measurement procedure, from the face of the housing to the converter weld nut in this case, to insure that the converter drive hub is seated. Refer to the individual manufacturers' specifications for the dimension.

Remember to line up your balance marks between the drive plate and converter. In some cases the balance marks are provided by the manufacturer. However, the better practice is to provide your own markings during removal in the event that the factory marks were omitted, Fig. 10-34.

Before installing the converter bolts or nuts, make certain that the converter is flush against the drive plate, but not binding. If the converter is binding, it means that the converter drive hub is not seated in the front pump drive gear. Hand start the converter bolts or nuts and tighten finger tight, then torque to specifications. This will insure proper converter alignment.

Transmission Disassembly

For our example transmission, the Chrysler TorqueFlite A-727 is selected, Fig. 10-35. The Torque-Flite housing is a one-piece aluminum casting which is favoritely used in current transmission design; therefore, the removal and installation of all sub-assemblies follow similar patterns, with slight variations.

Good shop practice techniques are the same for all transmissions. Keep in mind that complete shop

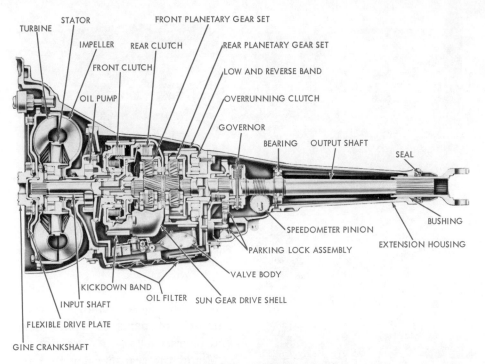

TURBINE
STATOR
IMPELLER
REAR CLUTCH
FRONT CLUTCH
OIL PUMP
FRONT PLANETARY GEAR SET
REAR PLANETARY GEAR SET
LOW AND REVERSE BAND
OVERRUNNING CLUTCH
GOVERNOR
BEARING   OUTPUT SHAFT
SEAL
BUSHING
SPEEDOMETER PINION
EXTENSION HOUSING
PARKING LOCK ASSEMBLY
VALVE BODY
KICKDOWN BAND
INPUT SHAFT
OIL FILTER   SUN GEAR DRIVE SHELL
FLEXIBLE DRIVE PLATE
GINE CRANKSHAFT

Fig. 10-35. TorqueFlite A-727 transmission.

manual details are not covered in our discussion.

All automatic transmissions have a special tool list provided by the manufacturer and it appears that a considerable capital investment is required to get into the business of major transmission repair. After carefully researching the situation, you'll find that many tools are interchangeable between Chrysler, Ford, and G.M. With a little thought, you can also engineer some of your own special tools at little or no expense. Fig. 10-36 shows some of the basic tools that

you will need for major transmission work.

Sub-Assembly Removal. Before removing any transmission sub-assemblies, thoroughly clean the exterior of the transmission, using either steam or a cold solvent wash, Fig. 10-37. As you are aware, when ever you are working with a hydraulic unit cleanliness cannot be over-emphasized as a little dirt can undo many hours of careful work. Therefore keep your work bench, tools, and the parts clean at all times. There are highly polished mating surfaces in the transmis-

257

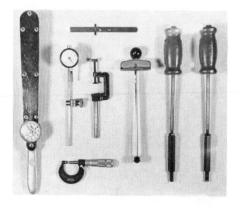

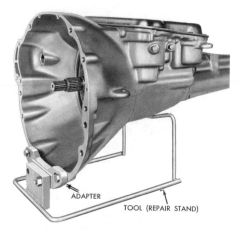

Fig. 10-38. Repair stand for transmission case.

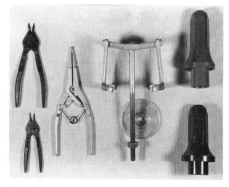

Fig. 10-36. Tools for major transmission repairs.

sion, and these require careful handling of parts to avoid nicks and burrs.

Mount the transmission in a repair stand, Fig. 10-38, and follow the general sequence for sub-assembly removal. Repair stands or fixtures are available for all transmissions and offer the advantage of working convenience to save repair time. After all, the name of the game is, *"speed, reliability, and profit."*

Fig. 10-37. Steam cleaning exterior.

PROCEDURE:

1. Remove the pump oil seal, (Fig. 10-18). It is convenient to perform this operation now because the transmission housing acts as a holding fixture.

2. Measure the drive train end-play (also referred to as input

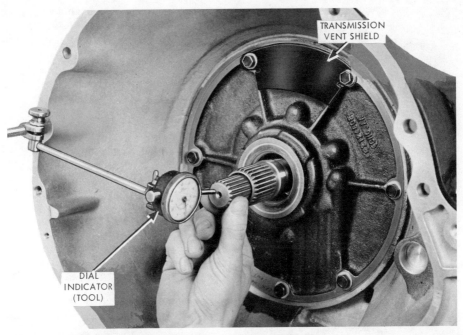

Fig. 10-39. Drive end-play measurement.

shaft end-play), Fig. 10-39. This is a requirement for all automatic transmissions and is controlled by a selective thrust washer in the transmission. By taking an end-play reading, you can determine if the thrust washer should be changed. If end-play is excessive, check for internal part damage.

3. Remove the oil pan and valve body assembly, Figs. 10-40 and 10-41.

4. Remove the accumulator piston and spring, Fig. 10-42.

5. Remove the extension housing and then the governor and support, Figs. 10-43, 10-44,

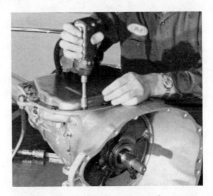

Fig. 10-40. Oil pan removal.

and 10-45. Observe the snap rings that must be removed in Fig. 10-46, and note that both contraction and expansion types are used. Be sure to use

Fig. 10-41. Removing the valve body bolts.

Fig. 10-44. Governor detachment.

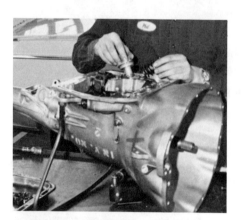

Fig. 10-42. Accumulator removal.

Fig. 10-45. Governor removal.

Fig. 10-43. Extension housing removal.

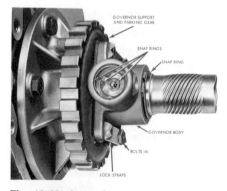

Fig. 10-46. Snap ring removal from governor assembly.

the appropriate snap ring pliers if you want to re-use the snap rings. Do not use screw drivers or ordinary pliers.

Once the valve body assembly, extension housing, and governor assembly have been removed, the remainder of the sub-assembly will come out the front of the transmission.

6. Remove the front pump and reaction shaft support assembly, Fig. 10-47. Slide hammers (Fig. 10-20) are essential.

7. Remove the front clutch and band, Fig. 10-48.

8. Remove input shaft and rear clutch, Fig. 10-49.

9. Remove planetary gear assembly, Fig. 10-50.

10. Remove low-reverse drum, rear band, and overrunning clutch rollers, Figs. 10-51.

11. Remove kickdown and low-reverse servos, Fig. 10-52.

Fig. 10-47. Front pump bolts are loosened.

Fig. 10-49. Input shaft comes next in removal.

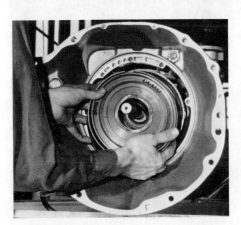

Fig. 10-48. The front clutch is removed.

Fig. 10-50. Planetary gear assembly comes out with output shaft.

Fig. 10-51. Low-reverse drum is removed.

Fig. 10-52. Kickdown and low-reverse servos disassembled.

Fig. 10-53. Sub-assemblies stored neatly to prevent mixing of parts.

All the sub-assemblies are now removed from the transmission case. Notice in Fig. 10-53 how they have been stored to avoid part damage.

Transmission and Sub-Assembly Reconditioning. In keeping with our objective, we will use only those examples of TorqueFlite sub-as-

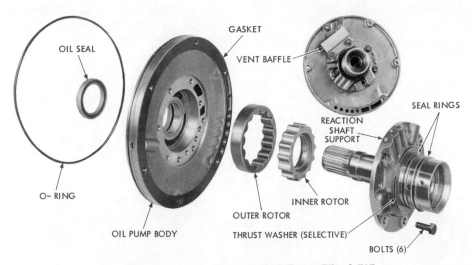

Fig. 10-54. Front pump disassembled, TorqueFlite A-727.

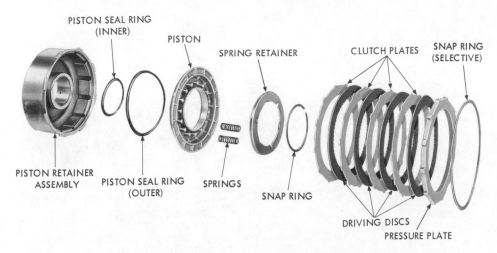

Fig. 10-55. Front clutch disassembled, TorqueFlite A-727.

sembly reconditioning which demonstrate a point in general practice pertaining to most all automatic transmissions.

When servicing sub-assemblies, work with one unit at a time; disassembly, cleaning, inspection and reassembly of each unit should be completed before disassembly of other units. This avoids confusion and interchanging of parts.

Figs. 10-54, 10-55, 10-56, and 10-57 show four major TorqueFlite subassembly units disassembled. It

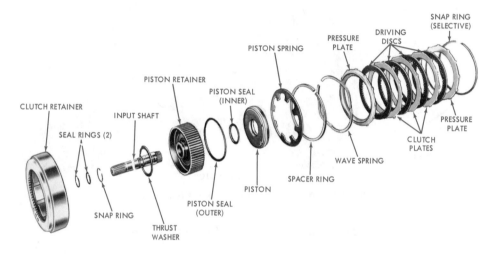

Fig. 10-56. Rear clutch disassembled, TorqueFlite A-727.

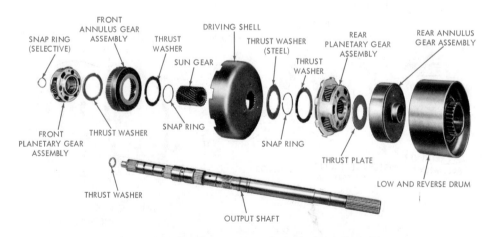

Fig. 10-57. Planetary gear train and output shaft disassembled, TorqueFlite A-727.

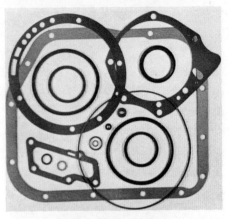

Fig. 10-58. Gasket and seal kit—not shown are the extension housing and front pump seals which should also be replaced.

Fig. 10-59. Overhaul kit.

doesn't take much imagination to realize the mass mix-up that could take place should these units be all disassembled at one time and spread over a work bench.

Note: Replace all O-rings, gaskets, and lip seals; do not re-use.

Shown in Fig. 10-58, is a typical *Gasket and Seal Kit* containing the above items and these are the absolute minimum needed in an overhaul. The job requirements will determine whatever additional parts are needed. These can usually be purchased as single items or assemblies.

Overhaul kits typically contain, in addition to the parts in a *Gasket and Seal Kit*, metal sealing rings and clutch plates, Fig. 10-59.

There are several service tips that apply to gaskets and seals:

1. Install metal encased oil seal assemblies, such as those used in the front pump or extension housing, with non-hardening sealing compound. Lube the lip seal area of these seals with transmission fluid before installing.

2. Do not use sealing compound on any paper, synthetic rubber, or cork gaskets.

3. Do not over-stretch O-ring or lip seals.

4. All O-ring and lip seals must be lubricated with transmission fluid or Door Ease before installation.

5. Remove all the dirt and old materials before installing new gaskets and seals.

6. Be sure to use correct valve-body gaskets. Compare the old to the

new. Gaskets for the separator plate, when required, cannot cover *any* holes in the separator plate.

After complete disassembly of a unit, all metal parts should be washed in a clean solvent and dried with compressed air. Shop towels or rags cannot be used to wipe parts during or after cleaning because of the lint that would adhere to the parts. Lint accumulation has been known to clog filter screens and also cause valving to seize.

During the drying process, be sure to blow out the fluid passages to remove any existing obstructions. Extra-small orificed passages need to be checked with tag wire. Fig. 10-60 demonstrates the cleaning operation of the transmission case. Note the bench center drain that helps keep the work area clean.

Fig. 10-61. Orifice cleaning demands close inspection and a fine wire.

The case fluid passages must be all blown out. In Fig. 10-61 top, the technician points to a lube orifice in the reaction shaft assembly of the front pump that will need to be checked with tag wire to eliminate the possibility of a clogged lube circuit, Fig. 10-61 bottom.

After cleaning, the unit parts are ready to be inspected to determine their condition for re-use or replacement. Fig. 10-62 shows a technician inspecting the pinion gears of the TorqueFlite front planetary for chipping, scoring, and excessive wear.

Fig. 10-60. Air drying transmission case.

Fig. 10-62. Pinion gear inspection for wear and loose pins.

Fig. 10-63. Snap ring removal.

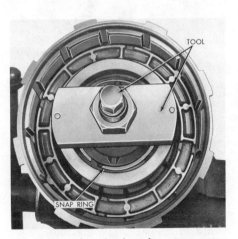

Fig. 10-64. Using clutch spring compressor.

Clutch servicing requires some special attention. We will use for example the front clutch assembly of the TorqueFlite to demonstrate disassembly, cleaning, inspection, and reassembly operations.

Clutch Disassembly. Fig. 10-55 showed a disassembled view of the front clutch.

DISASSEMBLY

1. Remove the selective snap ring and lift the pressure plate and clutch plates from the drum housing (clutch piston retainer), Fig. 10-63.
2. Use a clutch spring compressor to compress the spring retainer and springs and remove the snap ring that holds the retainer, Fig. 10-64. Clutch spring compressors are standard tooling items.
3. Gradually relax the spring tension until the retainer clears the hub. Remove the tool, retainer, and springs, Fig. 10-65.
4. Remove the piston and both the inner and outer piston seals.

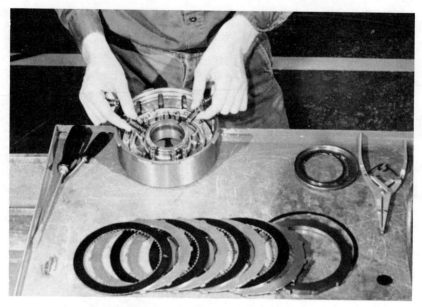

Fig. 10-65. Clutch retainer and springs removed.

CLEANING AND INSPECTION

1. Clean metal parts with a brush in solvent, dry in compressed air, Figs. 10-66 and 10-67.
2. Inspect the drum housing bushing support for wear or scoring, Fig. 10-68. Most transmission bushings are replaceable. Use the proper tool, Fig. 10-69.
3. Note the ball check in the drum housing, Fig. 10-70. Make sure that it moves freely. Most clutch assemblies have a ball check in either the drum housing or clutch piston. Should these ball checks freeze or drop out, the clutch discs will fail, and you will have to repeat your work.
4. Inspect the piston return

Fig. 10-66. Cleaning parts with brush and solvent.

Fig. 10-67. Drying parts with air pressure.

Fig. 10-68. Inspect bushing for marred surfaces or pitting.

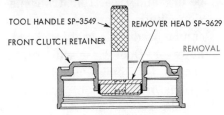

Fig. 10-69. Special tools are used to remove and replace bushings.

Fig. 10-70. Ball check inspection.

springs for distorted or collapsed coils.

5. Inspect the piston bore for score marks. Light scores can usually be removed with crocus cloth.

6. Inspect the steel clutch plates and pressure plate for scored or burned surfaces.

7. Inspect friction plates for pitted, flaked, or loose facing. If the facing material can be removed with the thumbnail, the plates should be replaced, Fig. 10-71. Always use new steel plates with new friction plates.

8. Friction plates that have seen service take on a natural dark discoloration. This should not be justification for replacement of the clutch plates.

9. Do not attempt to clean composition plates in any type of solvent if they are to be put back into service.

Fig. 10-71. Inspect friction plates.

Clutch Assembly. On any clutch service the assembly parts and specifications must match the engine displacement requirement, especially the steel and friction plate count.

PROCEDURE

1. Install the inner and outer piston seals—seal lips must face the pressure side. Lubricate the seals with a wax type lubricant

Fig. 10-72. Install new piston seals.

Fig. 10-73. Lubricating piston seals.

(Door Ease) for easier installation of the clutch piston in the bore, Figs. 10-72 and 10-73. When using this method of lubrication the piston bore must be dry and free from transmission fluid. Transmission fluid can be used for a seal lubricant; however, Door Ease will still be needed for some special installations or the clutch piston will not slip into its bore.

2. Install the piston return springs and retainer, using the spring compressor again.
3. Lubricate all clutch plates and install in the drum housing, Fig. 10-74. Note how a small pan filled with transmission fluid can be used for dipping parts for pre-lubrication.

Fig. 10-74. Lubricate plates before they are installed.

Fig. 10-76. Check assembly with air.

Fig. 10-75. Measuring plate clearance.

4. If new friction plates are used, they must be pre-soaked in transmission fluid for a minimum of 15 minutes.
5. After the clutch plates and pressure plate have been snapped into place, measure the clutch plate clearance between the selective snap ring and pressure plate, Fig. 10-75.
6. The clutch plate clearance is adjustable with the selective snap ring (available in three sizes).

7. Finally, check the reliability of your clutch reconditioning service. Shown in Fig. 10-76, the technician has mounted the clutch assembly on its support and is checking the apply and release action with air pressure. Note that the clutch mounts on the front pump assembly (see Fig. 10-54) and the apply circuit also passes through the pump housing.

Most clutch assembly units can be tested for operation on the bench with an air check. This is stressed in the shop manuals.

Valve Body Service. Valve body service demands extra clean handling and extra attention to detail. When repairing the valve body, here are some procedures and tips:

PROCEDURE

1. Disassemble the valve body over a parts tray or pan to catch the parts as they are removed;

271

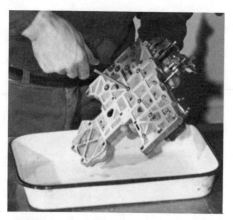

Fig. 10-77. Disassemble valve assembly.

otherwise, the springs, check balls and spool valves can easily roll off the bench and get lost. These parts are not normally replacement items, Fig. 10-77.

2. Keep the parts for each valve body section separated to prevent accidental interchange of springs that look alike. This practice also helps to keep track of the valves for reassembly and saves time.

3. Clean all parts by soaking them in a transmission cleaner. A carburetor cleaner could be used, but soak only long enough to remove the gum and varnish as some carburetor cleaners will etch or pit the parts if allowed to work too long.

Should the valve body appear free of excessive gum and varnish, a soak and flush operation with only cold solvent is acceptable.

Fig. 10-78. Checking valve for free fall.

4. After the cleaner soak period, flush the parts in clean solvent and dry with compressed air.

5. Do not lubricate the valve body parts for reassembly until after testing the valves for free movement. The spool valves must be tested for free movement in their bores under dry conditions during assembly of the valve body. Simply insert each valve in its bore and tip the valve body. The valve should fall free out of the bore when the body is shaken lightly, Fig. 10-78.

6. To remove burrs on a spool valve rotate the valve on crocus cloth on a flat plate. Do not round the corners! To prevent wedging, corners must be razor sharp to keep it clean as the valve moves.

272

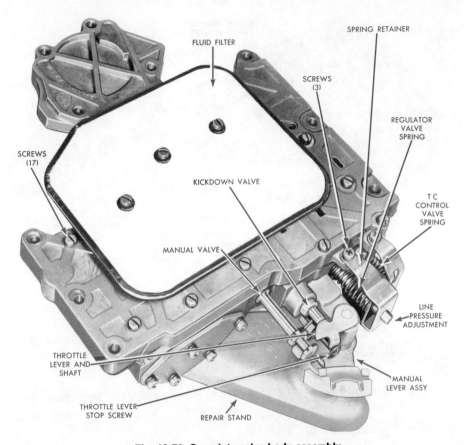

Fig. 10-79. Complete valve body assembly.

The TorqueFlite valve body is shown as an assembled and as a disassembled unit in Figs. 10-79, 10-80, 10-81, and 10-82. Most service manuals provide detailed exploded views of the valve body to assist any technician needing help on valve and spring location. In some instances, a spring chart is provided to identify each spring by number of coils, coil diameter, coil length, and color code.

Sprag Clutch Installation. If sprag clutch assemblies are used in the transmission, follow instructions exactly to get the proper freewheeling direction. Sprag clutches can easily be installed backwards and this results in wrong freewheeling action.

In Fig. 10-83, the intermediate sprag assembly (Turbo Hydra-Matic 400) is shown as it is installed in its outer race. One side

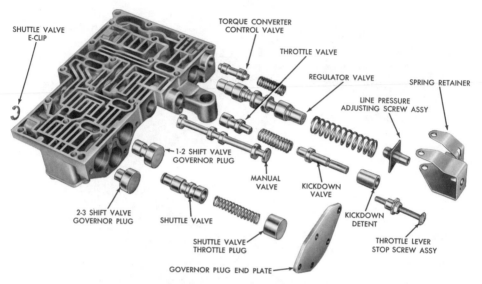

SHUTTLE VALVE
E-CLIP

TORQUE CONVERTER
CONTROL VALVE

THROTTLE VALVE

REGULATOR VALVE

SPRING RETAINER

LINE PRESSURE
ADJUSTING SCREW ASSY

1-2 SHIFT VALVE
GOVERNOR PLUG

MANUAL
VALVE

KICKDOWN
VALVE

2-3 SHIFT VALVE
GOVERNOR PLUG

SHUTTLE VALVE

KICKDOWN
DETENT

SHUTTLE VALVE
THROTTLE PLUG

THROTTLE LEVER
STOP SCREW ASSY

GOVERNOR PLUG END PLATE

Fig. 10-80. Manual shift body disassembled.

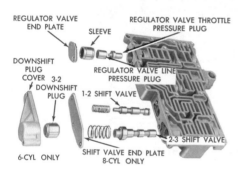

REGULATOR VALVE
END PLATE

SLEEVE

REGULATOR VALVE THROTTLE
PRESSURE PLUG

DOWNSHIFT
PLUG
COVER   3-2
DOWNSHIFT
PLUG

REGULATOR VALVE LINE
PRESSURE PLUG

1-2 SHIFT VALVE

2-3 SHIFT VALVE

6-CYL ONLY

SHIFT VALVE END PLATE
8-CYL ONLY

Fig. 10-81. Automatic shift body disassembled.

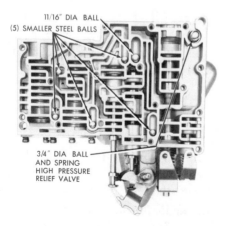

11/16" DIA BALL

(5) SMALLER STEEL BALLS

3/4" DIA BALL
AND SPRING
HIGH PRESSURE
RELIEF VALVE

Fig. 10-82. Valve body ball check valves.

Fig. 10-83. Sprag assembly removal. (Oldsmobile Div., General Motors Corp.)

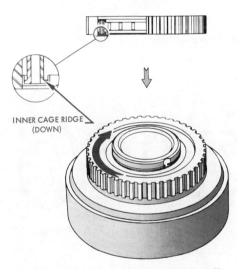

Fig. 10-84. Sprag positioning for installation. (Oldsmobile Div., General Motors Corp.)

of the sprag assembly has a shoulder which must face down to give the correct freewheeling direction, as illustrated in Fig. 10-84, when mounted on the direct clutch housing. The outer race of the sprag should not turn counterclockwise after installation.

Transmission Assembly

The installation of sub-assembly units in any transmission simply requires the reverse procedure in which they were removed. The main trick on installation is to carefully mate the sub-assemblies together along with their related parts. The transmission should go together with the same care given to a 21-jewel watch; excessive force is not needed. If parts do not assemble freely, find the cause and correct the trouble before proceeding with further assembly.

In our TorqueFlite example, the servo and accumulator parts should be installed in the case prior to transmission build-up. The parts make-up of these assemblies are shown in Figs. 10-85, 10-86, and 10-87. Other related assembly parts are the overrunning clutch, Fig. 10-88, the governor Fig. 10-89, the low-reverse band and linkage, Fig. 10-90 and the kickdown band and linkage, Fig. 10-91. The overrunning clutch and low-reverse band and linkage must be set up in the case before proceeding with sub-assembly installation. Here are some general service practices to follow on reassembly:

REASSEMBLY

1. Use the recommended transmission fluid to lubricate the transmission during assembly.

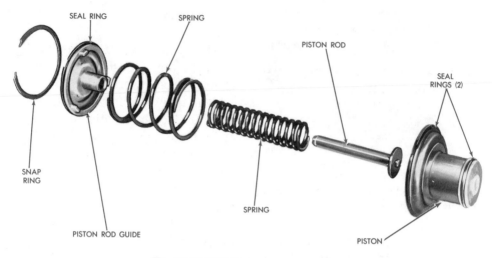

Fig. 10-85. Kickdown servo assembly.

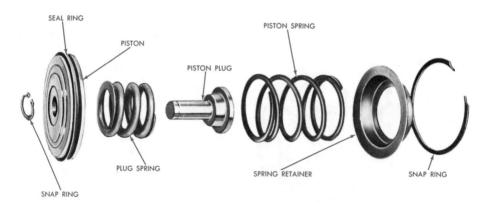

Fig. 10-86. Low and reverse servo assembly.

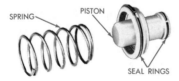

Fig. 10-87. Accumulator assembly.

2. Pre-soak new bands in transmission fluid 15 minutes.
3. If the drive train end-play was not within or on the high side of

specifications before disassembly, use a new selective thrust washer of proper thickness. In the TorqueFlite 727 the selec-

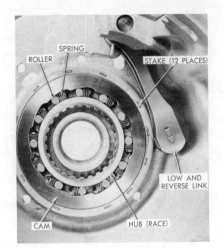

Fig. 10-88. Overrunning clutch assembly, (Chrysler Corp.)

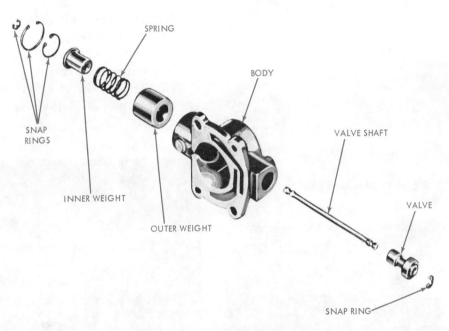

Fig. 10-89. Governor assembly.

tive washer comes in three sizes and is located on the re-action shaft support hub for the front clutch, Fig. 10-92. Al-

ways recheck the drive train end-play requirements on assembly.

4. Before installing the threaded

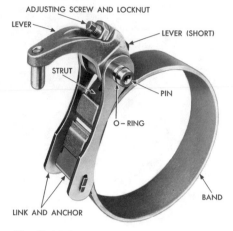

Fig. 10-90. Low-reverse band and linkage.

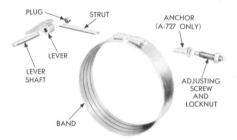

Fig. 10-91. Kickdown band and linkage.

bolts in the aluminum transmission case, dip the bolts in automatic transmission fluid to prevent galling the aluminum threads and to keep the bolts from seizing.

5. Use a torque wrench for final tightening. This prevents stripping of aluminum threads, or case warpage which leads to circuit leaks, or valve seizure in the valve body. Never use impact tools when tightening a valve body. Unless you are highly skilled, this could result in valve seizure.

6. If tapped aluminum threads are stripped or damaged, they can be made serviceable again by the use of Heli-Coils, Fig. 10-93.

Fig. 10-92. Selective washer location for controlling drive train end-play.

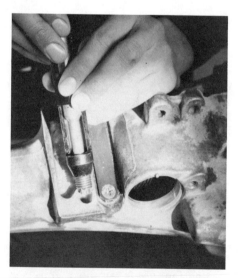

Fig. 10-93. Heli-coil repair on TorqueFlite extension housing.

Fig. 10-94. Torquing valve body.

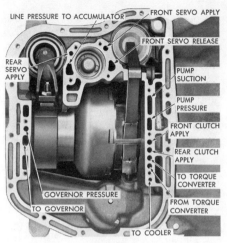

Fig. 10-95. Case feed holes to clutches, servos, and governor.

7. Be consistent on the use of the torque specifications; either stay entirely with the high side, or the low side, of the specifications throughout the transmission assembly. The mixing of the high and low side of the torque specifications has been known to cause case warpage and result in circuit leaks. The technician is shown, Fig. 10-94, torquing the valve body, which has critical mating areas where uneven torquing can cause warping, which in turn may cause internal leaks or possible valve seizure.

8. Installation of the front pump assembly also requires extra care. Use pilot studs on installation, (as in previous Fig. 10-23). Carefully tap the pump into place with a soft mallet, and gradually snug the body bolts prior to final torquing.

   The input and output shafts must be checked for rotation both after the pump body bolts have been snugged, and again after final torquing. If either shaft fails to rotate freely, the cause of the bind must be located and corrected.

9. On band adjustments, the adjustment specifications must match the engine displacement requirements.

10. For a reliability check on your workmanship, test the clutch, servo, and governor action whenever possible using compressed air. Illustrated in Fig. 10-95 are the feed holes in the case to these circuits in the TorqueFlite.

    The technician in Fig. 10-96 is running a check on the rear clutch apply circuit. You should be able to hear and feel the clutch apply and release. Air to

279

Fig. 10-96. Checking rear clutch apply circuit with air.

the governor circuit should result in either an audible thud or valve buzz; *no noise means trouble*. Both the front and rear servo operation can be visually observed.

When you've got the transmission back together, your hard work deserves a smile, Fig. 10-97. After installation in the car, always make a road test and pressure test to be sure the job is right.

Converter and Cooling System Service

Converter and cooling system service must be considered as part of the overhaul. This is an often neglected service which, if overlooked, can lead to a quickly repeated failure of the transmission. It should be obvious that if any varnish, loose friction material, or metallic deposits found in the transmission prior to overhaul have worked their way into the converter and cooling system, service is required. If ignored, this con-

Fig. 10-97. Completed job.

tamination will cycle itself back into the transmission and we will again have trouble. Return contaminates frequently cause seizing of the pressure regulator valve and cause a loss of operating pressure, or they also cause seizing of the governor valve and make for shift problems. A clogged cooler or cooler line results in immediate overheating and transmission failure.

Today's modern converters are of welded design, and therefore cannot be disassembled in the field for cleaning and inspection. With the aid of special tooling and modern equipment, the job can be done in the shop.

To clean the converter, mount the assembler in a converter flusher, Fig. 10-98. This piece of equipment slowly rotates the converter while a cleaning solvent is cycled in and out of the converter to purge any loose particles of contaminates. The machine automatically adds timed blasts of compressed air to the solvent as it enters the converter.

If the transmission is found to have heavy deposits, the best policy is to replace the converter for the flusher will not usually clean out this kind of excess.

The converter flusher can also be utilized to clean the cooler lines. Hose attachments from the flusher are connected to the lines and the cleaning solvent under pressure is

Fig. 10-98. Converter flushing.

Fig. 10-99. Using converter flusher to clean cooler lines.

Fig. 10-100. Cleaning cooler lines with air.

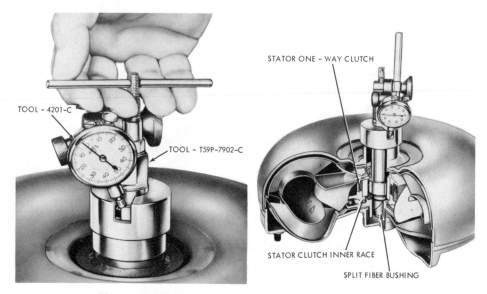

Fig. 10-101. Checking converter end-play. (Ford Motor Co.)

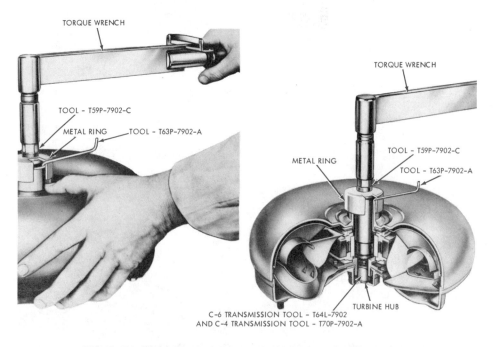

Fig. 10-102. Typical reactor (stator) clutch check. (Ford Motor Co.)

charged into the cooler feed line. The technician watches for a clear flow of solvent from the cooler return line and then stops the operation, Fig. 10-99. Compressed air is then used to clear solvent from cooler lines, Fig. 10-100.

If flushing equipment is not available, compressed air can be used to check the lines and the cooler for obstruction.

The converter can be checked for wear and reactor (stator) operation with the help of special tools. Typical set-ups for these checks are illustrated in Figs. 10-101 and 10-102. Procedure details are found in the shop manual.

Towing

As a general rule, if the vehicle drive train is in sound condition, it may be safely towed in *neutral* at a speed of not more than 30 mph and a distance not to exceed 50 miles. The reason for these limitations is to preserve the transmission. The current practice in transmission design is to eliminate the use of a rear pump which means that without a fluid pressure build-up, the transmission lube system is not working. Excessive towing speeds and distances would cause critical damage to clutches and bearings. Even if a rear pump did exist, the lube system would be inadequate for its job because of the high overdrive speeds inherited by the transmission as the drive wheels under tow serve as the transmission input rather than the engine.

Should the drive train be damaged, then the drive wheels must be off the ground or the propeller shaft disconnected.

For more specific details on towing, consult the manufacturer's shop or owner's manual.

Checking On Your Knowledge

The following questions give you the opportunity to check up on yourself. If you have read the chapter carefully, you should be able to answer the questions. If you have any difficulty, read the chapter over once more so that you have the information well in mind before you go on with your reading.

PART I—Periodic Maintenance:

1. Describe several automatic transmission operating conditions that would be termed as severe service.
2. What are some basic guidelines to follow when determining the time and mileage interval for a fluid change and band adjustment?
3. What type of fluid is used by the following car manufacturers for their automatic transmissions; American Motors, Chrysler, Ford, and General Motors.
4. What makes up a Transmission Tune-Up?

PART II—External Leaks:

1. Explain how locating a transmission leak may not be an easy problem.
2. Why is it a good policy to visually examine all the possibilities on an external leak problem?
3. On extension housing seal leaks, what are some other observations that need to be made by the technician?
4. On leaks located up front around the converter housing, how is engine oil distinguished from transmission fluid?
5. What are three sources of engine leaks, whereby, the oil works its way around the converter housing?
6. What are the three main leak possibilities that occur at the front pump?
7. Why is it a good policy to replace the extension housing seal and other transmission case seals, and perform a transmission tune-up as part of any front pump seal-up?
8. What would be some problems caused by a worn front pump body bushing?
9. Explain how a front pump body bushing inspection is a part of any front pump seal-up.
10. Explain why it is important to drop the oil pan as part of most oil leak problems.

11. What are two checks that can be made to determine a diaphragm leak in a vacuum modulator or throttle unit?
12. Briefly explain how a torque converter can be checked for leaks?

PART III—Overhaul:

1. List three important guidelines to follow for transmission removal.
2. Why must the converter attaching bolts be removed first before the transmission to engine block bolts?
3. When installing the transmission, what is a tip-off that the converter hub is not seated in the front pump drive gear?
4. How can you be positive that the converter hub is fully seated in the front pump drive gear?
5. Why is it best to measure transmission drive train end-play (same as input shaft end play) during disassembly?
6. Why are slide hammers usually needed as a special overhaul tool?
7. What is the rule on re-use of O-rings, gaskets, and lip seals for overhaul?
8. What are six guidelines to follow when working with automatic transmission gaskets and seals?
9. Explain: Automatic transmission parts must be air dried after cleaning in solvent. They cannot be wiped clean with shop towels or rags.
10. Is a clutch drum housing bushing support a replaceable item?
11. Explain why clutch friction plates that are to be put back in service should not be rinsed in any type of solvent.
12. How might the clutch assembly differ between a low torque and high torque capacity clutch?
13. How are new clutch friction plates treated before installation?
14. In which direction must the inner and outer clutch piston seal lips face? If a third or center piston seal

is included, in which direction would the lip seal face? (See T-400)

15. How are the piston seal lips treated before the clutch piston is installed in the clutch housing or drum bore?

16. How is the clutch plate clearance controlled in both the front and rear clutches of the TorqueFlite?

17. Explain how carburetor cleaner can be used to soak a valve body for cleaning purposes?

18. Explain the spool valve free fall test.

19. What type of edges are preferred on the spool valve lands, rounded or sharp? Why?

20. Explain why a sprag clutch assembly requires special attention during assembly operations?

21. How can stripped or damaged tapped aluminum threads be salvaged?

22. How can the action of the clutches, servos, and governor be bench tested?

23. How should governor action respond to an air check?

24. What are two types of service that can be performed by a converter flusher?

25. Why can't current type converters be disassembled for service?

26. What is a good guideline to follow on converter flushing when a transmission has been severely damaged?

27. What are some undesireable effects that can result from failure to clean the cooler and lines as part of the overhaul job?

28. Explain why it is not impossible to check a welded converter for wear and stator action?

29. Why would excessive towing speeds damage an automatic transmission? (rear wheels on the ground)

SPECIAL EXTRA ASSIGNMENT

Using an appropriate car manufacturers service manual, complete the following projects.

1. Write-up the band adjustment procedures for at least one of the following transmissions. Be sure that the adjustments cover all the requirements for the various engines used by the manufacturer: Torqueflite A-904 and A-727, Ford C-4 and C-6, Buick or Olds T-300 and Chevrolet Powerglide.

2. Select an automatic transmission of your choice and give the torque requirements for the following attaching bolts; extension housing or bearing retainer to case, valve body to case, front pump to case, reaction shaft support or pump cover to pump body, oil pan, converter drive plate to torque converter.

3. Investigate the service procedures of the clutch units in the following transmission; TorqueFlite A-904 and A-727, Ford C-4 and C-6, G.M. Turbo Hydra-Matic 350 and 400. Answer the following items for each clutch unit in the transmission.

   a. Name of clutch unit.

   b. Clearance check requirement (State *none* if not required).

   c. Clearance adjustment provision.

   d. Clearance specifications for the various engines used by the manufacturer.

   e. Number of drive and driven discs used in the assembly for the various engines used by the manufacturer.

   f. Any special instructions referring to installation of clutch discs.

Summary/ Characteristics of Current Automatic Transmissions

It would take volumes to make a complete coverage of operating characteristics for today's automatic transmissions. The information in this chapter attempts to bring it all together in brief form.

The discussion covers the development and essential characteristics of the transmissions in production since 1965. Some of the current transmissions, however, pre-date 1965.

Chrysler Corporation

Aluminum TorqueFlite (Chrysler, Dodge, Imperial, Plymouth)

This transmission was introduced in 1960 and was used with the newly developed Chrysler slant six engine. It was simply termed the TorqueFlite Six or A-904 transmission. By 1962 the cast iron TorqueFlite was phased out in

favor of a beefed up aluminum TorqueFlite to accommodate V-8 engine applications, and referred to as the TorqueFlite Eight or A-727 transmission. Both transmissions are currently in production; however, the A-904 has also been adapted to the smaller V-8 engines. The present practice, therefore, is to refer to the two as the A-904 and A-727. The band and clutch power flow is summarized in Table 11-1. Figs. 11-1 and 11-2 shows a comparison of the two.

The TorqueFlite has a three element torque converter and a 3 speed planetary gearbox. The drive goes through the converter which has a torque range of 2.0 to 2.2, depending on engine application. Regular drive starts with the converter and low gear (*breakaway*) ratio of 2.45:1, shifts to torque converter plus second gear ratio of 1.45:1, and then shifts to converter with the gear train locked in *direct*.

The transmission throttle and kickdown systems are mechanically operated by a common external linkage to the carburetor.

For added acceleration kickdown shifts 3-1 and 3-2 are available within safe vehicle speed ranges. This will vary according to engine torque design. The closed throttle downshift pattern is 3-1.

Drive-2 position provides a 1-2 shift and keeps the transmission in second gear. *Drive-1* maintains first gear only and is used for braking and heavy pulling. A shift from *D* to *D-1* results in a downshift to second gear until a safe vehicle speed is attained for first gear engagement. Once first gear is engaged, the transmission will not upshift. Selector lever pattern: P R N D 2 1.

Starting with production year 1966, the rear pump was eliminated in the TorqueFlite and push starts were no longer available for the TorqueFlite.

TABLE 11-1. POWERFLOW SUMMARY TORQUEFLITE A-904 AND A-727

SELECTOR LEVER PATTERN P R N D 2 1

RANGE	GEAR	FRONT CLUTCH	REAR CLUTCH	FRONT KICKDOWN BAND	REAR LOW-REVERSE BAND	OVER-RUNNING CLUTCH	PARK PAWL
PARK		OFF	OFF	OFF	OFF	NO MOVEMENT	IN
REVERSE		ON	OFF	OFF	ON	NO MOVEMENT	OUT
NEUTRAL		OFF	OFF	OFF	OFF	NO MOVEMENT	OUT
D-DRIVE	(BREAKAWAY) FIRST	OFF	ON	OFF	OFF	HOLDS	OUT
	SECOND	OFF	ON	ON	OFF	OVERRUNS	OUT
	THIRD	ON	ON	OFF	OFF	OVERRUNS	OUT
2-DRIVE	SECOND	OFF	ON	ON	OFF	OVERRUNS	OUT
	FIRST	OFF	ON	OFF	OFF	HOLDS	OUT
1-DRIVE	FIRST	OFF	ON	OFF	ON	HOLDS	OUT

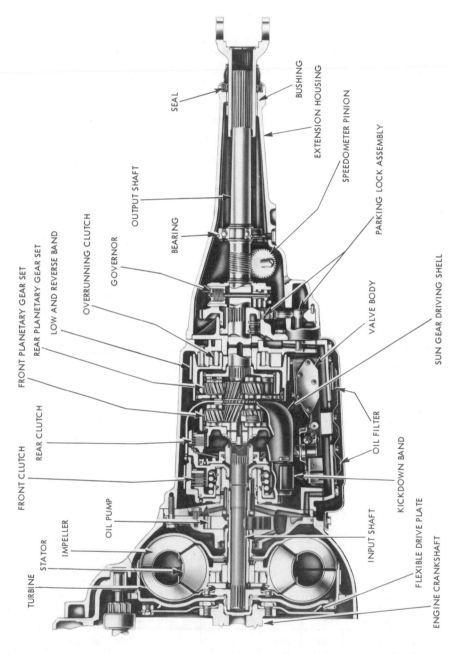

SEAL

BUSHING

EXTENSION HOUSING

SPEEDOMETER PINION

PARKING LOCK ASSEMBLY

OUTPUT SHAFT

BEARING

OVERRUNNING CLUTCH

GOVERNOR

LOW AND REVERSE BAND

REAR PLANETARY GEAR SET

FRONT PLANETARY GEAR SET

VALVE BODY

SUN GEAR DRIVING SHELL

REAR CLUTCH

FRONT CLUTCH

OIL FILTER

OIL PUMP

KICKDOWN BAND

IMPELLER

STATOR

TURBINE

INPUT SHAFT

FLEXIBLE DRIVE PLATE

ENGINE CRANKSHAFT

Fig. 11-1. TorqueFlite A-904 transmission. (Chrysler Corp.)

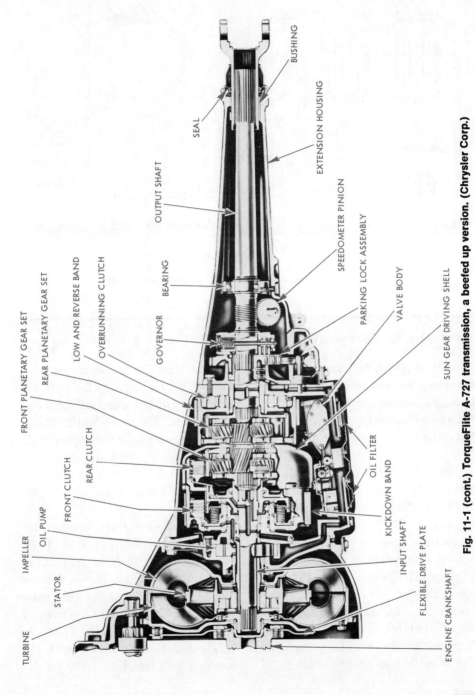

TURBINE

IMPELLER

STATOR

OIL PUMP

FRONT PLANETARY GEAR SET

REAR PLANETARY GEAR SET

LOW AND REVERSE BAND

OVERRUNNING CLUTCH

REAR CLUTCH

FRONT CLUTCH

GOVERNOR

BEARING

OUTPUT SHAFT

SEAL

BUSHING

EXTENSION HOUSING

SPEEDOMETER PINION

PARKING LOCK ASSEMBLY

VALVE BODY

OIL FILTER

KICKDOWN BAND

INPUT SHAFT

FLEXIBLE DRIVE PLATE

ENGINE CRANKSHAFT

SUN GEAR DRIVING SHELL

Fig. 11-1 (cont.) TorqueFlite A-727 transmission, a beefed up version. (Chrysler Corp.)

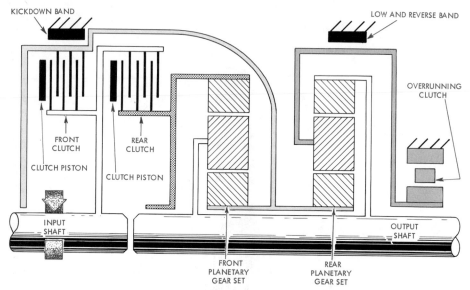

KICKDOWN BAND

LOW AND REVERSE BAND

OVERRUNNING CLUTCH

FRONT CLUTCH

REAR CLUTCH

CLUTCH PISTON

CLUTCH PISTON

INPUT SHAFT

OUTPUT SHAFT

FRONT PLANETARY GEAR SET

REAR PLANETARY GEAR SET

Fig. 11-2. TorqueFlite A-904 and A-727 powerflow schematic.

Ford Motor Company

C4 and C6 (Ford, Fairlane, Mercury, Montego, Torino, Falcon, Mustang, Cougar, Lincoln Continental, Thunderbird, Pinto, Maverick)

The C4 and C6 Cruise-O-Matics were introduced respectively in 1964 and 1966; hence the reference C4 and C6. Both transmissions use aluminum cases with the C-6 designed to handle the higher torque engines. The transmissions closely resemble one another, using gear trains of the same design and identical clutch and band combinations with only one exception. The C-6 has a low-reverse clutch in

place of the C-4 low-reverse band, 11-3, 11-4, and 11-5. Also note the similarity of the TorqueFlite (Fig. 11-1) and Cruise-O-Matic transmissions, especially their gear train design and clutch-band combinations. A power flow summary for the series is also included in Table 11-2.

In the Select-Shift version beginning in production year 1967, the D position is fully automatic; starting through a three element torque converter and low gear ratio (2.40 or 2.46) it shifts to converter and intermediate ratio (1.46 or 1.47), and then to *direct* with the converter furnishing the drive

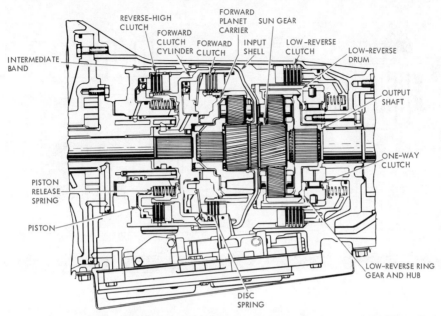

Fig. 11-3. C-6 automatic transmission, gear train, clutches and bands. (Ford Motor Co.)

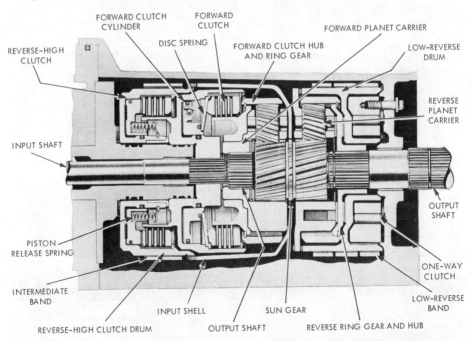

Fig. 11-4. C-4 automatic transmission, gear train, clutches and bands. (Ford Motor Co.)

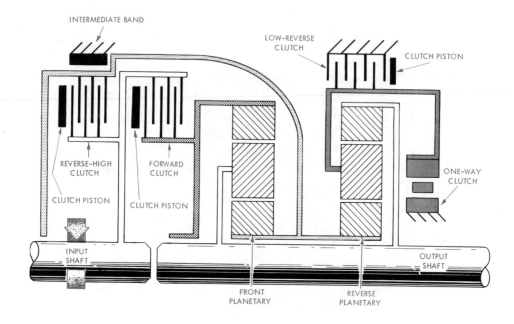

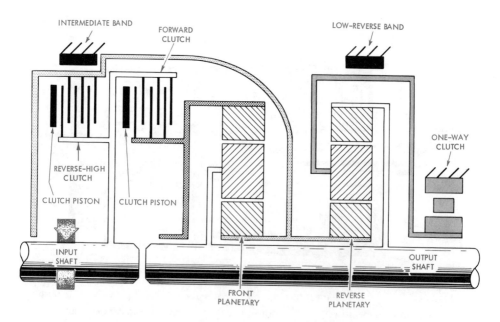

Fig. 11-5. Powerflow schematic for C-6 and the C-4/C-4S.

TABLE 11-2. POWERFLOW SUMMARY FOR FORD C-4 AND C-6 SELECT-SHIFT

SELECTOR LEVER PATTERN P R N D 2 1

RANGE	GEAR	FORWARD CLUTCH	REVERSE HIGH CLUTCH	INTERMEDIATE BAND	LOW REVERSE [CLUTCH C-6] [BAND C-4]	ONE-WAY CLUTCH	PARK PAWL
PARK		OFF	OFF	OFF	OFF	OFF	IN
REVERSE		OFF	ON	OFF	ON	NOT AFFECTED	OUT
NEUTRAL		OFF	OFF	OFF	OFF	OFF	OUT
D–DRIVE	FIRST	ON	OFF	OFF	OFF	HOLDS	OUT
	SECOND	ON	OFF	ON	OFF	OVER–RUNS	OUT
	THIRD	ON	ON	OFF	OFF	OVER–RUNS	OUT
2–DRIVE	SECOND	ON	OFF	ON	OFF	OVER–RUNS	OUT
1–DRIVE	FIRST	ON	OFF	OFF	ON	HOLDS	OUT

power. In the 1 position, the transmission is in low gear and will remain until shifted to 2 or D positions. In the 2 position, the transmission is in intermediate gear and will remain until shifted to D or 1 positions. With this shifting arrangement the driver can start in 1, then shift to 2 at any speed or peak rpm, and then into D. Or he can elect to have fully automatic shifting and use D. The transmission throttle system is vacuum controlled and the kickdown system is operated from a separate mechanical linkage to the carburetor.

For added acceleration kickdown shifts 3-1 and 3-2 are available within safe vehicle speed ranges. This will vary according to engine torque design. The closed throttle downshift pattern is 3-1.

Shifting from D to 2 immediately downshifts the transmission for extra passing power or for increased braking. Shifting from D to 1 results in a downshift to intermediate gear until a safe vehicle speed range is attained for low gear engagement. Selector lever pattern: P R N D 2 1. The Ford C-4 and C-6 have no rear pump design, so push starts are not available.

The C4 and C6 Dual Range, prior to 1967, had a slight variation in operation. It provided two drive positions—D_1 for full automatic shifting with a low gear start, and D_2, an intermediate gear start which shifts to *direct*. Manual low keeps the transmission in first gear. Selector lever pattern: P R N D_2 D_1 L.

293

C4S Semi-Automatic (Maverick limited production)

Introduced in 1970, the C4S is a semi-automatic powershift transmission using a 3 speed planetary gearbox similar to the C4 full automatic. The governor and throttle systems, and the shifter valves were eliminated. There is no clutch pedal and the driver has full manual control over the gear changes by simply repositioning the selector lever (P R N H₁ 2 1). H₁ gives direct only. Push starts not available with C-4S design.

Cast Iron Cruise-O-Matic (Ford, Mercury, Lincoln Continental, Comet, Fairlane, Thunderbird, and FX, MX)

The Cast Iron Cruise-O-Matic dates back to 1958 and is the sole survivor from the old line of cast iron transmissions since the age of aluminum took over in the construction of automatic transmission cases in the early 60's. It was first adapted to the Ford, Mercury, Edsel, Lincoln, and Continental and labeled by the various advertising names, Cruise-O-Matic, Multi-

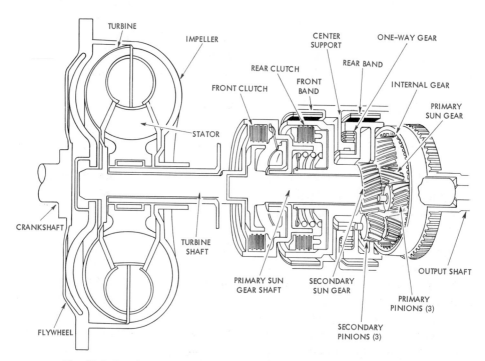

Fig. 11-6. Cast iron Cruise-O-Matic planetary gear train. (Ford Motor Co.)

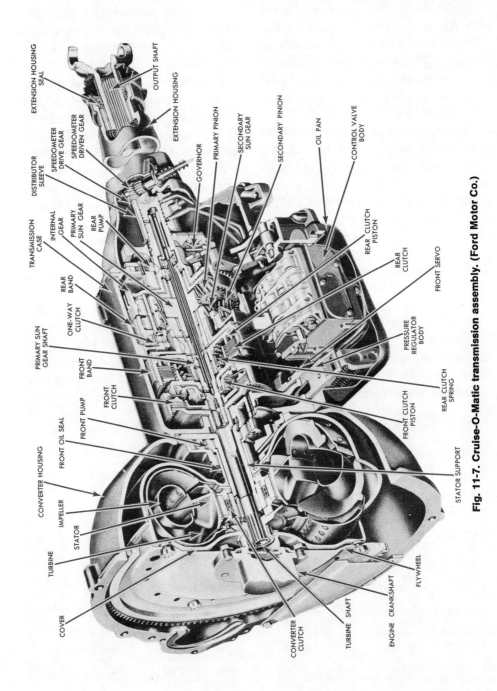

Fig. 11-7. Cruise-O-Matic transmission assembly. (Ford Motor Co.)

Drive, Dual Power, and Turbo-Drive. In more recent years it has been known as Cruise-O-Matic, Merc-O-Matic, and Turbo-Drive.

This transmission is a redesigned version of the original 3-speed automatic used by the Ford Motor Company. It is composed of a three element torque converter and a multiple-pinion planetary gear train to produce three forward speeds and reverse, Figs. 11-6 and 11-7.

In the Dual Range design, normal drive in D_1 position starts through the torque converter (maximum torque, 2.1) and low gear ratio (2.37, 2.40, or 2.46), shifts to torque converter plus intermediate ratio (1.46, 1.47, or 1.48), and finally to direct and converter drive. In D_2 position, the transmission starts in intermediate, then shifts to direct.

For added acceleration kickdown shifts 3-1 and 3-2 are available within safe vehicle speed ranges. This will vary according to engine torque design. The closed throttle downshift pattern is 3-2-1 or 3-2. Manual low keeps the transmission in first gear. A shift from D_1 or D_2 to manual low results in intermediate gear operation and low gear does not engage until a safe vehicle speed is attained. Once in low gear the transmission will not upshift. Selector lever pattern: P R N D_2 D_1 L.

The Cruise-O-Matic gear train operation is illustrated in Figs. 11-8, 11-9, 11-10, 11-11, 11-12, and 11-13. The power flow is summarized for all in Table 11-3.

Starting with the production year 1967, the cast iron Cruise-O-Matic was modified and converted

TABLE 11-3. POWERFLOW SUMMARY FOR FORD CAST-IRON CRUISE-O-MATIC SELECT-SHIFT

SELECTOR LEVER PATTERN P N R D 2 1

RANGE	GEAR	FRONT CLUTCH	REAR CLUTCH	FRONT BAND	REAR BAND	ONE-WAY CLUTCH	PARK PAWL
PARK		OFF	OFF	OFF	OFF	OFF	IN
REVERSE		OFF	ON	OFF	ON	NOT AFFECTED	OUT
NEUTRAL		OFF	OFF	OFF	OFF	OFF	OUT
D-DRIVE	FIRST	ON	OFF	OFF	OFF	HOLDS	OUT
	SECOND	ON	OFF	ON	OFF	OVERRUNS	OUT
	THIRD	ON	ON	OFF	OFF	OVERRUNS	OUT
2-DRIVE	SECOND	ON	OFF	ON	OFF	OVERRUNS	OUT
1-DRIVE	FIRST	ON	OFF	OFF	ON	HOLDS	OUT

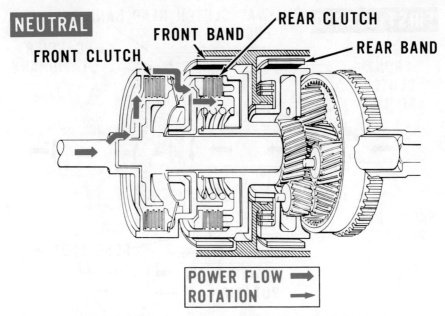

NEUTRAL

FRONT CLUTCH

FRONT BAND

REAR CLUTCH

REAR BAND

POWER FLOW
ROTATION

Fig. 11-8. Cruise-O-Matic operation-neutral. (Ford Motor Co.)

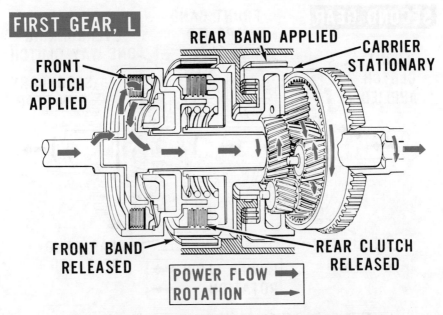

FIRST GEAR, L

REAR BAND APPLIED

CARRIER STATIONARY

FRONT CLUTCH APPLIED

FRONT BAND RELEASED

REAR CLUTCH RELEASED

POWER FLOW
ROTATION

Fig. 11-9. Cruise-O-Matic operation-first gear, 1. (Ford Motor Co.)

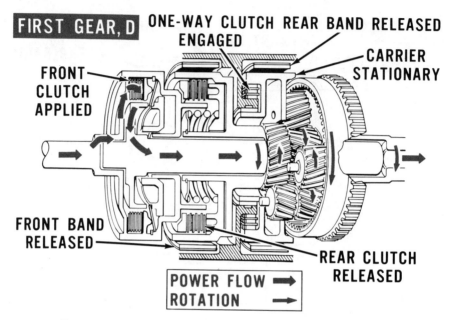

Fig. 11-10. Cruise-O-Matic operation-first gear, D. (Ford Motor Co.)

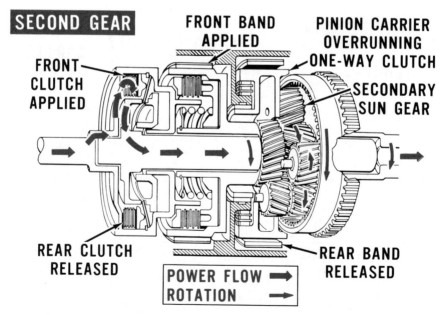

Fig. 11-11. Cruise-O-Matic operation-second gear. (Ford Motor Co.)

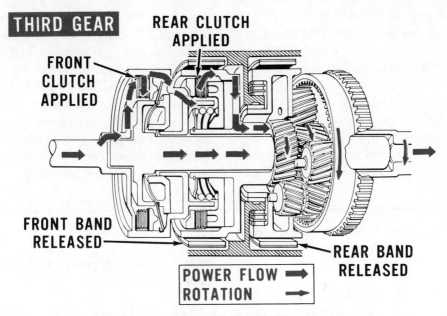

Fig. 11-12. Cruise-O-Matic operation-third gear. (Ford Motor Co.)

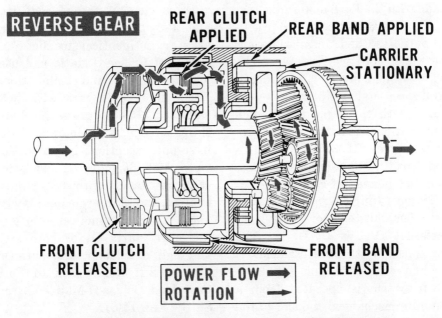

Fig. 11-13. Cruise-O-Matic operation-reverse gear. (Ford Motor Co.)

to a Select-Shift, P R N D 2 1. The operating characteristics are identical to the C4 and C6 Select-Shift, except for the closed throttle downshift in D which is still 3-2-1. Prior to 1967 the Select-Shift did exist for police cruisers and some sport model applications.

For service reference, the new design is referred to as the MX and the early design as the FX. The MX and FX designs use a vacuum controlled throttle system and a kickdown system operated by a separate mechanical linkage to the carburetor.

Starting with production year 1968, the rear pump was eliminated in the cast iron Cruise-O-Matic and push starts were not available.

American Motors Corporation

Flash-O-Matic

The Flash-O-Matic dates back to 1957, and after years of good service it was last used in 1967 production. A direct comparison can be made with the Ford dual range cast iron Cruise-O-Matic. For all practical purposes, the transmissions are the same, both using a three element torque converter, and identical 3-speed multiple planetary gear trains with the same band-clutch combinations. Starting in the production year 1963, the Flash-O-Matic had an aluminum transmission case instead of cast iron.

The operating characteristics are also identical. Selector Shift lever pattern: P R N D_2 D_1 L. The transmission throttle system is vacuum controlled and the kickdown system is operated from a separate mechanical linkage to the carburetor or by an internal electrical solenoid triggered by a throttle linkage switch.

Shift-Command

This transmission is composed of a three element torque converter and a 3-speed multiple planetary gear train identical to the Ford cast iron Cruise-O-Matic and uses identical clutch-band combinations. Used on 1965-71 cars with floor shift and 1968-71 cars with column shift, the operating characteristics have one exception: in production year 1965-66, the transmission starts in low D with six cylinder engines, and in intermediate D with V-8's. Current practice is to give low gear starts D for both six's and eight's. Selector lever pattern: P R N D 2 1. Refer back to Ford Cast Iron Cruise-O-Matic—Select-Shift (Fig. 11-6).

Low gear ratios are (2.39:1 or

2.40 :1). The maximum torque converter multiplication is 2.0. The transmission throttle system is vacuum controlled and the kickdown system is operated by an internal solenoid triggered by a throttle linkage switch.

Torque-Command

An adaption of the Chrysler Torque-Flite that replaces the Shift-Command for 1972. Chrysler Corporation furnishes the transmission which has the same construction and operating features as the Torque-Flite, including identical gear ratios. Selector lever pattern: P R N D 2 1. Push starts are not available as there is no rear pump.

General Motors

Powerglide, Tempest, Super Turbine 300, and Jetaway

These transmissions represent a family of 2-speed automatic transmissions used by General Motors in recent years. The transmissions closely resemble one another with all using a one-piece aluminium case, multiple pinion planetary gear trains of the same design providing for *neutral, low, direct,* and

TABLE 11-4.   RECENT GENERAL MOTORS TWO-SPEED APPLICATIONS

TRANSMISSION TYPE	G.M. PASSENGER CAR APPLICATION	PRODUCTION YEAR INTRODUCED	LAST PRODUCTION YEAR
ALUMINUM [1] POWERGLIDE	Chevrolet, Monte Carlo, Chevelle, Chevy Nova, Camaro, Corvair, and Vega	1963; EXCEPT CORVAIR—1961	CURRENT
SUPER TURBINE 300[2]	Buick Special, Skylark GS, and LeSabre	1964	1969
PONTIAC 2-SPEED[3]	Pontiac Tempest, GTO, Firebird, and Venturi II	1961	CURRENT
JETAWAY[2]	Oldsmobile F-85, 4-4-2, and Jetstar 88	1964	1969

[1] The Aluminum Powerglide is so-called to distinguish it from its ancestor, the Cast Iron Powerglide.

[2] The Super Turbine 300 and Jetaway used a three element convertor designed with a VP reactor(stator) from 1964 through production year 1967. The maximum torque multiplication of the convertor in low pitch angle was 1.95:1 (1.8 on V-8's), and in the high pitch angle 2.75:1 (2.45 on V-8's).

[3] Tempestorque 1961-63; Tempest T-300, 1964-69 (no VP); Tempest M-35, 1970-72.

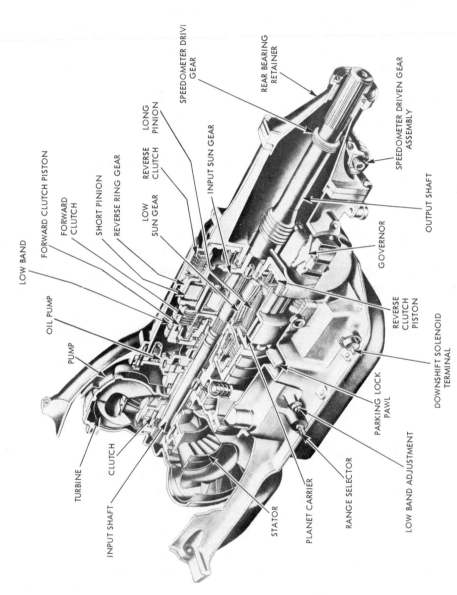

SPEEDOMETER DRIVI GEAR

REAR BEARING RETAINER

SPEEDOMETER DRIVEN GEAR ASSEMBLY

LONG PINION

INPUT SUN GEAR

REVERSE CLUTCH

OUTPUT SHAFT

FORWARD CLUTCH PISTON

FORWARD CLUTCH

SHORT PINION

REVERSE RING GEAR

LOW SUN GEAR

GOVERNOR

LOW BAND

REVERSE CLUTCH PISTON

OIL PUMP

PUMP

DOWNSHIFT SOLENOID TERMINAL

PARKING LOCK PAWL

TURBINE

CLUTCH

INPUT SHAFT

STATOR

PLANET CARRIER

RANGE SELECTOR

LOW BAND ADJUSTMENT

Fig. 11-14. Powerglide transmission. (General Motors Corp.)

reverse, and identical clutch and band combinations, Figs. 11-14 through 11-19. Table 11-4 gives a power flow summary.

Three element torque converters are used with the transmission having an array of maximum torque ratings from 1.95 to 2.8, depending

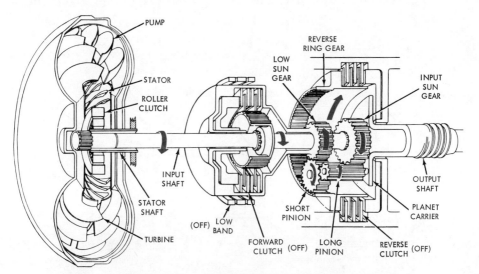

Fig. 11-15. Powerglide operation-neutral. (General Motors Corp.)

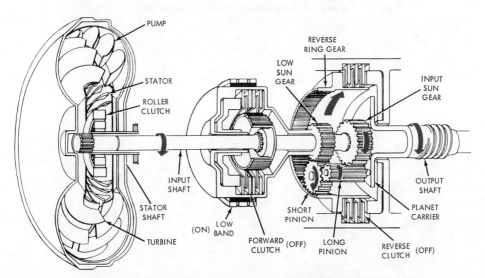

Fig. 11-16. Powerglide operation-low. (General Motors Corp.)

303

on engine application. In some cases a variable pitch reactor (stator) design is employed.

Manual low, Fig. 11-16 will engage at any vehicle speed, therefore, the vehicle operator needs to use some judgment. *Engagement of manual low is considered safe only below 40 mph!* Manual low keeps the transmission in low gear and provides no upshift. See Table 5.

Normal *drive*, Fig. 11-17, starts

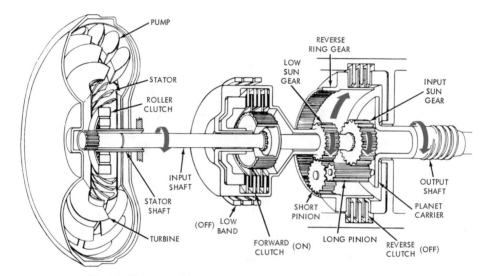

Fig. 11-17. Powerglide operation-direct. (General Motors Corp.)

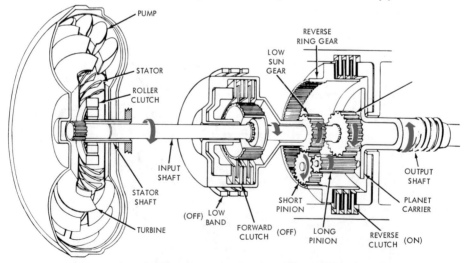

Fig. 11-18. Powerglide operation-reverse. (General Motors Corp.)

through the converter and low gear and then automatically upshifts to high gear and converter drive.

For added acceleration a kickdown or forced downshift, *high* to *low,* is available within safe ve-hicle speed ranges. This will vary according to engine torque design.

The transmission throttle and kickdown (detent) systems are mechanically operated by a common external linkage to the carbu-

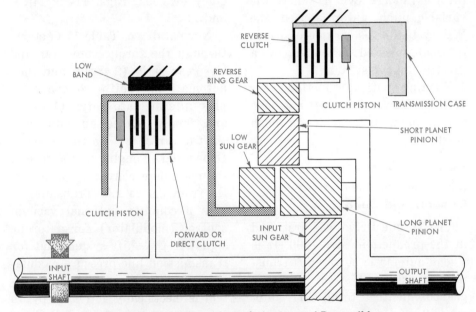

Fig. 11-19. Powerflow schematic for 2-speed Powerglide.

TABLE 11-5. POWERFLOW SUMMARY FOR SUPER TURBINE 300, JETAWAY, POWERGLIDE, AND PONTIAC 2-SPEED

SELECTOR LEVER PATTERN P R N D L

RANGE	GEAR	FORWARD CLUTCH	REVERSE CLUTCH	LOW BAND	PARK PAWL
PARK		OFF	OFF	OFF	IN
REVERSE		OFF	ON	OFF	OUT
NEUTRAL		OFF	OFF	OFF	OUT
DRIVE	LOW	OFF	OFF	ON	OUT
	HI	ON	OFF	OFF	OUT
LOW	LOW	OFF	OFF	ON	OUT

retor in the Powerglide or M-35. In the Super 300 and Jetaway, a vacuum controlled modulator is used for shifting and the kickdown (detent) system is operated by an internal solenoid activated by a throttle linkage switch. Where the variable pitch stator is used, the V.P. system is also triggered by an internal solenoid activated by a throttle linkage switch.

Starting with production year 1967 the Powerglide does not have a rear pump to provide for push starts.

Torque Drive Semi-Automatic (Chevy Nova, Chevy II, Camaro, and Vega)

The Torque Drive was first used in the production year 1969. It is a semi-automatic powershift transmission using a 2-speed planetary gearbox identical to all G.M. automatic 2-speed transmissions. It has no governor and throttle systems, and no shifter valve. A clutch pedal is not required and the driver has full manual control over the gear changes by simply repositioning the selector lever positions, P R N H$_1$ L. Push starts not available.

Turbo Hydra-Matic 400 (Chevrolet, Pontiac, Oldsmobile, Buick, and Cadillac)

1964 was the first production year for the T-400 when it was introduced in the Buick and Cadillac.

For 1965 it was added to Oldsmobile, Pontiac, and Chevrolet. The transmission consists of a three element torque converter (some with a VP stator or reactor) and a 3-speed compound planetary gearbox, Figs. 11-20, 11-21, and 11-22.

Normal drive, Table 11-6, starts through the torque converter and low gear ratio (2.48:1), and then automatically shifts to converter plus intermediate ratio (1.48:1), and finally makes an automatic shift to direct and converter drive. Depending on engine torque design, the maximum converter ratio varies from 2.0 to 2.5. Transmission uses a common external vacuum control (modulator) for a torque signal to the shift system and for transmission line pressure modulation. The detent or kickdown system is electrically activated by an internal solenoid triggered from the throttle linkage.

The T-400 Buick, Cadillac, and Oldsmobile used a three element torque converter with a VP stator through the production years 1965 through 1967. The maximum torque multiplication of the converter was 2.2:1 in the high pitch angle and 1.8:1 in the low pitch angle. The V.P. system is triggered by an internal solenoid activated by a throttle linkage switch.

For added acceleration, forced or kickdown shifts 3-1 or 3-2 are

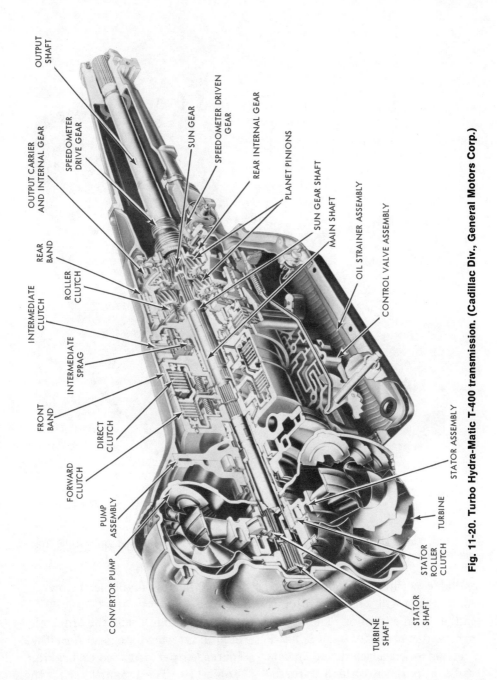

OUTPUT SHAFT

OUTPUT CARRIER AND INTERNAL GEAR

SPEEDOMETER DRIVE GEAR

REAR BAND

ROLLER CLUTCH

INTERMEDIATE CLUTCH

INTERMEDIATE SPRAG

FRONT BAND

DIRECT CLUTCH

FORWARD CLUTCH

PUMP ASSEMBLY

CONVERTOR PUMP

SUN GEAR

SPEEDOMETER DRIVEN GEAR

REAR INTERNAL GEAR

PLANET PINIONS

SUN GEAR SHAFT

MAIN SHAFT

OIL STRAINER ASSEMBLY

CONTROL VALVE ASSEMBLY

STATOR ASSEMBLY

TURBINE

STATOR ROLLER CLUTCH

STATOR SHAFT

TURBINE SHAFT

Fig. 11-20. Turbo Hydra-Matic T-400 transmission. (Cadillac Div., General Motors Corp.)

307

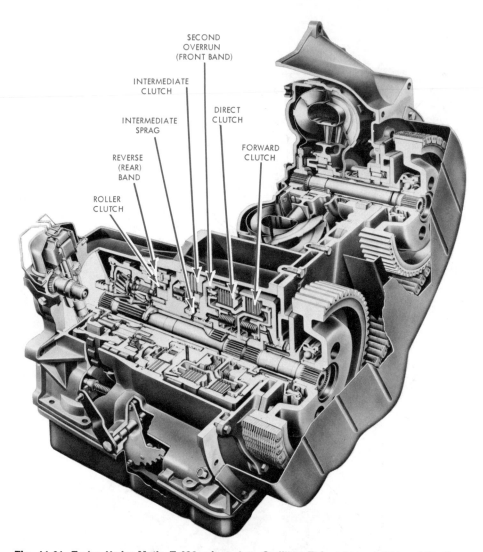

Fig. 11-21. Turbo Hydra-Matic T-400 adapted to Cadillac Eldorado and Oldsmobile Toronado. (General Motors Corp.)

available within safe vehicle speed ranges. This will vary according to engine torque design. The closed throttle downshift pattern is 3-2-1. For controlled acceleration in city traffic a part throttle 3-2 forced downshift is available below 30 mph.

Super range keeps the transmission in intermediate gear for either increased performance or braking, Table 11-6. The 1-2 shift occurs the same as in *drive;* however, there will not be a 2-3 shift regardless of vehicle speed. Super or intermediate range was not included in the original 1964 T-400. The manual shift selections take on the appearance of a 2-speed automatic: P N R D L.

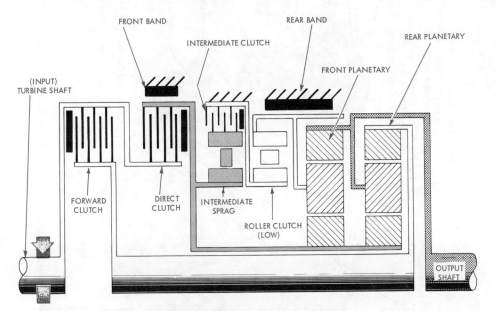

Fig. 11-22. Powerflow schematic for T-400.

TABLE 11-6. POWERFLOW SUMMARY FOR TURBO HYDRA–MATIC–400

TYPICAL SELECTOR LEVER PATTERN P R N D S L

SELECTOR POSITION	FORWARD CLUTCH	DIRECT CLUTCH	FRONT BAND	INTERMEDIATE CLUTCH	SPRAG	ROLLER CLUTCH	REAR BAND
PARK-NEUTRAL	OFF	OFF	OFF	OFF	OFF	OFF	OFF
DRIVE 1	ON	OFF	OFF	OFF	OFF	ON	OFF
2	ON	OFF	OFF	ON	ON	OFF	OFF
3	ON	ON	OFF	ON	OFF	OFF	OFF
SUPER 1	ON	OFF	OFF	OFF	OFF	ON	OFF
2	ON	OFF	ON	ON	ON	OFF	OFF
LO 1	ON	OFF	OFF	OFF	OFF	ON	ON
REVERSE	OFF	ON	OFF	OFF	OFF	OFF	ON

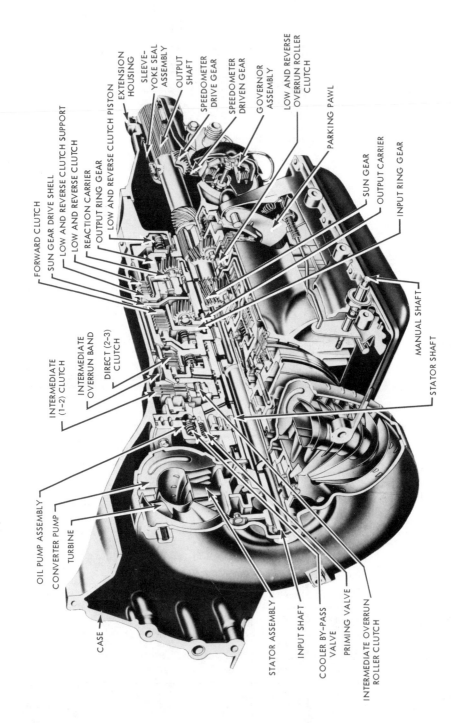

Fig. 11-23. Turbo Hydra-Matic 350. (Oldsmobile Div., General Motors Corp.)

In low range, Table 11-6, the transmission is kept in first gear for braking and extra torque. A shift from *drive* to *low* brings in intermediate gear until a safe vehicle speed range is reached. Once first gear engages, an upshift will not occur. Typical selector lever pattern: P R N D S L. Push starts are not available.

Turbo Hydra-Matic 350 (Chevrolet, Pontiac, Oldsmobile, Buick, and Cadillac)

This 3-speed transmission was added to the G.M. Hydra-Matic family in 1969, Figs. 11-23 and 11-24. Depending on engine application, it uses a three element torque converter varying in maximum torque from 2.0 to 2.5. The low gear ratio is 2.52:1 and intermediate ratio 1.52:1. The transmission vacuum modulator system is identical with that of the T-400. The detent or kickdown system is, however, mechanically controlled by the external throttle linkage.

Operating characteristics are identical to the T-400, Table 11-7. The reader should note the similarity of the gear train structure and

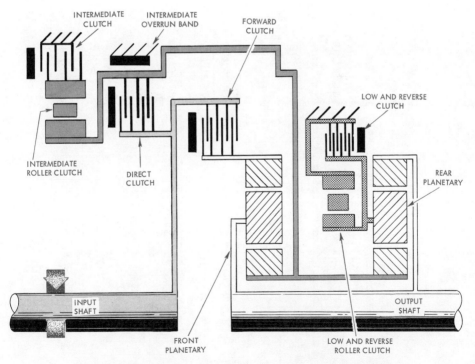

Fig. 11-24. Powerflow schematic for Turbo Hydra-Matic 350.

TABLE 11-7. POWERFLOW SUMMARY FOR TURBO HYDRA-MATIC-350.

TYPICAL SELECTOR LEVER PATTERN P R N D S L

RANGE	SPREAD	FORWARD CLUTCH	INTERMEDIATE CLUTCH	INTERMEDIATE ROLLER CLUTCH	INTERMEDIATE OVERRUN BAND	DIRECT CLUTCH	LOW & REVERSE CLUTCH	LOW & REVERSE ROLLER CLUTCH
PARK–NEUTRAL		OFF	OFF	INEFFECTIVE	OFF	OFF	OFF	INEFFECTIVE
REVERSE		OFF	OFF	INEFFECTIVE	OFF	ON	ON	INEFFECTIVE
DRIVE	FIRST	ON	OFF	EFFECTIVE NOT HOLDING	OFF	OFF	OFF	EFFECTIVE
	SECOND	ON	ON	EFFECTIVE HOLDING	OFF	OFF	OFF	INEFFECTIVE
	THIRD	ON	ON	INEFFECTIVE FREE WHEELING	OFF	ON	OFF	INEFFECTIVE
SUPER	FIRST	ON	OFF	EFFECTIVE NOT HOLDING	OFF	OFF	OFF	EFFECTIVE
	SECOND	ON	ON	EFFECTIVE HOLDING	ON	OFF	OFF	INEFFECTIVE
LOW	FIRST	ON	OFF	EFFECTIVE NOT HOLDING	OFF	OFF	ON	EFFECTIVE

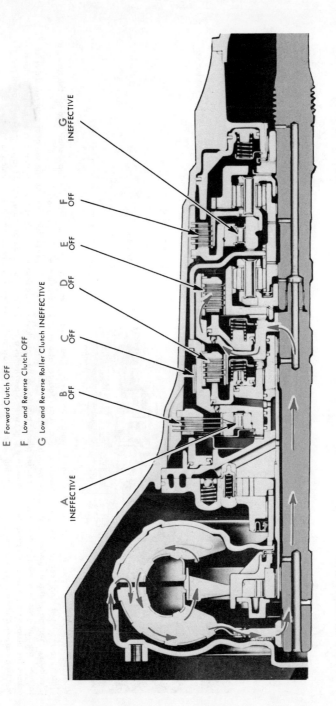

A Intermediate Overrun Roller Clutch INEFFECTIVE

B Intermediate Clutch OFF

C Intermediate Overrun Band OFF

D Direct Clutch OFF

E Forward Clutch OFF

F Low and Reverse Clutch OFF

G Low and Reverse Roller Clutch INEFFECTIVE

Fig. 11-25. Turbo Hydra-Matic 350—neutral. (Oldsmobile Div., General Motors Corp.)

In neutral, all clutches and the intermediate overrun band are released; therefore no power is transmitted from the torque converter turbine to plane-tary gear sets or output shaft.

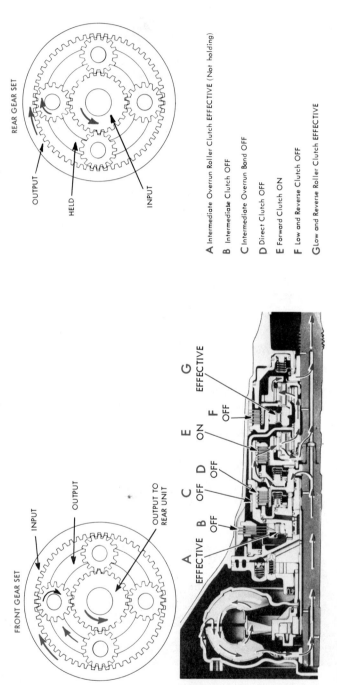

REAR GEAR SET

OUTPUT

HELD

INPUT

FRONT GEAR SET

INPUT

OUTPUT

OUTPUT TO REAR UNIT

EFFECTIVE B OFF D OFF ON F EFFECTIVE
A   C   E   G
OFF   OFF   OFF

A Intermediate Overrun Roller Clutch EFFECTIVE (Not holding)

B Intermediate Clutch OFF

C Intermediate Overrun Band OFF

D Direct Clutch OFF

E Forward Clutch ON

F Low and Reverse Clutch OFF

G low and Reverse Roller Clutch EFFECTIVE

With the range selector lever in Drive, D range, the forward clutch is applied. This delivers turbine torque from the input shaft through the forward clutch, to the input ring gear in a clockwise direction. (Converter torque ratio equals approximately 2:25 at stall.) Clockwise rotation of the input ring gear causes the output planet pinions to rotate in a clockwise direction, driving the sun gear counterclockwise. In turn, the sun gear turns causing the reaction carrier planet pinions to turn clockwise. Clockwise rotation of the reaction carrier planet pinions causes the output ring gear and output shaft to turn in a clockwise direction in a reduction ratio of approximately 2.52 to 1. The reaction of the reaction carrier planet pinions against the output ring gear is taken by the low and reverse roller clutch which is grounded to the case. To prepare the transmission for the shift into intermediate (Second gear) the intermediate roller clutch is locked. Therefore, the sun gear sun gear drive shell, direct clutch housing, intermediate roller clutch and the intermediate clutch faced plates are all turning in a counterclockwise direction.

Fig. 11-26. Turbo Hydra-Matic 350—D range (first gear). (Oldsmobile Div., General Motors Corp.)

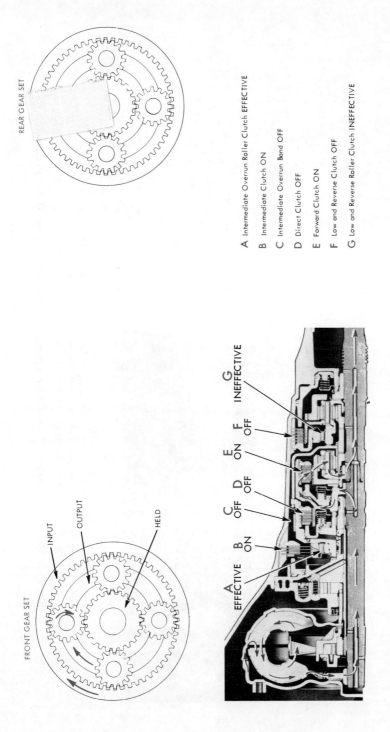

REAR GEAR SET

FRONT GEAR SET

INPUT

OUTPUT

HELD

A Intermediate Overrun Roller Clutch EFFECTIVE
B Intermediate Clutch ON
C Intermediate Overrun Band OFF
D Direct Clutch OFF
E Forward Clutch ON
F Low and Reverse Clutch OFF
G Low and Reverse Roller Clutch INEFFECTIVE

A EFFECTIVE B ON C OFF D OFF E ON F OFF G INEFFECTIVE

In Drive D range, intermediate (second gear), the intermediate clutch is applied to allow the intermediate overrun roller clutch to hold the shell and sun gear stationary (against counterclockwise rotation). Turbine torque, through the applied forward clutch is delivered to the input ring gear in a clockwise direction. Clockwise rotation of the input ring gear causes the output planet pinions to walk around the stationary sun gear in a clockwise direction. This causes the output shaft to turn in a clockwise direction in a reduction ratio of approximately 1.52 to 1.

Fig. 11-27. Turbo Hydra-Matic 350—D range intermediate (second gear). (Oldsmobile Div., General Motors Corp.)

315

REAR GEAR SET

FRONT GEAR SET

INPUT

OUTPUT

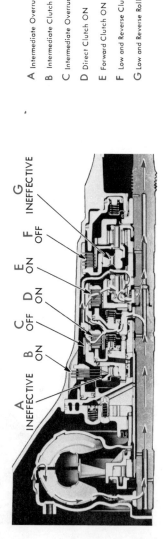

A INEFFECTIVE
B ON
C OFF
D ON
E ON
F OFF
G INEFFECTIVE

A Intermediate Overrun Roller Clutch INEFFECTIVE
B Intermediate Clutch ON
C Intermediate Overrun Band OFF
D Direct Clutch ON
E Forward Clutch ON
F Low and Reverse Clutch OFF
G Low and Reverse Roller Clutch INEFFECTIVE

In direct drive, engine torque is transmitted to the converter then through the forward clutch, to the input ring gear in a clockwise direction. The clutch is applied transmitting torque through the sun gear drive shell to the sun gear in a clockwise direction. Since both the sun gear and the input ring gear are turning in a clockwise direction at the same speed, the planetary gear sets are locked and turn as one unit at a ratio of 1:1.

Fig. 11-28 Turbo Hydra-Matic 350—direct drive range. (Oldsmobile Div. General Motors Corp.)

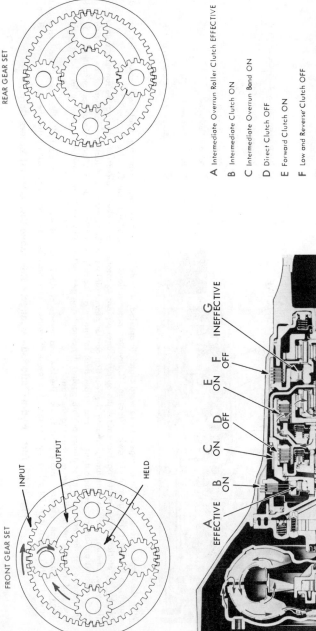

REAR GEAR SET

FRONT GEAR SET

INPUT

OUTPUT

HELD

A Intermediate Overrun Roller Clutch EFFECTIVE

B Intermediate Clutch ON

C Intermediate Overrun Band ON

D Direct Clutch OFF

E Forward Clutch ON

F Low and Reverse Clutch OFF

G Low and Reverse Roller Clutch INEFFECTIVE

A EFFECTIVE B ON C ON D OFF E ON F OFF G INEFFECTIVE

In S range, the intermediate clutch is applied to allow the intermediate overrun roller to hold the shell and sun gear stationary (against counterclockwise rotation). Turbine torque, through the applied forward clutch is delivered to the input ring gear in a clockwise direction. Clockwise rotation of the input ring gear causes the output planet pinions to walk around the stationary sun gear in a clockwise direction in a reduction ratio of approximately 1:52 to 1. The reaction of the output planet pinions against the sun gear is taken by either the intermediate overrun roller clutch or the intermediate overrun band. When the selector lever is moved to S range, the intermediate overrun band is applied in addition to the forward and intermediate clutches. The intermediate overrun band provides overrun braking as it holds the sun gear fixed.

Fig. 11-29. Turbo Hydra-Matic 350—S range. (Oldsmobile Div., General Motors Corp.)

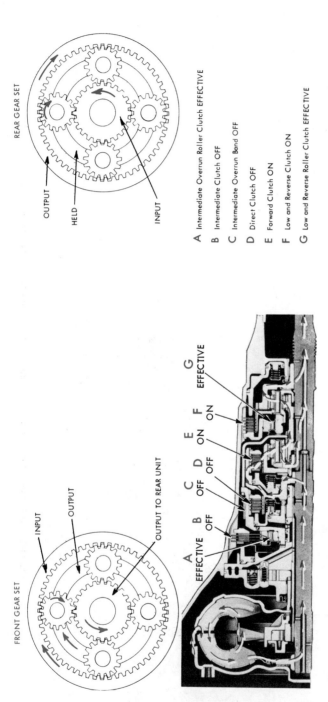

REAR GEAR SET

OUTPUT

HELD

INPUT

A Intermediate Overrun Roller Clutch EFFECTIVE

B Intermediate Clutch OFF

C Intermediate Overrun Band OFF

D Direct Clutch OFF

E Forward Clutch ON

F Low and Reverse Clutch ON

G Low and Reverse Roller Clutch EFFECTIVE

FRONT GEAR SET

INPUT

OUTPUT

OUTPUT TO REAR UNIT

A	B	C	D	E	F	G
EFFECTIVE	OFF	OFF	OFF	ON	ON	EFFECTIVE

With the range selector lever in L range, the forward clutch is applied. This delivers turbine torque from the input shaft through the forward clutch, to the input ring gear in clockwise direction. (Converter torque ratio equals approximately 2:3 at stall.) Clockwise rotation of the input ring gear causes the output planet pinions to rotate in a clockwise direction, driving the sun gear counter-clockwise. In turn, the sun gear turns, causing the reaction carrier planet pinions to turn clockwise. Clockwise rotation of the reaction of carrier planet pinions causes the reaction carrier and output shaft to turn in a clockwise direction in a reduction ratio of approximately 2.52 to 1. The reaction of the reaction carrier planet pinions against the output ring gear is taken by either the low and reverse roller clutch or the low and reverse clutch which are grounded to the case.

When the transmission is shifted into L (first gear), the low and reverse clutch is applied below a preset controlled car speed in addition to the forward clutch which is on for all forward ranges. The low and reverse clutch provides overrun braking as it holds the reaction carrier fixed.

Fig. 11-30. Turbo Hydra-Matic 350—L range. (Oldsmobile Div., General Motors Corp.)

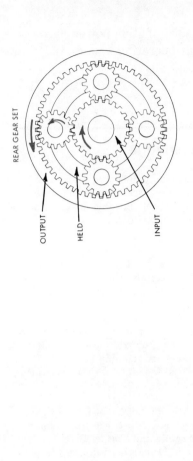

REAR GEAR SET

OUTPUT

HELD

INPUT

FRONT GEAR SET

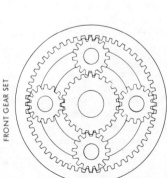

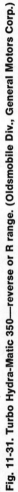

A Intermediate Overrun Roller Clutch INEFFECTIVE

B Intermediate Clutch OFF

C Intermediate Overrun Band OFF

D Direct Clutch ON

E Forward Clutch OFF

F Low and Reverse Clutch ON

G Low and Reverse Roller Clutch INEFFECTIVE

In Reverse R, the direct clutch is applied to transmit torque from the forward clutch housing to the sun gear drive shell and the sun gear. The low and reverse clutch is applied preventing the reaction carrier from turning. Clockwise rotation of the sun gear causes the reaction carrier pinions to turn counterclockwise, thus turning the output ring gear and output shaft counterclockwise in a reduction ratio of approximately 1.93 to 1.

Fig. 11-31. Turbo Hydra-Matic 350—reverse or R range. (Oldsmobile Div., General Motors Corp.)

power flow to the C4, C6, and TorqueFlite A-904, A-727. Figs. 11-25 thru 11-31 give a detailed summary of the power flows of various operating ranges and gear combinations.

Checking On Your Knowledge

The following questions give you the opportunity to check up on yourself. If you have read the chapter carefully, you should be able to answer the questions.

If you have any difficulty, read the chapter over once more so that you have the information well in mind before you go on with your reading.

1. In what production year were the following automatic transmissions introduced?
   a. American Motors
      Shift Command
      Torque Command
   b. Chrysler Corporation
      A-904 TorqueFlite
      A-727 TorqueFlite
   c. Ford Motor Company
      C-4 Cruise-O-Matic Dual Range, Select-Shift, and C4S
      C-6 Cruise-O-Matic Dual Range and Select-Shift
      Cast Iron Cruise-O-Matic Dual Range and Select-Shift
   d. General Motors
      Aluminum Powerglide and Torque Drive
      Super Turbine 300 and Jetaway
      Pontiac M-35
      Turbo Hydra-Matic 400
      Turbo Hydra-Matic 350
2. What is the difference in the American Motors' Shift-Command operating characteristics between the six and eight cylinder engine applications used in the production years 1965-66?
3. Make a comparison of the planetary gear trains used in the Aluminum Powerglide, Super Turbine 300, Jetaway, and Pontiac M-35.

4. Relating to the transmissions in Question 3; explain why their planetary gear trains are running in N and P? Referring to the Laws of Planetary Gear Operation; explain why the vehicle does not move even though the planetary gear train has an input and the gears are spinning?
5. What is the difference in operating characteristics between the C-4 and C4S?
6. What is the difference in operating characteristics between the Aluminum Powerglide and Torque Drive?
7. Make a comparison between the planetary gear trains used in the Chrysler Torqueflite A-904 and A-727, Ford C-4 and C-6, G.M. Turbo Hydra-Matic 350, and A.M. Torque Command.
8. Name the car make users and production years in which the variable pitch converter applied to the following automatic transmissions; Super T-300, Jetaway, and Turbo Hydra-Matic 400.
9. Study the gear train layout and powerflow summary for each transmission reviewed in this chapter. Be prepared to fill-in the ON and OFF applications of the friction and mechanical elements for each transmission on a powerflow summary chart.

Glossary

A

accumulator, hydraulic: A piston operated unit that is employed to absorb a volume of fluid at a controlled rate or interval of time. When incorporated in an apply circuit of a clutch or band in an automatic transmission the accumulator absorbs the apply pressure in relation to engine torque. When the accumulator quits working, the clutch or band is fully applied and the apply pressure jumps to full value. In essence, the accumulator controls shift quality.

annular groove: (see spool valve) The smaller diameter horizontal surface of a spool valve, the stem part. When an annular groove is aligned with an oil passage, fluid flows into and through that groove.

annulus gear: (see internal gear) Annulus means a ring like body or figure, Chrysler Corporation uses the term "annulus gear" in reference to the internal gear when describing the planetary gears in the TorqueFlite Transmission.

atmospheric pressure: One atmosphere is the weight at sea level of an air column one inch square and extending out to the farthest point of the earth's atmosphere. At sea level, the atmospheric pressure is approximately 14.7 pounds per square inch. For simplicity, 15 psi is sometimes used.

auxiliary pressure: (see balanced valve and regulator valve) An added fluid pressure that is introduced into a regulator or balanced valve system. It functions to either increase or decrease the response of the regulator valve to input, or supply pressure. The auxiliary pressure itself can be either a fixed or a variable value.

B

balanced valve: (see regulator valve) The same as a regulator valve as regulator valves work on the balanced valve principle. The balanced valve converts a fixed or variable mechanical force into a regulated hydraulic pressure signal known as the output, whereas the input fluid source is referred to as the supply source. In most cases, the transmission line or operating pressure is the supply source.

The force of the regulated pressure itself balances the valve action against the value of the mechanical force. Examples of balanced valve operation in automatic transmissions are the throttle valve and governor valve systems. The throttle valve output balances against a spring force that varies with engine torque while the governor valve output balances against the centrifugal force of a weight that varies with vehicle speed. In some cases, either a fixed or a variable auxiliary fluid pressure is introduced to modify the valve output. The pressure regulator valve is an example of this type of balanced valve design.

band: In automatic transmissions, a flexible external contracting band is a type of friction element commonly used to absorb the reaction force of a planetary gear train. The band is servo applied and always connects the planetary reaction member to ground through the case.

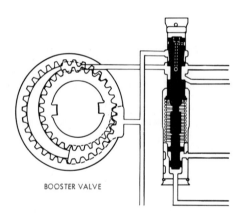

BOOSTER VALVE

booster valve: Refers to the transmission pressure regulator valve system. It is incorporated in the pressure regulator valve system so that auxiliary fluid pressures may be introduced to vary the spring load on the regulator valve and increase the transmission hydraulic pressure to higher values as needed.

Higher transmission operating or line pressures are needed for extra holding torque on the clutches and bands to match any increase in engine torque output. Added transmission line pressure is also needed for reverse operation and is obtained through the booster valve action.

brake horsepower (bhp): It is the actual horsepower available at the engine flywheel as measured by a dynamometer. In theory, brake horsepower is the available horsepower delivered by an engine after friction horsepower is subtracted from the indicated horsepower developed by the expansion of gases of burning fuel within a piston chamber: Ihp-Fhp = Ahp.

breakaway: A term used by Chrysler Corporation that refers to the actual first gear operation related to the TorqueFlite transmission (drive-breakaway).

C

centrifugal force: The force away from a center of revolution of a revolving weight. The force increases with the square of the speed of rotation.

check valve: A one-way directional valve in a hydraulic line, commonly either of a ball or poppet design.

CLUTCH ASSEMBLY

clutch assembly: (see clutch, friction) The parts make-up of a friction clutch unit that is representative of those used in various manually controlled transmissions.

322

clutch, fluid: (see clutch, friction and fluid coupling) The same as a fluid coupling. A fluid clutch or coupling performs the same functions as a friction clutch by utilizing fluid friction and inertia as opposed to solid friction used by a friction clutch.

clutch, friction: A coupling device that provides a means of smooth and positive engagement and disengagement of engine torque to the vehicle power train. Transmission of power through the clutch is accomplished by bringing one or more rotating drive members into contact with complimenting driven members.

In manually operated transmissions, the clutch is mounted on the engine flywheel and is pedal operated by the driver and usually of a single disc dry-type construction. Spring force from a pressure plate assembly presses the drive and the driven plate surfaces together to produce the necessary friction force to hold against vehicle load. See clutch assembly.

Automatic transmissions favor the use of a hydraulically operated multiple disc wet-type clutch construction to effect gear changes. The drive and driven clutch plate friction elements are applied for holding against the operating load by a hydraulic force acting on a clutch piston.

coast: A condition whereby the vehicle momentum drives the engine, used in retarding or engine braking. The drive wheels, through the power train, try to rotate the engine at a speed faster than its output, therefore engine compression can be used for slowing the vehicle. Coast conditions are brought about by deceleration and when descending steep or long road grades.

coefficient of friction: (see friction)

compound gear: A gear consisting of two or more simple gears with a common shaft. The two or more gears may be a one piece forging with the shaft, or may be keyed or splined to the shaft.

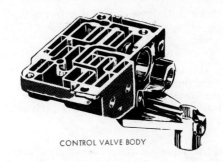

CONTROL VALVE BODY

control valve body: A multiple valve assembly for controlling the shifts and shift quality in automatic transmissions.

converter: (see fluid torque converter)

D

detent: A spring loaded plunger, pin, ball, or pawl used as a stop or checking device on a rachet wheel or shaft. In automatic transmissions, a detent mechanism is used for locking the manual valve in place for the selected operating range by engaging built-in notches on the valve.

detent downshift: (see kickdown)

diaphragm: A flexible membrane, often made up of fabric and rubber, clamped at the edges and usually spring-loaded, used in various pump and control devices such as the fuel pump, distributor vacuum advance, and automatic transmission vacuum throttle or modulator control.

differential areas: (see spool valve) When opposing faces of a spool valve are acted upon by the same pressure but their areas differ in size, the ratio of their surface area will be the strength of their relative effects, the face with the larger area producing a differential force.

differential force: (see differential areas) The ratio of forces of a pair of opposing spool valve face surfaces, usually dependent on square area.

323

direct drive: The gear ratio is 1:1 with no change occurring in the torque or speed input. Torque and speed input equals torque and speed output.

drive line: The drive connection between the transmission and the rear axle, consisting of the propeller shaft, universal joints and a slip joint.

drive torque: (see load torque) The torque which is produced by the engine and power train gear ratios to overcome the load torque. Should the drive torque at anytime exceed the vehicle load torque, then acceleration takes place. When the drive torque equals vehicle load torque and there is no drive torque reserve, then maximum vehicle speed has been attained and no further speed increase can take place.

E

efficiency: (see mechanical efficiency)

element: In reference to a hydrodynamic drive, an element is a single row of flow directing blades. In the simple torque converter the impeller, the turbine and stator each have a row of flow directing blades, thus the phrase, "three element torque converter".

energy: The ability or capacity to do work.

F

face: (see spool valve) In a spool valve, it is the vertical surface that connects the land to the annular groove. When an annular groove has one face larger than its other face, the fluid pressure acting in that annular groove exerts a greater effective force in the direction of the largest face.

fluid: A fluid can be either a liquid or gas. In hydraulics, a liquid is used for transmitting force or motion.

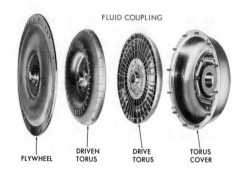

FLUID COUPLING

FLYWHEEL   DRIVEN TORUS   DRIVE TORUS   TORUS COVER

fluid coupling: (see hydrodynamic drive, and clutch, fluid) The simplest form of hydrodynamic unit. It consists of two members similar in construction and referred to as the pump (impeller) and the turbine. It transmits power at a 1:1 torque ratio and does not have the ability to change torque. In automobile applications it is used between the engine and the transmission and acts as a clutch, hence it is sometimes called a fluid clutch.

fluid drive: (see hydrodynamic) Either a fluid coupling, or a fluid torque converter.

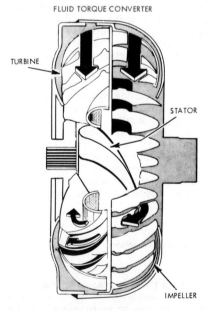

FLUID TORQUE CONVERTER

TURBINE

STATOR

IMPELLER

fluid torque converter: (see element, and hydrodynamic drive) A hydrodynamic drive that transmits power with ability to change torque. The basic design of a simple fluid converter consists of three elements, a pump (impeller), a turbine, and a stator (reaction member). The job of the stator is to collect the working fluid as it leaves the turbine and re-direct it into the pump for regeneration, permitting a torque boost.

fluid, transmission: A mineral oil fortified with additives. Two basic mineral oil formulas are currently used for passenger car automatic transmissions: Ford *Type F* for the Ford family, and *Dexron* for all others. Dexron is the trade name given to a G.M. transmission fluid development.

force: Force can be defined as a push or pull effort on an object mass, measured in units of weight.

freewheeling: (see one-way clutch)

friction: The resistance which is offered to the sliding or slipping between contacting surfaces of one solid body over another. The friction relationship between any particular pair of surfaces remains the same regardless of any change in weight or contact area. This relationship is expressed by a ratio called the coefficient of friction (μ). Each pair of contacting surfaces has its own coefficient of friction (μ). As an example, if it took a 100 lb effort to put a 500 lb block into motion over a flat surface then:

$$\mu = \frac{\text{Force of Friction}}{\text{Weight}} = \frac{100}{500} = 0.2$$

Should the weight increase to 1,000 lbs the force of friction would be

$$\begin{aligned} \text{Friction} &= (\mu) \times \text{Weight} \\ &= 0.2 \times 1,000 \\ &= 200 \text{ lbs} \end{aligned}$$

In an automatic transmission, friction is the loss of power due to dragging surfaces within the gears and rotating parts such as shafts and clutch drums, and even from the fluid action in the torque converter. The power loss from friction results in heat. Lubrication, bearings, and micro finished bearing surfaces are used to minimize effects of friction.

friction horsepower: (see indicated hp and brake hp) The amount of work which is lost in a mechanical system due to friction, abbreviated *Fhp*. When friction horsepower is subtracted from indicated horsepower, *Ihp*, the theoretical remainder is brake horsepower, *Bhp*, or available horsepower.

G

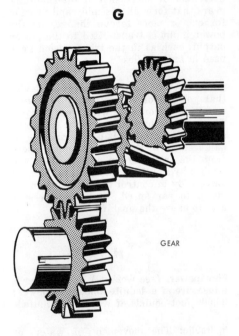

GEAR

gear: (see gear ratio) A toothed mechanical device that acts as a rotating lever to transmit power or turning effort from one shaft to another. Two or more gears are usually used in a combination to change the torque and speed of the power input. A gear combination may also function to reverse the powerflow.

gear ratio: The relative speed, in number of revolutions, which the input gear makes relative to one revolution of the output gear. In a simple gear combination, three revolutions of the input gear to one of the output gear gives a ratio of 3:1. The torque and speed changes that take place in a gear set is a function of the gear ratio.

gear reduction: Torque is multiplied and speed decreased by the factor of the gear ratio. For example, a 3:1 gear ratio will change an input torque of 180 lb-ft and an input of 2,700 rpm to 540 lb-ft and 900 rpm respectively. (No account is taken of frictional losses which are always present.)

gear train: A succession of intermeshing gears that form an assembly and provide for one or more torque changes as the power input is transmitted to the power output, such as in the transmission gear used in automobiles.

governor: (see balanced valve) A device that governs or controls another device, usually in accordance with speed or rpm. The governor used in automatic transmissions is an example. It is a regulating or balanced valve that senses vehicle speed from the transmission output shaft and sends a hydraulic speed signal to the shift valve body to control gear shifting in relation to car speed. Governor pressure acts to cause the upshift.

H

horsepower: (see work) A horsepower is a measure of a definite amount of power: 33,000 foot-pounds of work per minute.

hydraulic: The movement of water, or force exerted by water, oil or other liquids.

hydraulic control: Refers to the means of control used for machines and structures operating by hydraulic pressure. In automatic transmissions a control valve body directs the fluid flow to the various clutch and servo units in response to oil pressure changes, linkage settings, and car speed.

hydrodynamic drive: As contrasted with mechanical or electrical, it is a type of drive that transmits power solely by fluid action in a closed recirculation path. The fluid coupling and fluid torque converter are examples of hydrodynamic drives.

I

impeller: Designates the power input member of a hydrodynamic unit. Sometimes called the pump or driving member.

indicated horsepower: (Ihp) The theoretical horsepower that can be developed by a machine without consideration to frictional power losses inherent to the machine itself. In an internal combustion engine, Ihp is affected by such factors as combustion pressure, number of cylinders, cylinder bore size, piston stroke, and rpm.

inertia: The resistance of an object mass at rest to movement, or when in motion, its resistance to a change in speed or direction of travel. The resistance of a vehicle to being put in motion or to change its speed are examples. The auto engine teams up with the power transmission system to overcome inertia encountered when a vehicle is at rest or in motion.

input: The power, or energy supplied to a machine. In an automatic transmission, the source of power from the engine is absorbed by the torque converter which provides the power input into the transmission.

internal gear: The ring like outer gear of a planetary gear set with the gear teeth cut on the inside of the ring to provide a mesh with the planet pinions.

ix gear pump: A popular type of pump design used in automatic transmissions.

ix rotor pump: A popular type of pump design used in automatic transmissions.

K

kickdown: (detent downshift) To force a full throttle downshift by overruling the automatic transmission gear selection. A valve within the transmission is activated mechanically or electrically by external control which calls for the driver to floor the accelerator. A kickdown full throttle shift is not possible unless the vehicle is within a safe speed range for the engine. In a 3-speed automatic transmission a 3-2 or 3-1 kickdown is available, depending on vehicle speed.

kinetic energy: Energy, which is defined as the ability to do work, is further defined as either potential or kinetic. The energy of motion is called *kinetic energy*. Within a transmission, the turning of a shaft or gear set, or the movement of fluid is an example of kinetic energy.

L

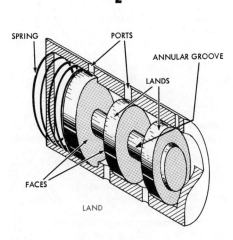

SPRING   PORTS   ANNULAR GROOVE   LANDS   FACES   LAND

land: (see spool valve) The larger diameter horizontal surface of a spool valve that is fitted into a valve bore. Spool valves usually have several lands which are utilized to block off fluid passages.

laws of planetary gear operation:

law of direct drive: Direct drive is obtained by clutching or locking any two planetary members together, or driving any two members at the same rpm and in the same direction.

law of neutral: When there is an input, but no reaction member, the condition is *neutral*.

law of overdrive: When there is a reaction member and the planet carrier is the input, the condition is *overdrive*. As in gear reduction, two possible combinations are possible: (1) sun gear is the reactionary member and the internal gear is the output, or (2) internal gear is the reactionary member and the sun gear is the output.

law of reduction: When there is a reaction member and the planet carrier is the output, the condition is *gear reduction*. The two possible combinations are: (1) sun gear driving with the internal gear as the reaction member, or (2) internal gear driving with the sun gear as the reaction member.

law of reverse: When the planet carrier is held, *reverse* is obtained by having either the sun gear or the internal gear act as the input. The sun gear driving gives a reverse reduction effect on the internal gear, while the internal gear driving gives a reverse overdrive effect on the sun gear.

load torque (see drive torque) The torque which the vehicle load presents to the output of a transmission.

M

manual linkage: (see manual valve) The driver controlled mechanical linkage to the transmission used for selecting the transmission operating range.

manual valve: A valve that derives its name from the fact that it is manually actuated by the driver of the vehicle through a linkage arrangement. In automatic transmissions, the driver selects the transmission operating range by manual selection.

MECHANICAL CLUTCH

mechanical clutch: (see clutch, friction) A device which allows manually operated transmissions to be engaged and disengaged from the engine crankshaft. Composed of a flywheel and pressure plate assembly as driving members on the crankshaft, and of a friction disc with a sliding hub as a driven member positioned on the splined input shaft of the transmission.

mechanical efficiency: (of an engine) The ratio of the actual input to the flywheel (brake horsepower = Bhp) to the power developed in the cylinders (indicated horsepower = Ihp). Calculated:

$$\text{Mechanical Efficiency} = \frac{\text{Bhp}}{\text{Ihp}}$$

$$= \% \text{ Efficiency}$$

member, hydrodynamic: (see hydrodynamic drive) A member is an independent component of a hydrodynamic unit such as an impeller (pump), a reactor (stator), or a turbine. Members are usually designed as single element members but may consist of more than one element in complex hydrodynamic drive configurations.

modulate: To change or adjust.

modulator valve: (see boost valve and throttle valve) A regulating or balanced valve that is sensitive to engine vacuum and to governor pressure. Its supply pressure is regulated to produce a hydraulic torque output signal to the boost valve in the pressure regulator valve assembly. This modifies line pressure in accordance with engine torque.

In some G.M. automatic transmissions, the modulator valve output has the addi-tional job of controlling the shifts in the shift valve body. Modulator pressure acts to delay the shifts as opposed to governor pressure that causes the shift.

N

needle valve: A valve which essentially has a needle nose that fits a conical seat and usually has screw type threads for fine adjustment. A spring loaded needle valve design is occasionally used as a relief valve.

O

oil seals: A seal placed around a rotating or static shaft, reciprocating piston, or other part to prevent escape of oil or to allow only partial escape. The oil seal designs used in automatic transmissions are the molded O-ring, lathe cut molded O-ring, lip, metallic, and the Teflon oil ring.

one-way clutch: A mechanical clutch of roller or sprag design that resists torque in one direction for the purpose of making a planetary member or torque converter stator member reactionary. It allows the members to rotate freely in the opposite direction when their function as a reaction member is not desired.

The one-way clutch is its own "boss" and needs no external control for operation.

orifice: A calibrated restriction in a hydraulic circuit line that controls fluid flow and pressure. By using an orifice, the restricted fluid flow delays the application of pressure as a pressure difference is maintained across the orifice (high potential side seeks to equalize the low potential side). When the fluid ceases to flow across the orifice an equilibrium has been reached on both sides and pressure is equal throughout the flow path.

o-ring: (see oil seals)

output: When referring to power, it is the actual power or energy delivered by a machine. When referring to torque, it is the actual torque delivered by a machine.

Since power is a function of torque and speed, a machine cannot multiply or decrease power by the factor of the gear ratio, but it can change torque and speed. Neglecting frictional heat losses the power input and output should theoretically remain the same regardless of the torque and speed changes that take place. Hence, power output and torque output are separate but interrelated terms.

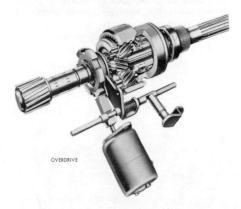

OVERDRIVE

overdrive: (see gear ratio, gear reduction, and automatic overdrive) A gear ratio that produces the opposite effect of a gear reduction. Torque is reduced and speed is increased by the factor of the gear ratio. A 1:3 gear ratio would change the 180 lb-ft input torque and speed of 2,700 rpm used for the gear reduction example to 60 lb-ft and 8,100 rpm.

overdrive transmission: (see overdrive) A semi-automatic controlled planetary gearing unit that is attached to the output end of a manually operated transmission. It utilizes a single planetary gear set which functions as either a direct drive or an overdrive, which ever is desired by the driver. In passenger car applications, the overdrive operation permits the engine to run at 30% less rpm than the drive shaft for any given roadspeed. The gear ratio expression would be 7:1.

overrunning clutch: (see one-way clutch) Same as one-way clutch.

P

pawl: A mechanically operated lever arm used as a locking device which fits into a detent slot to hold a moving part stationary. For example, the park pawl in an automatic transmission engages a slot in a lock gear or wheel that holds the output shaft.

piston: A disc fitted to slide in a cylinder bore. In hydraulics, it provides the means of converting hydraulic pressure into a useable force. In most cases, individual operating pistons in an automatic transmission are moved by the fluid along a cylinder to apply a load. When the fluid pressure is relieved, the piston may be returned to its original position by means of a mechanical spring compressed during the power stroke. Examples of piston applications are found in servo, clutch, and accumulator units.

planet carrier: (see planetary gear set) The rigid member of a planetary gear set that houses the planet gears. In addition, the carrier can act independently and serve as an output member, an input member, or a reaction member.

PLANETARY GEAR RATIO

planet pinions: (see planetary gear set) In a planetary gear set, the pinions are the gears that mesh with and revolve around the sun gear. They are also in mesh with the internal (ring) gear. The planet pinions may correctly be referred to as the planet gears.

planetary gear ratio: (see gear ratio) A planetary gear ratio produces the same results as any simple drive and driven gear set-up. Reduction, overdrive, and direct drive set-ups are attainable. The relationship of the planetary gears in their assembly, however, dictates more complex approaches to gear ratio calculations with gear teeth numbers on the sun and internal gears used in various formula combinations.

A direct comparison of the input speed to output speed, however, can still be used:

$$\text{Gear Ratio} = \frac{\text{Input Rpm}}{\text{Output Rpm}}$$

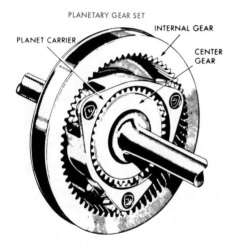

PLANETARY GEAR SET

INTERNAL GEAR

PLANET CARRIER

CENTER GEAR

planetary gear set: A group of gears arranged in a sun-and-planet fashion, in which planet gears may rotate on their own independent centers as well as around the sun gear which also has its own center of rotation. The planet gears in a planetary gear set are mounted in a common planet carrier, are identical, and perform the same functions. Usually, there are three or four planet gears mounted in a carrier.

The planet gears sometimes referred to as planet pinions are in constant mesh with both the sun gear and an internal gear which surrounds the pinions.

planetary gear set, simple: The simplest form of planetary gear set made up of the three basic elements: sun gear, planet carrier and pinions, and internal gear.

planetary gear set, compound: A gear set which has more than three elements of the type found in a simple gear set. For example, the gear set found in a two-speed automatic transmission consists of two sun gears, a dual set of planet pinion gears, and a single internal gear.

pounds per square inch: This is the unit for measuring pressure of liquids or gases. It is abbreviated *psi*.

power: (see work) The ability to do work per unit of time, as expressed in horsepower: one horsepower equals 33,000 ft-lbs of work per minute, or 550 ft-lbs of work per second. The rate at which work is done (power) is calculated:

$$\frac{\text{Force} \times \text{Distance}}{\text{Time}} = \frac{\text{Work}}{\text{Time}}$$

power flow: The flow of power from an input shaft through a set of gears, or

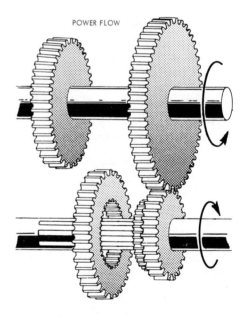

POWER FLOW

through a full automatic transmission to an output shaft. This power flow includes only those elements in operation at any particular time.

power train: (rear wheel drive) A total automotive power train includes the engine, a mechanical clutch, or fluid drive, a manual or automatic transmission, a drive shaft and U-joints, a rear axle drive and rear drive wheels.

pressure: Pressure is *force*, divided by *area*, or force per unit area. Usually, it is measured in pounds per square inch, or *psi:*

$$PSI = \frac{Force}{Area}$$

pressure gage: An instrument used for measuring the existing fluid pressure in a pressure circuit or chamber. The unit of measure is pounds per square inch, *psi.*

pressure regulating valve: In automatic transmissions its purpose is to regulate the pressure of the pump output and supply the basic fluid pressure necessary to operate the transmission. The regulated fluid pressure may be referred to as mainline pressure, line pressure, or control pressure. It regulates according to a fixed spring force and other auxiliary fluid pressures used for modulation.

The pressure regulator valve is sometimes assigned the auxiliary task of controlling the flow of fluid that charges the converter, feeds the oil cooler, and provides a lubrication feed for the transmission.

pump, automatic transmission: (see IX gear pump and IX rotor pump) An engine driven mechanical device of rotary design that creates the fluid flow and pressure build-up for operation of the transmission.

pump, torque converter: (see impeller) Means the same as impeller.

R

reaction member: In a planetary gear set, reference is made to any one of the planetary members that may be grounded to the transmission case during operation.

This is accomplished through the use of friction and wedging devices known as bands, disc clutches, and one-way clutches.

In physics, the second law of motion states that for every action an equal and opposite force is exerted. In a planetary gear set, the planet pinions react to a fixed sun gear or internal gear by setting up a walking motion as they rotate on their centers to produce a reduction or overdrive effect. The stator in a fluid torque converter is another example of a reaction member.

reaction pressure: A fluid pressure that opposes a spring pressure or combination of spring pressure and fluid pressure on the opposite end of a spool valve. The area on which it acts is called a reaction area. The strengths of the opposing pressures determine the position of the valve.

reactor, torque converter: (see stator) The reaction member of a fluid torque converter more commonly called a stator. The use of the term *reactor*, however, is descriptive of the function and is commonly used in engineering papers.

reduction: (see gear reduction) Gearing down as in gear reduction.

regulator valve: (see balanced valve) It is a spring loaded balanced valve mechanism that has the capability of responding to auxiliary hydraulic pressure signals as well as to the spring load. In automatic transmissions, the regulator valve is in series with the pump output and maintains the required system operating pressure.

relay valve: A directional valve of spool design which directs fluid flow and pressure in hydraulic circuitry. The shift valve in the shift system of an automatic transmission is an example of a relay valve.

relief valve: A safety valve that protects a hydraulic system from an accidental build-up of excessive pressure. The valve triggers when a pre-set pressure is reached, usually diverting the excess to a reservoir.

reservoir: (see sump) Same as a sump.

ring gear: (see internal gear) Same as an internal gear.

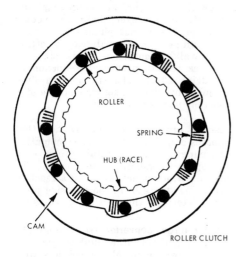

roller clutch: (see one-way clutch) A type of one-way clutch design using cams and rollers.

rotary flow: In a fluid drive unit, it is the flow of fluid trapped in the blade members of the impeller and follows the same direction as impeller and turbine spin.

S

sealing, non-positive: A fluid sealing method which allows some leakage for lubrication.

sealing, positive: A fluid sealing method which completely prevents leakage of fluid.

servo: In an automatic transmission, it is a piston in a cylinder assembly which converts hydraulic pressure into mechanical force and movement. Used in the control of brake or friction bands.

shift valve: Classified as a relay valve. It triggers the automatic shift in response to a governor and a throttle signal by di-

recting fluid to the appropriate band and clutch apply combination to cause the shift to occur.

speed ratio: Expressed in percentage, it reflects the efficiency of a fluid drive, impeller speed vs. turbine speed.

$$\text{Speed Ratio} = \frac{\text{Turbine Speed}}{\text{Impeller Speed}}$$

spool valve: (see annular groove, land, and face) A valve that fits into a cylindrical bore and consists of two or more pistons or spools that are part of a valve stem of smaller diameter. Spool valve nomenclature makes reference to lands, valleys or annular grooves, and to faces. The valve itself determines the flow of fluid between two or more possible paths. Spool valve movement can be controlled manually, by hydraulic pressure, or by spring pressure. This type of valve design is used extensively in hydraulic control assemblies.

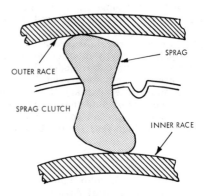

sprag clutch: (see one-way clutch) A type of one-way clutch design using cams or contoured, shaped sprags.

spring force: The tension in a spring when it is compressed or stretched.

stall: In fluid drive transmission applications, stall refers to engine rpm with the transmission engaged and the vehicle stationary; carburetor throttle valve can be in any position between closed and wide open.

stall speed: (see stall) In fluid drive transmission applications stall speed refers to the maximum engine rpm with the transmission engaged and vehicle stationary, when the carburetor throttle valve is wide open.

stall torque: (see stall speed) It is the maximum design or engineered torque ratio of a fluid torque converter and is produced under stall speed conditions.

stator: (see reactor) In a fluid torque converter, the stator is the reaction member that changes the direction of the fluid as it leaves the turbine to enter the pump so as to assist the pump to spin. This assist acts much the same as a lever arm or fulcrum and results in fluid torque multiplication.

sump: The storage vessel or reservoir that provides a ready source of fluid to the pump. In an automatic transmission the sump is the oil pan. All fluid eventually returns back to the sump for recycling into the hydraulic system.

sun gear: (see planetary gear set) In a planetary gear system, the center gear which meshes with a cluster of planet pinions is the sun gear.

T

tachometer: An instrument used for measuring engine revolutions per minute (rpm).

throttle linkage: The mechanical linkage between the driver's accelerator pedal and the throttle opening in the carburetor. In automatic transmission equipped cars, the throttle linkage may be an additional attached relay linkage connected to the transmission to operate a throttle and/or kickdown system.

The throttle linkage to carburetor to transmission relationship is critical to automatic transmission operation.

throttle valve, automatic transmission: (see balanced valve and modulator valve) It is a regulating or balanced valve that is controlled mechanically by throttle linkage or engine vacuum and sends a hydraulic torque signal to the shift valve body to control shifting in relation to engine torque. Throttle pressure acts to delay shifts, as opposed to governor pressure that causes a shift. Throttle pressure is also used as an auxiliary boost pressure in the pressure regulator valve system to modify line pressure with engine torque requirements.

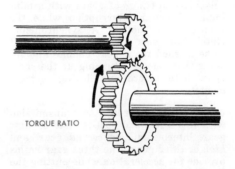

TORQUE RATIO

torque ratio: (see gear ratio) An expression of the gear ratio factor on torque effect. A 3:1 gear ratio or 3:1 torque ratio increases the torque input by the ratio factor of (3):

Input Torque (100 lb-ft) $\times$ 3 = Output Torque (300 lb-ft)

torus member: Another name for the drive and driven members of a fluid coupling or a torque converter.

transmission: A gear box is used for power transmission. In passenger cars it provides for torque and speed changes as an assist to engine performance, a reverse, and a neutral. Transmissions are designed for either manual or automatic control.

TRANSMISSION SYNCHROMESH

transmission, synchromesh: A manually operated transmission that permits "clashless shifting" of gears with a minimum of power interruption while the vehicle is in motion. A synchronizing clutch unit acts upon the parts about to be meshed for a gear change and insures that they are turning at the same speed both before and during engagement.

transmission, 3-speed: A transmission with three forward speeds: *low* or first gear, intermediate or *second* gear, and *high* or third gear. The three gear ratios provide for acceleration while putting the car in motion.

transmission, 2-speed: A transmission with two forward speeds: *low* and *high* gear.

turbine: (see fluid torque converter and fluid coupling) Designates the output or driven member of a fluid coupling or a fluid torque converter.

turbulence: The interference of molecules of a fluid (or vapor) with each other in a fluid flow as when eddies or swirling currents interfere with the linear flow of a stream.

V

vacuum: (see atmospheric pressure) The negative pressure (or lack of pressure) which in an auto engine or automatic transmission allows another force or pressure to move a valve, or change the flow of a fluid. When referring to a vacuum, a negative pressure is considered to be any pressure less than atmospheric.

vacuum gage: An instrument used for measuring the existing vacuum in a vacuum circuit or chamber. The unit of measure is in *inches* (of mercury in a barometer).

valley: (see annular groove) Same as annular groove.

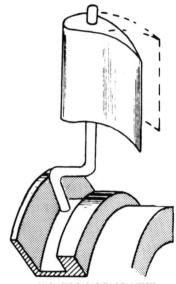

VARIABLE CAPACITY CONVERTER

variable capacity converter: A fluid torque converter designed with a two position stator blade angle, high and low. The high angle position gives an increased power input by permitting a higher rate of fluid flow return into the converter pump. This results in an increased engine speed input to the converter pump for improved acceleration. The converter torque output is also changed to a higher value, and thus power performance is achieved. For normal acceleration and cruising conditions, the stator operates in low angle (widest opening) position.

volumetric efficiency: Refers to the breathing ability of an internal combustion engine. It is a comparison of the actual volume of fuel-air mixture drawn in on the intake stroke to the maximum volume that it would take to completely fill the cylinder. Volumetric efficiency is related to the carburetor throttle valve opening and other normal restrictions in the engine intake system, and to engine rpm.

vortex flow: (see rotary flow) In a fluid drive, it is the fluid force generated by the centrifugal pumping action of the impeller or pump. This pumping action on the fluid cycles the fluid between the impeller and turbine members.

Vortex flow and rotary flow are two forces imposed on the fluid as a result of the impeller spin. Their influence on fluid drive operation is dependent on vehicle load and engine output.

W

work: The force exerted to move a mass or object. Work involves motion; should a force be exerted and no motion takes place then no work is done. Work per unit of time is called power:

Work = Force × Distance = ft-lbs
33,000 ft-lbs in one minute =
1 Horsepower

Index

Numerals in **bold type** refer to illustrations.

A

Absolute pressure, 153
Acceleration, 4, 40
Accumulator units, 187, 188, 276, 321
Actuators, 120
Annular grooves, **136**, 321
Annulus gear (Chrysler terminology for internal gear), 90, 91, 93, 97, 321
Applied band, 69, 95
Apply (condition of applying a brake band), 164
Apply chambers, 132
AQ-ATF, 192
Atmospheric pressure, 120, 121, 153
Automatic drive range, 170, 171, 175
Automatic low, 22
Automatic overdrive, 62
  introduced by Borg-Warner, 62

introduced by Chrysler, 62
Automatic shift timing, 184
Automatic shifting, 15, 166, 176, 183-187
Auxiliary pressure, 139, 321

B

Band, 163, 164, 322
  applied, 163, 164
  friction, 110
  kickdown, 262, 326
  low, 22
Band apply circuits, 163
Balanced valve principle, 321
Ball check valve, 133, 269
Ballooning, 146
Boost valve, 145, 158, 322
Borg-Warner, 13, 14

Brake horsepower, 3, 322
Breakaway, 88, 90, **90-91**, 322

C

C-4, 67, 87, 98, 100, 231, 290-300, **291, 292**
C-6, 67, 87, 98, 100, 290-300, **291, 292**
C-4S (semi-automatic), 292, 294
Cavitation, 146
Centrifugal force, 37, 39, 42, 322
Check valve, 133, 322
  ball type, 133, 269, 274
  poppet type, 133, 134
  relief valve, 123, 134, 135, 331
Closed throttle down-shift, 179, 180
Clutch, 34, 43, 67, 164,

264, 267, 267-271
apply, 133, **176**
assemblies, 163-166, 267
fluid, 323
friction type, 323, 328
multiple disc, 164, **165**
one-way, 34, 43, 67, 328
overrunning, 14, 34, 277, 329
pistons, 119, 268
roller, 332
sprag, 67, 92, 271, 273-275, 332
Clutch apply, 133
Clutch piston, 198
Clutch slip point, 55
Coast (the condition of coasting), 70, 95, 179-181, 323
coast breakaway, 92, 95
freewheeling, 92
Coast breakaway, 92
Coefficient of friction, 194, **195**, 323
Compound gear train, 64, 326
Compound planetary gear system, 65
Confined fluid, 113-116
Control valve body, 118
Control valve body assembly, 17, 18, 18, 130, **131**
Controlled coupling, 77
Converter charging circuit, **169**

Converter coupling, 30, 46, 54
capacity, 55
Dynaflow, 31
fill, 41
freewheeling devices, 31
roller clutches, 332
stall, 55
Converter efficiency, 33, 39
(see speed ratio)
Converter, flushing, **281**
Converter service, 332
Converter torque capacity, 55, 56, 57
high capacity, 56
low capacity, 56
Cooling shroud cover, 52, 53, 54
Cooling system service, 88, 105, 170, 280, 281
Coupling, 40, 41, 51
full torque, 41
slip, 41
start condition, 42, 51
Coupling fill, 80, 82
Coupling members, 40 45
drive, 36
driving input member, 36, 65
driven member, 36, 80
reaction member, 48, 65, 331
two member fluid coupling, 29, 31

Coupling phase, **51**
Coupling full torque, 41
Coupling slip, 41
Coupling start condition, 41
Cruise-O-Matic (Ford), 15, 99, 179, 294-300, 294, 297-299
cast iron Cruise-O-Matic, 294

D

Detent valve, 176, 179
through-detent, 179-181
to-detent, 179-181
Dexron, 194, **195**, 241, 242
Diagnostic procedure, 207-237
Differential force, 137
Direct drive, 65, 76-83, **76-81**, 106
Direct (third) gear, 94 95
Directional valves, 130
Disc clutch assembly, **164**, **165**
Downshift (see forced downshift)
Downshift valve, 179
Drive, 22, **22**, 80, 95, 101-102, 161
automatic low, 23
direct drive, **23**, 95, 102, 324

Drive oil, 160
Drive power, 91
Drive shaft load, 4, 24
Driven member, 36, 80
Driveshaft torque curve, 324
Driving input member, 36, 65
Driving shell, 92, 94, 96
Driving torque, 38
Dynaflow, **32**
  (introduced by Buick, 1948), 8, 32
  fluid torque converter, 8

E

Element, 33, 324
  coupling members, 33
  drive, 22, 80, 95, **101**, **102**, 161
  driven member, 36, 46, 80, 326, 331
  driving shell, 44
  impeller, 34, 38, 43
  stator, 33, 42, 47, 59, 333
Engine characteristics, 3, 3
Engine performance, **3**, 4
Exit angle, 57, 58
Exhaust valve, 80

F

Fail-safe, 155

Feed oil, 52
1st gear, 4
First gear, 4
First position (low), 89
  low (first position), 89
Five laws of planetary operation:
  law of direct drive, 94
  law of neutral, 94
  law of overdrive, 94
  law of reduction, 92
  law of reverse, 96
Fixed gear ratio, 325
Flash-O-Matic, 179, 300
Flexible drive plate, 88
Flight pitch Dynaflow, 32
Fluid, 111, 192-196, 324, 325
  conditions, 193, 209, 212-213, 243
  Dexron, 194, **195**, 241
  M-2C33-F, 194, 241
  properties, 193, 325
Fluid clutch, **79**, 82
Fluid coupling, 7, 12, 29, **31**, 32, 34, **35**, 37, 48, 324
  Alan Coats, inventor, 31
  introduced by Chrysler, 1938, 7, 12, 31
  last used, 1965, 32
Fluid flywheel, 31
  adopted by Chrysler, 1938, 31
  developed by Harold Sinclair, 31

Fluid leaks, 245-253, 246, 248
Fluid level, 209-212
  high level, 210, 213
  low level, 210, 213
Fluid shock absorber, 31
  (fluid coupling as shock absorber)
Fluid torque converter, 2, 15, 29, 32, 324
  (see torque converter)
  Chrysler-Plymouth Torque-Drive, 12, 306
  Plymouth Hydrive, 7
Foot pounds, 116
Force, 112, **113**, 120, 136, 325
  power, 114, 136
Forced downshift
  (kickdown), 24, 99, 179
  hill grades, 24
  kickdown band, 99
Ford fluid,
  M-2C33-F, 241, 242
Ford-O-Matic, 11, **11**
  introduced by Ford, 1951, 11
Four speed planetary, 7
Free flow, 117
Freewheeling, 31, 65, 69, 93, 325
  action, 69, 71
Freewheeling devices, 31
  converter coupling,

31
roller clutches, 332
Friction, 325
Friction bands, 110
Friction clutch, 7
in semi-automatic
transmissions, 6
introduced by Reo,
1933, 6
Friction elements, **167**
Friction plates, 269, **270,**
271
Frictional losses, 325
Front planetary, 90
Front pump, 118, **168,**
250, 251

G

Gasket seal kit, 265, 265
Gear ratio, 4, 15, 22, 62,
64, 84, 325
fixed gear ratios, 62,
325
gear set ratio, 62, 64
Gear ratio change, 4, 22,
84
broad ratio, 32
defined, 84
fixed, 62
set ratio, 64
Gear reduction, 65, 81,
326
Gear set ratio, 15, 84
Gear train, **165,** 326
Gearing power flow, 70
Gears, 62, 64, 84, 325

General Motors fluid,
Dexron, 194, **195,**
241, 242
Governor system, 17,
24, 159-161, **161,**
173, 260, 277, 326
Governor valve, **160**
Grounding media (or
medium), 66
Gyromatic, 7
introduced by Chrys-
ler, 1938 or after, 7

H

Heli-Coil, 278
High angle position, 57
Horsepower (defined),
3, 326
brake horsepower, 3
Hydra-Matic, 15, 17, 62,
87, 179
fluid coupling with 4-
speed planetary, 7
introduced by Olds,
1940, 7
Hydraulic control sys-
tem, 17, 18, **18,** 326
Hydraulic hoist, 122-
123
Hydraulic jack, 120-
122, **121**
Hydraulic pump, 125-
130
Hydraulic systems, 116-
118, **116,** 119
Hydraulics (the science

of moving fluids),
100-123, **111,** 125,
326
Hydrive (Plymouth), 7
Hydrodynamic drive,
34, 326
Hydrodynamic units,
29, 328
fluid coupling, 29
torque converter, 29

I

Idle, 214
Impeller (pump), 34,
38, 43, 46, 326, 331
driving input mem-
ber, 34, 47
driving shell, 44
hydraulic pump, 47
vanes, 43, 47
Impeller vanes, 43, 47
Inch pounds (in-lb),
116
$$\frac{\text{ft lbs}}{12} = \text{in-lbs, a}$$
unit of distance
and mass
Inlet, 127, 129
Inner drive member,
125
Intake manifold vac-
uum, 153
Internal (annulus)
gear, 63, 66, 326
IX gear pump (inter-
nal/external gear

pump), 127-129, 326

IX rotor pump (internal/external rotor pump), 127-129, 326

J

Jetaway (GM), 1, 18, 65, 104, 203, 301

K

Kickdown band, 262, 326
Kinetic energy, 327

L

Land, 327
Lathe-cut O-ring, 199, 200, 201
Law of conservation of energy, 51, 115, 116
Laws of planetary gear operation, 65-81, 327
Light oil feed pressure, 52
    feed oil, 52
Line pressure boost, 159
Lip seal, 199, 199

Lock-up, 70, 91
Low, 89, 95, 96, **107**, 171
Low angle position, 57
Low range, 25, 181
Low servo piston, 115
Lugging, 33

M

Manual low, 99, 106, 166-170, **181**, 304
Manual valve, 18, **23**, 25, 161-162, 372
Manual valve linkage, 16, 215-216, **215**, 327
Mechanical clutch, 328
Mechanical efficiency, 328
Member, 34, 328
Merc-O-Matic, 11
    introduced by Mercury, 1951, 11
Metal seal, 202, 203, **203**
Milky fluid, 213
Modulator boost, 152, 171
Modulator (throttle) booster signal, 156
Modulator pressure circuit, 158, **159**
Modulator valve, 328
Multiple disc clutch, 67, 78, 81, 98, 110, 164, **164**

N

Needle valve, 121, 328
Newton's law, 51, 52, 115, 116
Neutral, 20, 21, 65, 66, 77, 90, 101, 105, 161, 170, 327
Non-positive sealing, 196-205

O

Oil cooling system, 88, 105, 170, 280, 281
Oil fill, 82
Oil pump circuit, 168, **169**
Oil seals, 328
One way clutch, 34, 43, 67, 328
Open position (open blade position), 57
Orifice, 131, **132**, **266**, 328
O-ring, 328
Output, 329
Overdrive, 6, 65, 74, 75, 76, 327, 329
Overhauling a transmission, 254-283, **255**, **265**
Overrunning clutch, 14, 34, 277, 329
Oxidation stability, 192-196

P

Park, 20, 21, 98, 108, 161, 170
Parking pawl, 98
Pascal's law, 111-113, 116, 132
Pawl (parking pawl), 98
Periodic maintenance, 240-245
Planet carrier, 63, 94, 96
Planet pinions, 63
Planetary gears, 63, 63, 84, 330
  ratio, 15
Planetary gear set, 20, 66, 75, 76, 77, 261, 330
  lock up, 70, 91
  ratio, 15, 84
Planetary gear system, 2, 62, 64, 86-108, 89
Planetary gear train, 5, 64, 89, 264
  in planetary transmission, 64
  planetary gear system, 89, 89
Planetary lock-up, 94
Planetary transmission, 62, 88, 102
Poppet check valve, 133, 134
Positive delivery, 130
Positive planet carrier lock, 108
Positive sealing, 196-

205
Pound, 112
Pound feet (lb-ft), 116
Pounds per square inch (psi), 113, 331
Power, 330
  drive power, 20, 330
  gearing power flow, 20
  horsepower, 3, 326
  power flow, 20
  power train, 330
  reduction power flow, 20
PowerFlite, 11, 12
Power flow, 20, 89, 165
Power train, 2, 4
Powerglide, 65, 104, 242, 301-306, 302-304
  aluminum Powerglide, 302-304
  introduced by Chevrolet, 65
Pressure, 112, 116, 118, 131, 145, 230, 331
Pressure/force relationship, 112, 113
  energy, 119
Pressure gage, 331
Pressure lines, 143, 157, 171
Pressure testing, 228-237, 228-231, 253, 331
Prestomatic, 7
  introduced by Chrysler, 1938, 7
Primary weights, 161

Program (programming), 160
  shift scheduling, 160, 174
Pump efficiency, 130
Pumps, 117, 331
  rotary, 118, 125-127, 331
  reciprocating piston type, 118
  front, 118
  rear, 118

R

Reaction internal gear, 66
Reaction member, 48, 65, 331
  area, 136
  element, 33, 324
  freewheeling stator, 31
  pressure, 136, 331
  stator, 33, 43, 47, 59, 333
  variable pitch stator, 56-59
Reactionary, 91
Reactor (stator), 30, 33, 45, 48, 331
Rear pump, 287, 293
Reciprocating piston pump, 118
Reduction gears, 63, 66, 327
  gear ratio, 63

gear reduction, 66-75, 327, 331
reduction power flow, 66-74, **67**, **68**, 72
Reduction power flow, 66-74, **67**, **68**, 72
Regulator valve assembly, 157
Regulator valves, 119, 130, 138, 144, 331
Relay valves, 140, 331
Relief valve, 123, 134, **134-135**, 331
Reservoir (sump), 332
Reverse, 26, **26**, 81, 161, 327
law of reverse, 81, 96, 327
reverse operation, 26, **26**, 80, 98, 182-183, **183**
Reverse torque, **103**
gearing power flow, 97, 163
law of reverse, 81
Ring gear (internal gear), 332
annulus gear, 90
Road load, 4, 5
Road test, 220-228
procedure, 221
Roller clutches, 332
Rotary flow, 37, **37**, 39, **39**, 42, 332
rotational movement, 37, 38, **38**
spinning mass, 39
Rotary pump, 118, 125-

127, 331
Rotational movement, 37, 38, **38**
centrifugal force, 37

S

Sealing, 196-205, **196**, **197**, 250, 251, 332
Second gear, 92
Second position, 88, 93, 99
Secondary weights, 161
Select-Shift, 98, **100**, **185**, **186**
Semi-automatic transmission, 29, 105, 187
introduced by Reo, 1933
Servo pistons, 115
Servo unit and band, 115, 163, **163**, 176, 279, 332
Severe driving conditions, 241
Shift-Command, 179, 300, 301
Shift point, 183
Shift quality, 225
Shift scheduling, 160
Shifting timing, 225-227
Shift valve spring, 1-9
Shifter valve, 24, 183,

184, 332
Slipping, 221
Sniff test, 243
Soft shift feel, 189
Speed ratio (defined), 39, 40, 332
(see converter efficiency)
Spinning mass, 38
rotational movement, 38
Spline (key type lock), 90
Split guide ring, 42
Spool valve, 122, 136, **137**, 332
Sports-Shift, 99
Sprag clutch, 67, 92, 271-273, 332
Sprag clutch assemblies, **272**
Spring force, 112, 138, 332
Spring tension, 153
Stall, 49, 51, 332
Stall speed, 333
Stall test, 216-219, **217**, **222-223**
Stall torque, 49, 333
Stator (reactor), 33, 42, 47, 59, 333
Sump (reservoir for driving fluid), 117, 333
Sun gear, **63**, 65, 83, 333
Synchromesh, 6, 334
introduced by Cadillac, 1928, 6

T

TV (throttle valve) diaphragm test, 115, 231-237
Tachometer, 333
Teflon seals, 205
Three element torque converter, 33, 42, 48, 287, 296
3-Speed transmission, 183-186, 311, 334
Throttle linkage, 22, 214-215, 215, 221, 333
Throttle system, 16, 24, 152-156, 173, 174
Through-detent, 24, 177, 178, 179, 180, 181
Tip-Toe shift, 7
  introduced by Chrysler, 1938, 7
To-detent, 176, 179-181
Torque, 3, 3
  torque drop, 3, 3
  torque flow, 48
  torque multiplication range, 3, 48, 49, 59
Torque-command, 301
Torque converter, 11, 32, 33, 33, 34, 34
  efficiency, 33
  Fottinger, 29, 30
  performance curve, 33
  stall speed, 333
  three element, 33, 34
Torque-Drive (Chrys-

ler), 7, 104, 105, 306
TorqueFlite, 15, 67, 86, 88, 93, 96, 98, 102, 179, 217, 279, 286-290, 301
  A-904, 86, 88, 288
  A-727, 86, 88, 289
Torque flow, 48
Torque multiplication range, 3, 4, 48, 59, 333
Towing cars with automatic transmissions, 283
Transmission function, 5, 333
Transmission removal, 254-274, 255, 275
  disassembly, 256
  installation, 255, 256, 256
  sub-assemblies, 257
Turbine, 33, 35, 36, 46, 334
  curvature of vanes, 43, 47
Turbine out-flow, 47, 48
Turbo-Hydra-Matic, 18
Turbine-300 (T-300), 18, 67, 104-105, 104, 301
Turbine-350 (T-350) 310, 313-319, 320
Turbine-400 (T-400), 204, 306, 307, 308, 309
Turbulence, 42, 334

Two-speed transmissions, 9, 19, 104, 301-306, 305, 334

U

Ultramatic, 12, 13
  introduced by Packard, 1949, 12
Up-shift, 176-179

V

Vacuum (defined), 120, 121, 334
  gage, 334
Vacuum leak test, 254
Vacuum modulator diaphragm, 153, 154
  (leaky modulator)
Vacuum modulator system, 156
Vacuum throttle system, 153-154, 214-215, 231-237, 231
Valve
  assembly, 16
  ball check, 134, 269
  boost, 145, 158, 322
  check, 133
  control, 130
  directional, 130
  downshift, 179
  needle, 121, 328

poppet, 133, 134
regulator, 119, 130, 131, 138-141, **138, 139**
relay, 140-141, 173
relief, 123, **134, 135,** 136, **137,** 331
spool, 122
Valve body, 16, 17, 24, 24, 147, 271-273, 272
control valve body, 24, 143, 271-273
control valve body as-sembly, 130, 272-273, **279**
Valve land, 327
Vanes, 50, 57
closed position, 57
open position, 57
Variable capacity con-verter, 56, 60, 334
Variable pitch stator (reactor) blades, 56, 57, 58, 59
Varnished fluid, 213
Viscosity index improv-ers, 193

Void, 127
Vortex flow, 37, **37,** 38, 39, **39,** 40, **41,** 42, 49, 335
(crosswise or circula-tory flow)

W

Wedging devices, 65, **69**
Work, 335